ENERGY

BRUCE CHALMERS

Gordon McKay Professor of Metallurgy
Division of Engineering and Applied Physics
Harvard University
Cambridge, Massachusetts

ACADEMIC PRESS

New York and London

ACADEMIC PRESS INC.
111 Fifth Avenue, New York, New York 10003

United Kingdom Edition published by
ACADEMIC PRESS INC. (LONDON) LTD.
Berkeley Square House, London W.1

LIBRARY OF CONGRESS CATALOG CARD NUMBER: 63-12920

First Printing, 1963

Second Printing, 1964

PRINTED IN THE UNITED STATES OF AMERICA.

PREFACE

The development of society in the past 200 years has been characterized by the progressive substitution of machine power for muscle power. Agriculture has evolved from oxen to tractors, transportation from horses to jet airplanes, war from gunpowder to thermonuclear bombs, astronomy from telescopes to interplanetary rockets, and comfort from paper fans to air conditioners. Moreover, the techniques of building machines have evolved from the blacksmith's forge to the automated plants of modern industry.

The key to these changes is the exploitation of natural sources of energy: fossil fuels (coal and oil), water power, solar radiation, and the nucleus of the atom. The utilization of the energy from these sources depends upon its conversion into forms in which it can be transported, transmitted or stored, and applied at the appropriate time and place. Energy has become the world's most important economic commodity; more of it is bought and sold than any other item, although it is not always obvious that it is energy that is changing hands.

But what is energy? There is no simple description which really answers this question; in this book we shall develop the concept of "energy" by discussing and explaining the various forms of energy and how it can be converted from one form to another for man's enjoyment or advantage. First we shall discuss the energy of moving objects (kinetic energy), and the energy that can be stored in objects by various operations such as lifting or deforming them; energy in these forms is called potential energy. These are the most familiar and the most useful forms of energy, since much of the world's work takes the form of setting objects in motion or lifting them. Next we shall consider heat as a form of energy; heat is important in its own right and because it is often an intermediate stage between the source of energy and its final form (for example, current methods for the production of electricity from coal depend upon first changing the energy of the coal into heat), and because almost all the energy used by man finally ends up as heat. Then we shall examine radiation, the means by which the sun's energy reaches the earth, and chemical energy, the form in which energy lies dormant in our fuels and our foods. This is followed by a discussion of electrical energy, a very convenient and widely used form of energy, and by a section on nuclear energy, at once the newest form of energy, because its exploitation on earth is just beginning, and the oldest, because almost all our energy comes from the sun, a giant thermonuclear reactor.

The final chapter is an attempt to answer the questions: How much energy do we use? In what forms and for what purposes do we use it? Where does it come from? What is the outlook on the adequacy of energy for the future needs of mankind?

The ultimate usefulness of the energy from a given source, such as a lump of coal, depends upon how much energy it contains and how efficiently this energy can be converted to the required form at the required place, such as for the heating or cooling of a house. In other words, we must think of energy in quantitative terms: in terms of how much of it is used and how much of it is wasted in conversion systems like power plants, automobiles, lamps, and nuclear reactors. All energy conversion systems are subject to a basic limitation: you cannot get more energy out of a system than you put in; an understanding of the "rate of exchange" between different forms of energy allows us to tell how close to the ideal we have come. Many of the current methods do not approach this ultimate efficiency limit. In addition to examining these methods, we shall also explore methods contemplated for future use. These include thermoelectric conversion of heat to electric power, thermoelectric cooling, direct conversion of solar energy to electrical energy, and fuel cells, which convert chemical energy directly to electricity.

This treatment will allow us to discuss the basic possibilities and limitations involved in the use of energy, and to determine the possibility, or impossibility of perpetual motion, whether a flashlight battery can be devised that will last forever, to what extent sunshine can be used for heating our houses, and what we buy when we pay our electricity bills. The reader should then be able to distinguish between applications of energy which are ultimately and fundamentally impossible and those which are not possible at present, but which await only the development of sufficient technical skill in exploiting the forces of nature.

The main purpose of this book is to give the reader a better appreciation of the achievements, potentialities, and limitations in the use of energy; but there is also another purpose. The implications of the conquest of energy, and the resulting technological revolution, are apparent to everyone. But the concurrent advances in science, without which the technological developments would have been impossible, are much less obvious and less well understood. It is not, of course, possible for the "nonscientist" to acquire professional competence in science, any more than a "nonhistorian" can in history, or a "nonclassicist" can in Greek; but since science is an important part of the intellectual output of the 20th century, and an equally important part of our cultural heritage, an educated man can and should be as "literate" in science as he is in history and in literature. He should have a general grasp of the meaning and purpose of science. This can be approached in various ways, among which is the study of a "unifying" topic, such as energy. This does not imply that an understanding of energy is a passport to all science, but it should provide a basis for understanding the nature of physical laws and how a scientist can use them to make detailed predictions outside the range of his experience.

For the reader who wishes to invest a substantial amount of effort in the subject, this book presents the methods of calculation as well as the results; the problems intended for such readers are included at the end of each chapter. The numerical answers to the problems are given in Appendix C. Other readers may prefer to concentrate their attention on the results; it is my hope that they, too, will acquire a more precise and comprehensive understanding of energy from this book.

The author wishes to express his thanks to many students and colleagues who helped him during the development of this material, and in particular, to Mr. R. Brady Williamson, who by discussion and comment clarified many questions both of content and presentation.

The author is also indebted to Addison-Wesley Publishing Company, Viking Press, and Johns Hopkins Press for permission to use figures and data.

BRUCE CHALMERS

February 1963

CONTENTS

PREFACE v

Chapter 1

INTRODUCTION
  Motion 2
  Instantaneous Velocity 2
  Rotation 3
  Acceleration 3
  Problems 6

Chapter 2

FORCE
  First Law of Motion 7
  Acceleration of Gravity 7
  Terminal Velocity 8
  Second Law of Motion; Force 8
  Mass and Weight 9
  Resultant Forces 12
  Angular Acceleration: Moment of a Force 13
  The Lever 14
  Machines 16
  Trajectories 18
  Motion in a Circle 21
  Friction 23
  Universal Gravitation 24
  Orbits of Planets, the Moon, the Other Satellites . . . 25
  Weightlessness 26
  Tides 27
  Problems 28

Chapter 3

MOMENTUM
  Reaction: Third Law of Motion 30
  Conservation of Momentum 30
  Angular Momentum 33

Reaction Propulsion: Rockets 34
Jet Propulsion 35
Problems 37

Chapter 4

WORK, KINETIC ENERGY, AND POTENTIAL ENERGY

Energy, the Capacity to Do Work 40
The Conservation of Energy 43
Machines 43
"Perpetual Motion" Machines 44
Water Power 46
Tidal Power 46
Power 46
Elastic Energy 49
Energy Stored in a Compressed Gas 50
Energy Storage in a Compressed Liquid 52
Energy Stored in an Elastic Solid 53
The Flywheel 56
Problems 57

Chapter 5

THE NATURE OF HEAT

Temperature and Quantity of Heat 59
Quantity of Heat 61
Latent Heat 64
The Nature of Heat 65
Effect of Temperature and Pressure 69
The Absolute Zero of Temperature 71
Absolute Scale of Temperature 71
Liquefaction of Gases 73
Temperature as a Measure of Energy 73
The Distribution of Energy 76
Temperature of Solids and Liquids 79
Evaporation and Latent Heat 80
Boiling of a Liquid 81
The Conversion of Work into Heat 82
The Mechanical Equivalent of Heat 82
Refrigeration and Air Conditioning 85
Air Conditioners 86
The Heat Pump 88
Problems 90

Chapter 6

HEAT TRANSFER

Conduction 91
Convection 92
Radiation 93

Evaporation 94
Newton's Law of Cooling 94
Thermal Conductivity 95
Heat Transmission Coefficient: Domestic Heating 97
Heat Insulation 99
Aerodynamic Heating 100
Problems 102

Chapter 7

THE CONVERSION OF HEAT INTO WORK

Heat Engines 103
Efficiency 104
Types of Heat Engines 107
Reciprocating Steam Engine 108
Steam Turbines 110
Internal Combustion Engines 111
Gas Turbines 112
Problems 114

Chapter 8

RADIATION

Infrared Radiation 117
Radiation of Energy 120
Solar Radiation 125
Solar Heating 131
Solar Furnaces 132
Solar Cooking 133
Solar Energy 133
Solar Energy for Spaceships 134
Temperature of a Satellite 134
Illumination 136
Sound 138
Problems 140

Chapter 9

CHEMICAL ENERGY

The Elements 141
The Atom 142
Chemical Energy and Life 150
Photosynthesis 152
Energy Conversion by Muscles 155
The Fossil Fuels 156
The Conversion of Chemical Energy into Electrical Energy 159
Polarization 163
The Dry Cell 164
Storage Battery 164
Conversion of Electrical to Chemical Energy 166

Production of Aluminum by Electrolysis 167
Fuel Cells 167
Bacterial Fuel Cell 169
Desalting of Sea Water 169
Problems 174

Chapter 10

ELECTRICAL ENERGY

Electrostatic Forces 176
Electric Currents 188
Electric Circuits 188
Heating Effect of a Current 192
Thermoelectric Effects 196
Thermoelectric Cooling 198
Thermionic Conversion 199
Photoelectric Effect 200
Solar Battery 201
"Direct" Conversion of Solar Energy 201
Fluorescent Lighting 202
Radio-Frequency Heating 202
Magnetic Effects of a Current 203
Forces between Magnetic Poles 204
Magnetic Units 205
Magnetic "Lines of Force" 205
The Origin of Magnetism 207
Ferromagnetic Substances 207
Magnetically Hard and Soft Materials 208
Effect of Temperature on Magnetization 209
Strength of Magnetic Field Due to a Current 210
The Hysteresis Loop 214
The Electromagnet 214
"Degaussing of Ships" 215
Motors, Generators, and Transformers 216
The Electric Motor 219
The Generator 224
Alternating Current 224
Transformers 225
Ignition System for Automobiles 228
Eddy Currents 228
Magneto-hydrodynamics 230
The MHD Generator 230
The MHD Motor 231
Problems 233

Chapter 11

NUCLEAR ENERGY

Radioactivity 235
Half-Life 236

Radiation Damage 237
Increase of Mass with Velocity 237
Relationship between Mass and Energy 239
Isotopes 239
Packing Fraction 240
Fission 241
The Fission Chain Reaction 242
Critical Mass 243
The Atomic Bomb 243
Natural Uranium as a Nuclear Fuel 244
Nuclear Reactor 245
Shielding 247
"Breeder" Reactors 248
Fusion 248
Problems 249

Chapter 12

THE SOURCES AND USES OF ENERGY

Domestic Heating 254
Energy for Spaceships 255
Energy Consumption 256
The World's Food Supply 260
The Sources of Energy 263
World Fuel Reserves 267

Appendix A

BIBLIOGRAPHY 269

Appendix B

CONVERSIONS 271

Appendix C

ANSWERS TO PROBLEMS 272

Index 275

Chapter 1

INTRODUCTION

Energy, according to Webster, is the capacity to do work. This definition is correct, but incomplete. To make it more complete, we must first define "work"; then it becomes apparent that we must consider the question of *how much* energy and *how much* work. This leads to the conclusion that the term "energy" may be used either in a qualitative or quantitative sense. But it is useful only if treated quantitatively, in much the same way that the concept of money is useful only if it is treated quantitatively. The subject will therefore be developed in terms of the units in which energy is measured and the "rate of exchange" between the different forms of energy (such as the energy of motion of an object and the heat energy which is developed as a result of friction).

In discussing the various forms of energy, it will be necessary to refer to many different quantities that can be measured or calculated; a few examples are length, time, speed, volume, fuel consumption, and power. All the quantities considered here will be measured in units that can be related, directly or indirectly, to three primary units, those of mass, length, and time. These have been chosen arbitrarily, as there is nothing in nature that specifies a standard, for example, of length. There are, in fact, two sets of units in such widespread use that the reader should be familiar with both of them; they are the pound, the foot, and the second, in the English system of units; and the kilogram, the meter, and the second, in the metric system. Since both systems are widely used, it is desirable to be able to make conversions between them. For many purposes, high precision is not required, and it is sufficient to use the following approximate values:

$$1 \text{ pound} \simeq \tfrac{1}{2} \text{ kilogram}$$
$$1 \text{ meter} \simeq 3 \text{ feet}$$
$$1 \text{ kilogram} \simeq 2 \text{ pounds}$$
$$1 \text{ foot} \simeq \tfrac{1}{3} \text{ meter}$$

It is fortunate that the same units of time are used in both systems. Many other units are derived directly from these primary units. A good example is *speed*, which is expressed in feet per second, meters per second, or miles per hour.

Motion   An important form of energy is the energy of a moving object. A convenient starting point for the study of energy, therefore, is to examine the ways in which motion can be described and measured. At this point, a distinction must be made between two concepts which are often used interchangeably: speed and velocity. Speed means rate of motion, regardless of the direction in which the motion takes place, whereas velocity means speed in a definite direction. When we describe velocity, the direction is as important as the unit and the number.

Instantaneous Velocity   The expression "a velocity of 30 miles per hour" means that if an object continues to move at the same velocity for 1 hour, it will cover a distance of 30 miles. However, since it can move at 30 miles per hour without traveling for 1 full hour, it is frequently necessary to use the concept of *instantaneous velocity*. The significance

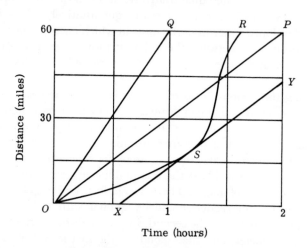

Fig. 1.1. Distance-time graph illustrating constant speed, 60 miles/hr (OP), constant speed, 30 miles/hr (OQ), varying speed (OR), and instantaneous speed at S, the point where XY is tangent to the curve.

of this is apparent if one plots a graph of the relationship between the time elapsed and the distance traveled (see Fig. 1.1). If the speed of an object is constant, that is, if equal distances are covered in equal times, the line representing the relationship between the distance and the time elapsed will be a straight line. The straight line *OP* in Fig. 1.1 represents a constant speed of 30 miles per hour; the straight line *OQ* represents a constant speed of 60 miles per hour. The slope of each line corresponds to the speed. If the speed is not constant the slope of the line will not be constant and the line will be a curve like line *OR* in Fig. 1.1.

Although the speed of the object changes continuously, at any given moment it is traveling at an instantaneous speed. This speed is represented by the slope of the line at that time. The slope is found by drawing a tangent to the line at the appropriate point. For example, line *XY* is the tangent to the curve at point *S*. Since it is parallel to line *OP*, it shows that at the time corresponding to *S*, the instantaneous speed is 30 miles per hour.

Rotation It has been assumed thus far that all parts of a moving object move at the same speed and that therefore a single speed or velocity is adequate to describe the speed or velocity of the whole object. However, this is no longer true when the object is rotating, because different parts necessarily move at different speeds; the speed increases with increasing distance from the center of rotation. Therefore, we cannot describe rotary motion in terms of feet per second, but must use revolutions per minute, degrees per second, or radians per second.

The conversions between the different units of angular velocity are as follows. Consider an object rotating at 100 revolutions per minute. Since there are 360 degrees in one complete rotation, 100 revolutions per minute is equal to 100 times 360 degrees per minute, which is $(100 \times 360)/60$ degrees per second, or 600 degrees per second. This is roughly equal to 10 radians per second. (A radian is the angle subtended at the center of a circle by an arc of length equal to the radius. One radian is about 57 degrees.)

Acceleration The velocity of a moving body does not necessarily remain constant. If the velocity changes, the body is said to be accelerating. Acceleration is measured as a rate of change of velocity. If an object moving at the rate of 10 feet per second at one instant is found 10 seconds later to be moving at 20 feet per second, its speed will have changed by 10 feet per second in 10 seconds. This is written as 1 foot per second per second or 1 ft/sec². Uniform acceleration occurs when the rate of change of velocity is constant, that is, when the velocity increases or decreases by equal amounts in equal periods of time. Uniform acceleration can be demonstrated by a steel ball rolling down a smooth slope (see Fig. 1.2). The position of the ball is observed at various times after it is released, either by high-speed photography with a strobe light, or, less accurately, with a stop watch. The positions after successive intervals of 1 second are shown in Fig. 1.2.

Figure 1.3 plots these results in a graph to show the relationship between the distance *D* that the ball travels and the time that it takes to cover that distance. The curved line in Fig. 1.3 represents the distance traveled at all

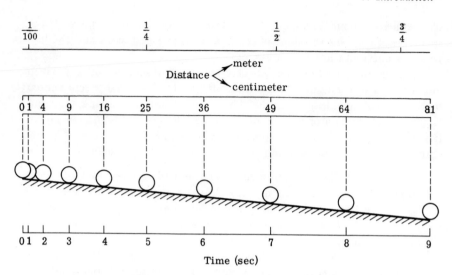

Fig. 1.2. The position, at intervals of one second, of a ball rolling down a slope.

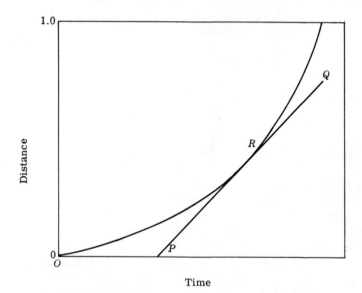

Fig. 1.3. Graph for distance and time of a ball rolling down a slope.

times, not only the measured ones. From this figure the speed can be calculated for any required instant, because the speed is the distance the ball would have traveled if it had continued to roll at the same speed for one second. Line PQ represents the behavior of a ball traveling at the speed which it had at point R, provided that this speed remained unchanged. From the slope of this line we can calculate the instantaneous speed at point R. The results of calculating the speed at various times are shown in Fig. 1.4.

It will be seen that the speed increased evenly with time, that is, the acceleration was uniform; the slope of this line shows that the acceleration was 0.02 meter per second per second, because the speed was 0.02 meter per second after 1 second, 0.04 meter per second after 2 seconds, and so on. It

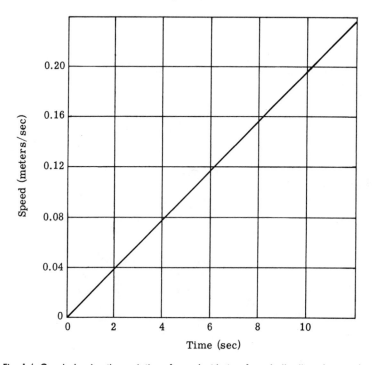

Fig. 1.4. Graph showing the variation of speed with time for a ball rolling down a slope.

should be evident that the distance traveled, time taken, speed, and acceleration are interrelated. Their relationship is expressed by three formulas:

$$V = U + AT,$$
$$D = UT + \tfrac{1}{2}AT^2,$$
$$V^2 - U^2 = 2AD,$$

where U and V represent the velocity at the beginning and the end of time T, A represents the acceleration, and D represents the distance traveled during time T. Thus, if any three of these quantities are known (including the fact that $U = 0$ in the case of an object starting at rest), the others can be found.

Example: An object starting from rest and uniformly accelerated travels 32 feet in 2 seconds. Calculate the acceleration:

$$D = UT + \tfrac{1}{2}AT^2$$
$$U = 0$$
$$32 = \tfrac{1}{2} \times A \times 2^2$$
$$2A = 32$$
$$A = 16 \text{ ft/sec/sec.}$$

It is apparent that there is a very clear distinction between "velocity" and "acceleration"; an object undergoes acceleration when its velocity is changing; if it is moving without acceleration, it has a constant speed in a constant direction.

Problems

1.1 (a) How many kilograms are there in 1 lb?
  (b) How many inches in 1 meter?
  (c) How many pints in 1 liter?
  (d) Convert 60 miles/hr to feet/second.
  (e) Convert 100 km/hr to miles/hour.

1.2 The earth rotates in 24 hours. What is its angular velocity?

1.3 Draw a graph of distance against time for a car starting from rest and moving with an acceleration of 1 ft/sec. From the graph find (a) how far it will have traveled in 30 seconds and (b) its speed at that time.

1.4 An object moves with an acceleration of 0.10 meter/sec/sec. (a) How far does it go, starting from rest, in 1 minute, and (b) how fast is it traveling at the end of that time?

1.5 (a) What is the average acceleration of a car that reaches a speed of 60 miles/hr from a standing start in 1 minute?
  (b) How far has it gone by the time it reaches 60 miles/hr?

Chapter 2

FORCE

First Law of Motion   Newton's first law of motion states that an object remains in its state of rest or of uniform motion in a straight line unless it is acted upon by an external force. This statement may at first appear to conflict with the familiar idea that a moving object will slow down and stop unless we continue to exert some force upon it. However, a little consideration will show that this is not the case. Consider a chair standing on a floor; the chair can be moved from one place to another by pushing it, and it will stop moving when it is no longer pushed unless it is moving rather fast. If, however, instead of a chair, we push a table on wheels, it is obvious that the table would continue to roll for an appreciable distance after we stopped pushing it. The same is true of a skater on ice. Having acquired some speed, the skater can coast for a considerable distance without applying any force at all.

The difference between these three cases is the amount of friction which opposes the motion of the object. If this is large, then the object stops quickly; if it is small, then the object continues to move for a great distance. This experience may be extrapolated in support of the first law of motion. That is, it may be accepted that if there were no friction, the object would move indefinitely. Another way of stating the first law of motion is that acceleration and deceleration are caused only by the application of a force.

Acceleration of Gravity   The most familiar example of accelerated motion caused by a force is that of a falling object. Here the force is the gravitational attraction that the earth exerts upon the object. It can be shown by simple experiments that all objects, unless they are very light, take just about the same time to fall the same distance. For example, if a cork and a piece of lead are released at the same instant from a point eight feet above the floor, they hit the floor at the same time, as nearly as one can observe. If we used a stop watch to time their fall, we should find that they hit the floor in about 0.7 of a second. (A more realistic estimate would be 0.7 plus or minus 0.1 second, that is, somewhere between 0.6 and 0.8 second.)

The acceleration caused by the force of gravity can be calculated from these rough measurements, using the equation $D = UT + \frac{1}{2}AT^2$; it is found that the acceleration, based on the estimate of 0.7 second for 8 feet, is 33 feet per second per second. However, the measurement is not precise and if 0.6 and 0.8 seconds are used as the lower and upper limits, it is found that the acceleration works out to 45 and 25 feet per second per second, respectively. Thus we conclude that the actual value is somewhere between 25 and 45 feet per second per second. Measurements of much higher precision made with high-speed photography indicate that the acceleration is about 32.2 feet per second per second or 9.81 meters per second per second. It must be clearly stated that this acceleration is caused by the gravitational attraction of the earth for the falling object and these numbers only apply at or near the surface of the earth; they vary slightly from one place to another on the surface of the earth. The acceleration caused by the moon's gravity acting upon an object near the surface of the moon would be about 1.60 meters per second per second.

Terminal Velocity The acceleration due to gravity is not the only force that acts upon a falling body. The air through which the body is falling offers some resistance to its motion. This force acts in the direction opposite to that of the motion. The speed of a falling object increases until the air resistance exerts a force equal to that of gravity, when the resultant force is zero and there is no further acceleration. The velocity at which this happens is called the terminal velocity; it is lower for very small or very light objects (such as raindrops) than for large or heavy ones (such as a bomb). For example, a water drop whose diameter is 0.01 millimeter has a terminal velocity of fall equal to 0.01 meter per second or about 2 feet per minute. Clouds very often form in air which is rising at a rate that is equal to or greater than 0.01 meter per second. A larger drop with a diameter of 0.1 millimeter has a terminal velocity of 1 meter per second, so drops of this size can therefore fall as rain. One of the major problems in meteorology is to understand why the small drops sometimes coalesce to form large ones that have a high terminal velocity.

Shape is an important factor in determining terminal velocity, because air resistance increases with increasing cross section of the object meeting the air, whereas the force of gravity depends only upon its mass. A parachute has a low terminal velocity (about 15 feet per second) because of its large cross section and relatively small mass.

Second Law of Motion; Force The first law of motion can be rephrased by the very plausible statement that acceleration takes place only if a force is applied. Newton's second law of motion goes further. It uses this statement as a definition of a force and it uses the implications of the statement to define the unit of force. Newton's second law may be stated in the form "force equals mass times acceleration," or $F = M \times A$. The unit of force is the force that will cause a unit mass to move with unit acceleration.

Mass The force that will cause a mass of 1 pound to move with
and an acceleration of 1 foot per second per second is called the
Weight *poundal*. The force that will cause a mass of 1 kilogram to move with an acceleration of 1 meter per second per second is called the *newton*. The force of gravity causes a mass of 1 pound to move with an acceleration of 32 feet per second per second and therefore the force which gravity exerts upon a mass of 1 pound is 32 poundals, and the force which

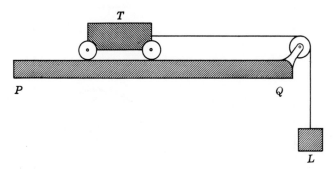

Fig. 2.1. Measurement of the relationship between mass and weight.

gravity exerts upon a mass of 1 kilogram is 9.81 newtons. *The force which gravity exerts* is known as the *weight*. The weight of an object is not necessarily constant since it would change substantially if the object were moved to the moon or to one of the other planets or to some other point in space, and in fact is slightly different at different places on the earth. But the mass of an object is constant and corresponds to the amount of matter in the object.

The experiment illustrated in Fig. 2.1 demonstrates the validity of the relationship between force, acceleration, and mass. *PQ* is a horizontal surface along which the trolley *T* may roll. It is attached to the load *L* by a thread. The force that moves this system is the force that gravity exerts on the load *L* and is therefore the weight of the load. The mass to be moved is the sum of the mass of *L* and the mass of the trolley *T*. It can readily be seen that reducing the load *L* or increasing the mass *T* decreases the acceleration with which the trolley and the load move. The system can also be used to give us a better estimate of the acceleration of gravity.

It is found that if no force is applied to the thread, the trolley comes to rest, as a result of the force of friction, which is always in the direction that *opposes* the motion that causes it. If the total force on the trolley is to be found, it is necessary to subtract the friction from the force applied by the load. The magnitude of the friction can be measured by determining what load will just keep the trolley moving at constant speed (no acceleration). The weight of this load is equal to the force of friction.

The following results were obtained in such an experiment. The load L was 0.200 kilogram, the mass of the trolley 1,468 kilograms, and it was established by a trial that the force of friction was equal to 0.060 kilogram. In

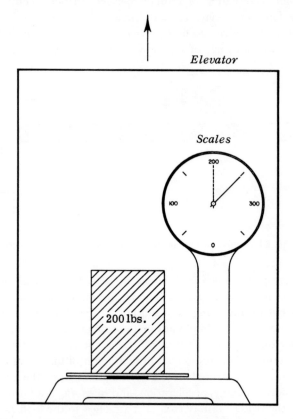

Fig. 2.2. Increase of apparent weight during upward acceleration of an elevator.

other words, a load of 0.060 kilogram (60 grams) would just keep the trolley moving. Therefore the total force acting upon the trolley was a weight of 0.140 kilogram. The experiment consisted in determining how long it took for the trolley, starting from rest, to move a distance of 1 meter. The average of a number of observations showed that the time was about 1.55 seconds. Using the formula $D = \frac{1}{2}AT^2$ the acceleration is 83.5 centimeters per second per second. The force, in newtons, that corresponds to the weight of 1 kilogram is calculated as follows: the force acting upon the system is $0.140 \times g$, where g is the required number, and that is equal to the mass, 1.668 times the acceleration, 83.5. Working out the value of g gives a result of 9.90 meters per second per second.

Since the weight of 1 pound is about 32 poundals, it is necessary to exert a force of 32 poundals to prevent a mass of 1 pound from falling. To lift a mass of 1 pound, it is necessary to accelerate it upward, and this requires a force of 32 poundals, which balances the force of gravity, plus whatever force is required to cause an upward acceleration. Thus, to lift it with an acceleration of 5 feet per second per second would require a force of 32 + 5.5

50 lbs.   50 lbs.

Fig. 2.3. The monkey on the rope.

poundals, that is, 37.5 poundals, which is equivalent to a weight of 37.5/32 pounds, or about 1 pound 3 ounces. Similarly, if the mass is allowed to descend with an acceleration of 16 feet per second per second, the apparent weight would be $\frac{1}{2}$ pound.

A familiar example of the change of apparent weight resulting from vertical acceleration is the sensation experienced in a high-speed elevator while it is accelerating or decelerating (Fig. 2.2). During upward acceleration one's apparent weight is greater than one's real weight; this could be measured if one stood on scales. During the deceleration at the top, one's apparent weight is less than one's real weight because the upward acceleration is negative. The situation is reversed during downward acceleration and deceleration. A classical problem which demonstrates the principles involved in acceleration and force is illustrated in Fig. 2.3. A large frictionless pulley supports a weightless rope which is tied to a weight of 50 pounds. On the other end of the rope is a monkey that also weighs 50 pounds. What happens if the monkey starts to climb the rope? Would the monkey move upwards, would the weight move upwards, or would they both move?

Resultant Forces The acceleration experienced by a body depends only on its mass and the force acting upon it; but the force must be considered as the total or net force. This may be a result of the action of more than one independent force, such as the tension in the string in one direction and the force of friction in the other, in Fig. 2.1. If the forces act in the same or opposite directions (vertically up or down, for

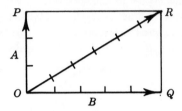

Fig. 2.4. Graphical method for finding the resultant, OR, of two forces, OP and OQ.

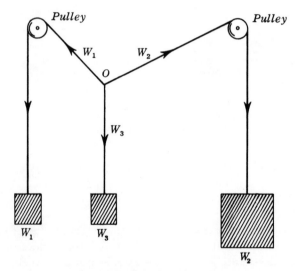

Fig. 2.5. The resultant of two forces.

example), it is easy to find the resultant by adding or subtracting. If they act in different directions, for example, one vertically and one horizontally, then the determination of the resultant force is not quite so simple. The problem is complicated by the fact that we have a physical quantity—in this case, force—which depends not only upon magnitude but also upon direction. One pound of apples plus 1 pound of apples is always equal to 2 pounds of apples, but it would not always be correct to say that the resultant of a force of 32 poundals and another force of 16 poundals is 48 poundals. Figure

2.4 shows the graphical method of finding the resultant of two forces A and B, whose directions and magnitudes are represented by the lines OP and OQ. The line QR, equal in length and parallel to OP, is added to the end of line OQ, and the line OR represents the resultant, both in direction and in extent. Thus, if the line OQ is drawn to represent a force of 5 poundals, and the line QR is drawn on the same scale to represent a force of 3 poundals, it will be seen that the line OR has a length of 6 on the same scale. The resultant is therefore 6 poundals in the direction OR. An experiment to demonstrate the validity of this method is illustrated schematically in Fig. 2.5. A string passes over two pulleys, and weights W_1 and W_2 are attached to the ends of

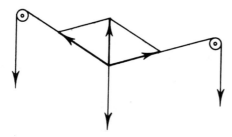

Fig. 2.6. Measurement and calculation of the resultant of two forces.

the string. The tension in the string is a force equal in magnitude to the weight it supports. The direction of the force must be along the length of the string, because the string is not rigid and consequently will not support a force in any other direction. The magnitudes and the directions of the forces exerted on the string at the point O are therefore known. The resultant of these two forces will cause the point O to move, since it will remain at rest only if the net force acting upon it is zero. If a load W_3, which is just equal and opposite to the resultant of W_1 and W_2, is attached to the string at the point O, then the string will remain stationary. Figure 2.6 shows such an experiment with the appropriate graphical construction superimposed. By a similar method, a single force can be *resolved* into two or more components.

Angular Acceleration: Moment of a Force The discussion so far has been confined to acceleration in a straight line, but it is clear that rotating objects can also accelerate; this type of motion is called angular acceleration, and is discussed in terms of analogous but slightly different concepts. The effect of a force on an object which can rotate depends not only upon the magnitude of the force, but also upon where it is applied; and the effective mass of a rotating object depends not only on its actual mass but also on how the mass is distributed; that is, upon how far away it is from the center of rotation. Figure 2.7 represents a wheel which can rotate about its axis O. It will be seen that a force acting on the wheel in the direction and along the line OA will not tend to make it rotate, but a force acting along the line PQ will do so. The turning effect of such a force is given by the product of the magnitude of the force and the distance OP of its line of action from the center of rotation. This is called the *torque*, or *moment* of the force about the center of rotation. Similarly the mass is least effective if it is at the center of rotation and most effective if it is far from the center of rotation. The effective mass is called the *moment of inertia*. The angular acceleration is given by a formula analogous to the one discussed

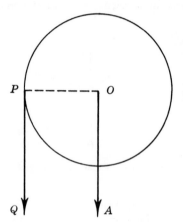

Fig. 2.7. Forces acting upon a wheel.

previously, and the *torque* or *moment* is equal to the *moment of inertia* times the *angular acceleration*.

The Lever　　The fact that the "turning effort" is equivalent to the moment, can be demonstrated by means of a lever. Figure 2.8 represents a bar resting upon a fulcrum F; the bar is placed so that it just balances. If we place a mass of 1 pound at A, a distance of 2 feet from F, it will unbalance the lever. To balance the lever again, we place a mass upon the lever to the right of the point F. We may use either a small mass far from the fulcrum or a large mass close to it. A simple experiment shows that we can balance the lever by placing 2 pounds at 1 foot, or 1 pound at 2 feet or $\frac{1}{2}$ pound at 4 feet, and so on. In fact any combination of mass and distance will balance the lever if their product is equal to 2, which is the moment of the mass A about the fulcrum F. This principle is used in the crowbar, which makes it possible for a relatively small force to lift a much larger weight. In Figs. 2.9a and b, if the weight W is close to the fulcrum F, then a smaller force P, much further away from the fulcrum, can

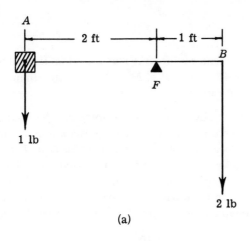

(a)

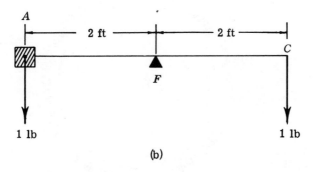

(b)

Fig. 2.8. The lever. The mass of 1 pound at A can be balanced by 2 pounds at B, or 1 pound at C, etc.

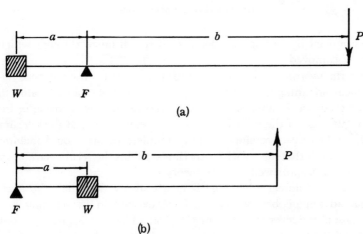

(a)

(b)

Fig. 2.9. The crowbar. A relatively small force P is used to lift the large weight W.

produce a moment sufficient to lift W. The criterion for balancing the crowbar would be that $W \times a = P \times b$. If P is greater than this it will exert net force which will raise the weight W.

Machines   Any device by which a small force can be used to exert a larger force is technically known as a *machine*. A measure of the performance of a machine is its *mechanical advantage*, the ratio of the force exerted by the machine to that exerted on it. The lever is a very simple machine; in the example shown in Fig. 2.9, the mechanical advantage is W/P. If there is no friction to overcome, this is equal to a/b, which is the *ideal* mechanical advantage. This is equal to the ratio of the

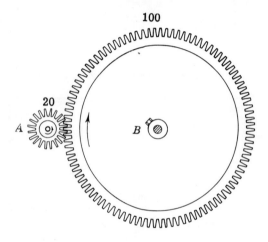

Fig. 2.10. A pair of gear wheels.

distance moved by the applied force P to the distance through which the weight W is moved.

The term *theoretical* mechanical advantage is often used instead of *ideal* mechanical advantage; however, this implies that the actual value differs from the theoretical value, which means that the theory is wrong or incomplete. In the case of the lever it would mean that friction at the fulcrum had not been taken into account. A more complete theory would include this and give a result that agrees with experiment. Thus the term *theoretical* should not be used without specifying the theory.

The *real* mechanical advantage is nearly always less than the *ideal* mechanical advantage because of the force exerted in overcoming friction. In the case of the lever the ideal mechanical advantage is given not only by the ratio of the forces that should be exerted but also by the ratio of the distance moved by the applied force and by the force exerted by the machine,

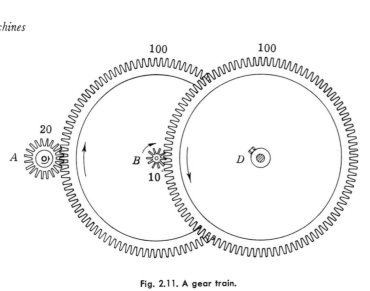

Fig. 2.11. A gear train.

for example, by the ratio a/b in Fig. 2.9. A pair of gear wheels is another
example of a very simple machine. In Fig. 2.10, A represents a small wheel
and B a larger wheel. The wheels can rotate about their centers and are
provided with meshing gear teeth, so that where the two wheels are in
contact, they must always move at the same speed. If the
small wheel A has 20 teeth and the large wheel B has 100,
the large wheel rotates by 1/5 turn while the small wheel
rotates once, and the ratio of their speeds is 5 to 1. The
ideal mechanical advantage of this pair of gears would
therefore be 5. Because the large wheel rotates at only 1/5
the speed of the small one, it should apply a torque of 5
times the magnitude. The actual mechanical advantage
would be somewhat less because of the torque required to
overcome friction.

Figure 2.11 shows a slightly more complicated gear
system with 4 wheels: A, B, C, and D. A drives B, C is
attached to the same shaft as B (and hence must rotate at
the same speed), and C drives D. If the numbers of teeth
are respectively 20, 100, 10, and 100, then it requires 50
rotations of wheel A to produce 1 rotation of wheel D, producing an ideal mechanical advantage of 50.

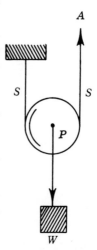

Fig. 2.12. A single
pulley.

Yet another simple type of machine is the pulley system.
In Fig. 2.12 a pulley P is supported by a string S, and
carries a load W. The tension in the string is 1/2 of the load, since the load is
shared by the two parts of the string. If the point A on the string is raised by 1
foot, the load is raised 6 inches; the ideal mechanical advantage is therefore 2.

Figure 2.13 represents a rather more complicated system consisting of four pulleys. The upper pulleys A and B are attached to a support, and the lower ones C and D, are attached to the weight W. A string passes around all the pulleys as shown. The weight W is shared between the four parts of the string P, Q, R, and S. If there is no friction, the load will be shared equally, and the

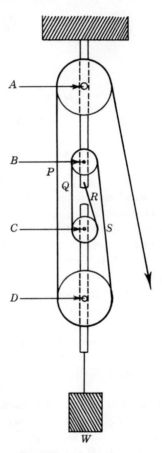

Fig. 2.13. A system of pulleys.

tension in the string required to support the load would be 1/4 of the weight W. The ideal mechanical advantage is therefore 4.

Trajectories   Newton's first two laws of motion make it possible to calculate the path or trajectory of a moving object that is acted upon by a force such as gravity. We must remember, however, that the net or resultant force exerted on an object is not necessarily the same as the force which appears to be exerted, because a force acting upon an object may be partly or completely balanced by some other force. For example, if a man tried to push a box that was too heavy for him to move, his pushing would be balanced by the force of friction between the box and the floor. Conversely, if the force that he applies is not balanced by friction or some other force, then the box must accelerate in the direction of the resultant force. The implications of this example are apparent in the case of the motion of a rifle bullet fired horizontally. The horizontal line *AB* in Fig. 2.14 represents the path that the bullet would follow if the initial horizontal force were the only one acting on it. But there are two other forces which

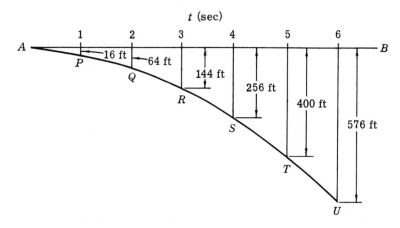

Fig. 2.14. The trajectory of a bullet fired horizontally.

affect it. One is the resistance of the air through which the bullet is traveling; this will be ignored. The other is the effect of gravity, which accelerates the bullet downward. For simplicity, let us assume that the initial velocity of the bullet is 1000 feet per second; the diagram of Fig. 2.14 shows the positions of the bullet after 1, 2, 3, 4, 5, and 6 seconds, respectively. The horizontal distance traveled in those periods of time are 1000, 2000, 3000, 4000, 5000, and 6000 feet, respectively.

Since this motion is horizontal, and the force of gravity is vertical, the *horizontal* velocity will be unchanged, but the bullet will also fall vertically because of the force of gravity. We can calculate the extent of this vertical motion from the formula $D = UT + \frac{1}{2}AT^2$, where U is zero because there was no initial vertical velocity. Using this formula and taking 32 feet per second per second as the acceleration, we find that the vertical distance traveled in 1, 2, 3, and 4 seconds, respectively, are 16, 64, 144, and 256 feet. Therefore, after 1 second the bullet has traveled 1000 feet horizontally and

16 feet vertically; this is plotted as the point P in Fig. 2.14. After 2 seconds it has traveled 2000 feet horizontally and 64 feet vertically, giving the point Q. The point R, after 3 seconds travel, corresponds to 3000 feet horizontally and 144 feet vertically, while the point S, after 4 seconds, corresponds to 4000 feet horizontally and 256 feet vertically. This illustrates the use of a graphical method for combining a constant horizontal velocity with an accelerated vertical motion. The path followed is no longer a straight line but is part of a parabola. The problem becomes slightly more complicated if the initial direction is not horizontal. Figure 2.15 represents the following problem. A ball is thrown at an angle of 30 degrees at a speed of 40 feet per second. How far does it go? It is necessary first to resolve its velocity of 40 feet per second into the horizontal component and the vertical component. This is

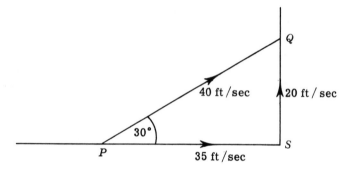

Fig. 2.15. Construction for finding horizontal and vertical components of a velocity.

done graphically in Fig. 2.15. The line PQ represents initial velocity and is 4 units in length. It is drawn at an angle of 30 degrees to the horizontal PS. The lengths PS and QS correspond, respectively, to 35 and 20 feet per second. This means that in 1 second, the ball would rise through a vertical distance of 20 feet while traveling 35 feet horizontally. The initial vertical velocity is 20 feet per second and as $V = U + AT$, where V is zero and U is 20 and $A = -32$ (because the upward velocity decreases), T equals about 0.63 second. This is the time for the vertical velocity to decrease from 20 to zero as a result of deceleration due to gravity and is therefore the time taken to reach the highest point. The time taken to fall from the top of the trajectory to the ground can also be shown to be 0.63 second. In other words, the ball would take just as long to fall as it does to reach the top of its trajectory. The total time of flight is therefore approximately 1.26 seconds, that is, twice 0.63. The horizontal range can now be calculated. The total time of travel is 1.26 seconds; the horizontal speed, which remains unchanged, is 35 feet per second. The distance traveled is therefore $35 \times 1.25 = 44$ feet.

Motion in a Circle   Newton's laws of motion refer to velocity and not to speed; therefore, an object traveling at a constant speed can change its direction only as a result of the application of a force. An example is the motion of an object that must follow a circular path, such as a weight attached to a string, swung so that it travels in a circle at a constant speed. The velocity of the weight is constantly changing because the direction of motion does not remain the same. We know that any change in velocity is equivalent to acceleration. But since the speed of rotation is constant there is no acceleration along the direction of motion; the motion and the acceleration must therefore be at right angles to each other. The only direction which is always at right angles to a circle is the line joining a point on the circle to the center, that is, the radius. It follows that uniform motion in a circle corresponds to acceleration that is at all times directed toward the center. To produce such acceleration a force must be applied and the direction of this force must always be toward the center of the circle. The force which must be applied toward the center of the circle to cause motion in a circle is called *centripetal force*. The acceleration is given by the formula

$$A = \frac{V^2}{R} = \Omega^2 R$$

and the force is given by

$$F = MA = \frac{MV^2}{R} \quad \text{or} \quad M\Omega^2 R,$$

where Ω is the angular velocity, in radians per second.

The centripetal force is the force which must be exerted on the string to cause the weight to move in a circle; it is therefore the tension in the string. It would be equally correct to state that the weight rotating in the circle exerts a force on the string. This is also given by the formula MV^2/R and is called the *centrifugal* force, that is, the force with which the rotating object tends to move away from the circular path. If the string were to break, the weight would continue to move without any further change in direction, since there would no longer be any force; it would go in a straight line which would be a tangent to the circle.

A well-known example of centrifugal force is the force experienced by the pilot of an aircraft when he changes direction of flight. An aircraft traveling at 400 miles per hour follows a curved path, the radius of the curve at a particular instant being 2000 feet. The acceleration toward the center which is required to achieve this is calculated from the speed, which is equivalent to approximately 587 feet per second; the acceleration is given by the formula $A = V^2/R$, is $587^2/2000$ which works out to about 172 feet per second per second. It is customary to express this result in terms of the acceleration of gravity, by dividing the actual acceleration by the acceleration of gravity: $\frac{172}{32}$ equals about 5.5. In other words, the acceleration experienced by the pilot is about 5.5 times as great as the acceleration of gravity, or 5.5g. The force required to achieve this acceleration is applied to the pilot by the seat of his chair. The less rigid parts of his body tend to move outward; the relative displacement of the more rigid

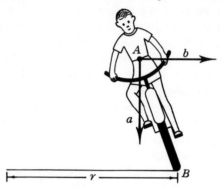

Fig. 2.16. Graphical construction for the angle for a bicycle making a turn.

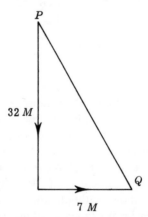

Fig. 2.17. Graphical construction for the angle of a bicycle.

parts and the blood may cause him to "black out" (lose consciousness). A similar centrifugal force is exerted on a cyclist who wishes to change direction. To do this he must lean toward the center of the circle of rotation through which he is going. This is necessary so that the resultant force acting upon him and his bicycle will not apply a torque to it, tending to tip it in either the inward or the outward direction. In Fig. 2.16 the line AB represents the bicycle, B being its point of contact with the ground. The resultant force on the bicycle must therefore be along the line AB. This is the resultant of the mass a of the bicycle and the centrifugal force b. The appropriate angle for a given speed and radius of turn can be calculated as follows: Let the speed be 10 miles per hour (15 feet per second) and the turning radius 30 feet. The centrifugal force is MV^2/R, which is $M \times 15^2/30$ or about $7M$, where M is the mass of the bicycle and rider. This is the force b in Fig. 2.17. Force a in Fig. 2.16 is the weight of the bicycle and rider expressed in poundals, that is, $M \times 32$. The angle at which the bicycle must lean can therefore be determined by a graphical construction, Fig. 2.17, in which we construct a triangle with a base $7M$ long and a height of $32M$. The direction of the line PQ is the required angle of tilt. The value of M need not be known because both sides of the triangle are scaled up or down according to the value of M.

Friction   It has already been mentioned that friction gives rise to forces that always tend to prevent an object from sliding over another; that is, the force of friction always acts in the opposite direction to the motion that causes it. The magnitude of the force of friction depends upon the nature of the two surfaces (what they are made of, their smoothness or roughness, and whether there is any lubricant between them) and on the force that presses them together (which is known as the normal force). The frictional force increases as the normal force increases, and the ratio of the two forces is called the *coefficient of friction*. The coefficient of friction for the trolley in Fig. 2.1 is the ratio of the force required to move it without acceleration (the weight of 0.060 kilogram) to the normal force (a weight of 1.468 kilograms). The ratio of the forces is 0.060/1.468, which equals 0.041; this is the coefficient of friction for the trolley assembly.

A coefficient of friction can also be measured by the method shown in Fig. 2.18. A block of wood rests on a board which can be tilted to any angle. The slope is increased until the block just slides down the board, that is, when the force acting on the block parallel to the surface of the board equals the force of friction. The weight of the block acts vertically, and is represented by the line OA. This is resolved, by the graphical construction, into two components at right angles to each other, OC, parallel to the board, and CA perpendicular to it. OC is equal to the frictional force and CA is the normal force; the coefficient of friction is therefore OC/CA, or $2.6/3.5 = 0.74$, since the lengths of OC and CA are 2.6 and 3.5 centimeters, respectively.

The problem of the bicycle turning a corner can also be considered in terms of friction. The centripetal force required to make the bicycle change direction must be applied to the tires by friction with the ground; if the friction is insufficient, the wheels will slip outward. The frictional force, in the example (top of page), must therefore be equal to $7M$ poundals, while the normal force is $32M$ poundals; the coefficient of friction must therefore be at least $\frac{7}{32} = 0.22$. On a slippery surface the coefficient of friction may easily be as low as 0.1; in this case the cyclist would have to resort to a larger radius of turn or a lower speed to avoid skidding.

The coefficient of friction between two surfaces is seldom greater than 1.0. Assuming a coefficient of friction of 1.0 between the tires of an automobile and a road (good, dry surface, and good tires) we can calculate how fast, and in what distance, it is possible to slow down from 60 miles per hour. The frictional force and the normal force are both equal to $M \times g$, so that the maximum acceleration that could be attained on a level surface is given by $M \times g = M \times A$; the M's cancel, leaving $A = g$ or 32 feet per second

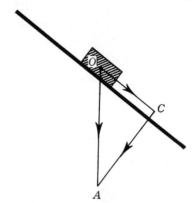

Fig. 2.18. Measurement of the coefficient of friction.

per second. To find the minimum braking distance necessary under these optimum conditions, we can use the equation

$$V^2 = U^2 + 2\,AD.$$

We insert the values

$$U = 88 \text{ ft/sec}, \qquad V = 0, \qquad A = 32 \text{ ft/sec}^2;$$

we find that

$$D = 120 \text{ ft.}$$

To find the minimum stopping time, we use

$$V = V + At$$
$$0 = 88 - 32t$$
$$t = \tfrac{88}{32} = 2.75 \text{ sec.}$$

Universal Gravitation   It has long been recognized that the centripetal force that causes the earth and the other planets to rotate about the sun, and the moon to rotate about the earth (instead of moving in straight lines), are manifestations of the same kind of force that causes objects near the earth to be attracted toward it. This is the force of *gravitation*. It is expressed in quantitative form as the *law of universal gravitation*, which states that an attractive force F acts between any two masses, M_1

and M_2. The magnitude of this force is given by the formula $F = GM_1M_2/D^2$, where D is the distance between them and G is the universal gravitational constant, which is equal to 6.67×10^{-11} newtons per meter^2 per kilogram^2. The force acts upon both bodies along the line joining them, and pulls them toward each other. If we know the masses of any two bodies, such as the earth and the moon, we can calculate the gravitational force between them:

$$M_1 = \text{mass of the earth} = 6 \times 10^{21} \text{ tons or } 6 \times 10^{24} \text{ kg}$$
$$M_2 = \text{mass of the moon} = 6.6 \times 10^{29} \text{ tons or } 6.6 \times 10^{22} \text{ kg}$$
$$D = \text{distance} = 2.4 \times 10^5 \text{ miles or } 3.8 \times 10^8 \text{ meters}$$
$$F = GM_1M_2/D^2 = 6.67 \times 10^{-11} \times 6 \times 10^{24} \times 6.6 \times 10^{22}/(3.8 \times 10^5)^2$$
$$= 1.8 \times 10^{20} \text{ newtons or } 1.8 \times 10^{16} \text{ tons weight.}$$

We can also calculate the very small forces between ordinary terrestrial objects. The force acting between two masses, each 1 kilogram, placed 10 centimeters apart is found by using the formula $F = GM_1/M_2/D^2$; the force is equal to 6.67×10^{-4} newtons, or less than one billionth (10^{-9}) of the weight of a kilogram. If this force were the only one acting between the two masses, they would accelerate toward each other (according to the formula $F = Ma$) with an acceleration of 6×10^{-9} meters per second per second. If this acceleration were maintained at the same value, the masses would meet in a little over 6 hours. In practice it is not possible to eliminate the forces of friction that would prevent an experiment of this kind being carried out successfully.

Orbits of Planets, the Moon, and Other Satellites Although an object at the end of a string can rotate only in a circular path with constant centrifugal force and constant speed, a planet or satellite subject to the law of universal gravitation can rotate in a path which is either circular or elliptical. The planets all follow paths which are elliptical. There is always some acceleration or deceleration along the orbit, but the main component of the acceleration is still directed toward the center of the orbit, that is, toward the sun. As would be expected in an orbit controlled by gravity, the time taken to circle the orbit once depends upon its radius (or in the case of an ellipse, the average distance).

The time of rotation of an artificial satellite about the earth can be calculated as follows: the satellite is at a height of 500 miles above the surface of the earth; that is, at a distance of 4500 miles from the center of the earth. The force between the earth and a satellite is equal to G times the product of the mass of the earth and the mass of the satellite, divided by the square of the distance between their centers: $F = GM_1M_2/D^2$, where F is the force between earth and satellite, M_1 and M_2 are the mass of the earth and of the satellite respectively, and D is the distance. If the satellite is in a circular orbit, the force of gravity holding it in the orbit must just equal the centrifugal force.

The centripetal force is equal to MV^2/R, where M is the mass of the satellite, V is its velocity at the instant considered, and R is the radius of its orbit (the distance between the orbit and the center of the earth). Using accepted figures for the mass of the earth and for G, we set up the equation

$$\text{Centripetal force} = GM_1M_2/D^2$$

where M_1, the mass of the earth $= 6 \times 10^{24}$ kg

M_2, the mass of the satellite, need not be known

D, the radius of the orbit, $= 4500$ miles $= 7.6 \times 10^6$ meters. We find that

$$F = \frac{6.67 \times 10^{-11} \times 6 \times 10^{24} \times M}{(7.6 \times 10^6)^2} = \frac{4 \times 10^{14}}{5.7 \times 10^{13}} = 7M \text{ newtons}$$

but

$$F = \frac{MV^2}{R},$$

therefore,

$$0.7M = \frac{MV^2}{7.6 \times 10^6}$$
$$V^2 = 7 \times 7.6 \times 10^6 = 5.3 \times 10^7$$
$$V = 7 \times 10^3 \text{ meters/sec.}$$

The circumference of the orbit is $2\pi R = 4.8 \times 10^7$ meters, therefore, the satellite completes it once in

$$4.8 \times 10^7/7 \times 10^3 = 6800 \text{ sec}$$
$$= 111 \text{ min}$$
$$= 1.8 \text{ hr.}$$

It will be noted that the mass of the satellite does not enter into the result; any part of the satellite would follow the same orbit even if it is separated from all the other parts.

Weightlessness One of the problems often discussed in connection with space travel is that of weightlessness. A simple but inaccurate view of the meaning of the term weightlessness would be to assume that it refers to the conditions existing at a point (whose location could be calculated) between the earth and the moon and the sun, where the gravitational attraction of the three objects cancels; that is, the point where there is no resultant gravitational attraction and where an object would not tend to fall in any direction. An object at that point would be weightless in the sense that no gravity would act upon it. But the problem of weightlessness during space travel is much more serious. The sensation of weight resulting from the action of gravity depends upon the support that the body receives from a chair (if one is sitting) or from the ground (if one is standing). Not only does the body press downward upon whatever supports it, but also the chair or the ground pushes upward on the various parts of the body which rest on them. It is the sum of all these forces that adds up to the sensation of weight. Weightlessness arises whenever the supporting forces cease to act. A simple example of this would occur in an elevator falling with the acceleration of gravity. The elevator and everything within it falls with the same acceleration, and therefore no force is required to support any part, since forces would produce accelerations different from that of gravity. A passenger would not exert any force upon the floor of the elevator, and the various parts of his anatomy would not be supported by one another. The obvious difficulties of conducting experiments in free-falling elevators have led to the use of other methods. An analogous situation arises in a projectile traveling in its own trajectory so long as there is no external force except gravity acting upon it. For this condition to be strictly satisfied, the projectile would have to be outside the earth's atmosphere, as otherwise there would be a retarding force due to air resistance. An occupant of a projectile tends to follow exactly the same path or orbit as the projectile itself, and therefore he does not require or receive support from below, nor do the various parts of his body. Before a man was put into orbit, it was necessary to use high-speed aircraft (which can fly in a free trajectory outside the effective limits of the atmosphere for a short time) to observe and measure the effects of a few seconds of weightlessness. These times were not long enough to make useful psychological observations, but recent orbital flights have provided longer periods of weightlessness. It is reported that the subjects experienced no severe mental or physical discomfort.

Tides It is well known that tides are caused by the gravitational attraction of the moon; but if the gravitational attraction is sufficiently large to cause the water in the oceans to change their level by 10 or 20 feet, then why, for example, does not the gravitational attraction of the moon cause our hair to stand up and point toward the moon? This question can be answered by calculating the force that the moon exerts upon an object on the surface of the earth, and comparing this force with that of the earth's gravity on the same object. It is convenient to calculate the forces exerted by the moon and by the earth upon a mass of 1 kilogram. The force due to the moon will be calculated first. This is given by

$$F = \frac{GM_1M_2}{D^2}$$
$$G = 6.7 \times 10^{-11}$$
$$M_1 = \tfrac{1}{80} \times 6 \times 10^{24} \text{ kg}$$
$$M_2 = 1 \text{ kg}$$
$$D = 4 \times 10^8 \text{ meters.}$$

Substituting these numbers in the equation $F = GM_1M_2/D^2$, we find that

$$F = \frac{6.67 \times 10^{-11} \times 6 \times 10^{24}}{80 \times 16 \times 10^{16}} \text{ newtons}$$

which is approximately equal to 3×10^{-5} newtons. The force exerted by the earth upon the same object is a weight of 1 kilogram: a force of approximately 10 newtons. Therefore, the earth exerts on the object a force equal to about 333,000 times that exerted by the moon. The same proportion applies regardless of the size or mass of the object.

This force might seem too small to cause observable tides. But we should remember that a tide of 10 feet is an extremely small proportion of the radius of the earth (about 4000 miles, or 20,000,000 feet). The height of the tide is thus only about one-millionth of the radius of the earth; from this point of view, it is an extremely small change in the shape of the layer of water that partly covers the earth.

Problems

2.1 (a) How long would it take an object weighing 10 lb to fall 64 ft, starting at rest? (b) How long would it take if the weight of the object were 1 lb?

2.2 A ball is thrown vertically upward at a speed of 16 ft/sec. (a) How high will it go, and (b) how long will it take to come down again?

2.3 A rifle bullet is fired with a velocity of 1000 ft/sec, at an angle of 45°. What is its range (assuming no air resistance)?

2.4 A force causes a mass to move with a known acceleration; the force is equal to the mass multiplied by the acceleration ($F = MA$). Does this still apply if you try to push (i.e., apply a force to) an object that is too heavy for you to move (acceleration is zero)?

2.5 A stone weighing 10 lb is attached to the end of a string which can just support a weight of 30 lb. (a) With what acceleration can the stone be lifted without breaking the string, and (b) how fast can the stone be swung in a horizontal circle if the length of the string is 2 ft? (c) What happens to the stone if the string breaks?

2.6 A pilot is flying an aircraft at 400 miles/hr. What is the sharpest turn he can make so that his acceleration does not exceed $4g$?

2.7 Explain why a bicyclist must lean inward when cornering. At what angle must he lean if he is traveling at 5 miles/hr and turns along an arc of a circle of radius 15 ft?

2.8 The coefficient of friction between the tires of a bicycle and a slippery road is 0.1. What is the sharpest turn that can be made at 10 miles/hr?

2.9 What is the minimum stopping distance for a car traveling at 60 miles/hr if the coefficient of friction between the tires and the road is 0.2?

2.10 If a man can jump 7 ft high on the earth, how high should he be able to jump on the moon?

2.11 Calculate the speed in a circular orbit of a satellite at a height of 500 miles above the earth.

Chapter 3

MOMENTUM

There are several ways to describe or measure the motion of an object. As we have already seen, one of these methods is in terms of the object's speed or velocity. But this method takes no account of the amount of material that is moving; and for many purposes the amount of moving material is just as important as its speed. An automobile moving at 10 miles per hour can do far more damage before it comes to rest than a bicycle traveling at the same speed. The reason is that the automobile has much more *momentum*. *Momentum* is a measure of the motion of a body that takes into account both its mass and its velocity. The momentum is calculated by multiplying the mass and the velocity of the moving object. Thus a 2000-pound automobile traveling at 10 miles per hour would have a momentum equal to 2000 times 10 pound-miles per hour, that is, 20,000 pound-miles per hour. For a bicycle and rider with a total weight of 200 pounds to have the same momentum as the automobile, they would have to travel at 100 miles per hour.

The simplest way of explaining the concept of momentum is as follows. To move a body or to change its velocity it is necessary to apply a force to it. Both the magnitude of the applied force and the length of time during which it is applied determine how much motion results. A force applied for a long time will produce more change in velocity than a force applied for a short time, and we can show that the momentum imparted to a body by the application of a force for a given time is equal to the product of the force and the time. The change of velocity of an accelerated body is given by $V - U$, where U and V are the velocities at the beginning and the end of the time under consideration. Using the relationship of $V = U + At$, it follows that $V - U = At$; but, since $F = MA$, $A = F/M$, where F is the resultant force acting and M is the mass. Therefore,

$$V - U = \frac{F}{M} \times t$$

or $\quad (V - U)M = F \times t, \quad$ or $\quad VM - UM = Ft.$

This shows that the change of momentum, $VM - UM$, is equal to the product of the force and the time during which it acted, assuming that the force is constant. If the force changes, then it is necessary to divide the time into short intervals in which the force remained almost constant, and to add together the force multiplied by the time for each interval.

Reaction: Third Law of Motion   There are many ways in which force may be exerted upon an object: another object may press against it; the two may be pulled together by a taut string which is in tension, or by gravitational attraction; or one object may exert a frictional force by sliding over the other one. It will be realized that in each of these cases, two objects, not one, are involved; the object to which the force is applied and the one which applies the force. It will be seen that in all cases both objects experience force. The forces on the two objects are equal in magnitude but opposite in direction. We have already seen that the force of gravity applies equally to the two objects between which gravitational attraction exists. The force of friction not only tends to slow down the moving object but also to speed up the object over which it slides. A taut string exerts a force on the object attached to one end, and an equal force on the object attached to the other end. These statements are generalized in Newton's third law of motion: *to every force there is an equal and opposite reaction.*

Conservation of Momentum   It follows that when a force applied to an object causes a change in its momentum, there must be an equal and opposite force on some other body for an equal time; this body must suffer an equal and opposite change of momentum because the product of the force and the time during which it is acting must be the same in magnitude and opposite in direction for the two objects. Thus, when one object experiences a change in momentum, some other object must experience an equal and opposite change in momentum, and the total momentum of all the objects concerned does not change. This is *the principle of the conservation of momentum.* A few examples will illustrate this. In Fig. 3.1, two balls of equal weight, A and B, are suspended from strings so that they can swing freely. If A is held at the point P and then released so that it strikes B, A will be stopped by the impact and B will move to the point Q, the same distance from B as P is from A. It will then swing back and strike A, sending A back to the point P, and so on. This description is not quite realistic, because air resistance will slow down the motion slightly so that each successive swing will be somewhat shorter than the one before, but to a very good approximation the ball B would move off from the impact with the same velocity that A had when the impact occurred. Thus the momentum of A and the momemtum of B change by an equal and opposite amount, and the total momentum of the whole system is unchanged. Figure 3.2 shows a variation of the same experiment with four balls. After ball A has struck ball *B*, *A*, *B*, and *C* will be at rest and *D* will swing to the right at a speed equal to that at which *A* hit *B*. Again, the momentum is conserved.

A different and slightly more complicated situation exists if the balls are not of equal mass. In Fig. 3.3, *A* is of smaller mass than *B*. Here *B* swings

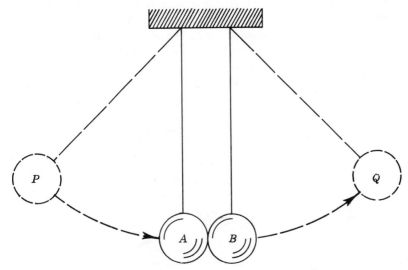

Fig. 3.1. Collision between two spheres of equal mass.

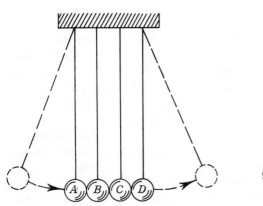

Fig. 3.2. Transfer of momentum.

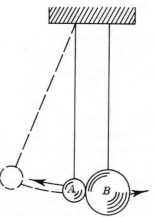

Fig. 3.3. Collision of unequal spheres.

to the right and *A* recoils to the left. If we measured the velocities of *A* and *B* immediately after impact, and multiplied them by the appropriate mass, we would find that the total momentum is unchanged. Similarly, if one ball on a pool table strikes two others simultaneously (see Fig. 3.4), the velocities after impact must add up to the initial velocity in the initial direction of travel.

The conservation of momentum can also be demonstrated by an experiment involving a person wearing roller skates (which for the moment are assumed to be frictionless) and standing on a horizontal floor. He holds a medicine ball. If he throws it forward he will roll backward, so that his momentum plus the momentum of the medicine ball remains zero. We must remember that momentum, like velocity, is a directional quantity and therefore we must subtract momentums that are in opposite directions. If the medicine ball is thrown back to him, his velocity will change in such a way that the total momentum of himself and the medicine ball remains constant

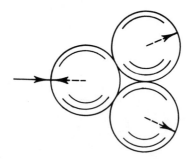

Fig. 3.4. Collision between one moving ball and two stationary balls. Velocity before impact, →; velocity after impact, ⋯→.

The roller skates are, in fact, not frictionless, so that when the subject catches the medicine ball he may either remain at rest or move in the direction in which the medicine ball was thrown. We can explain this by assuming that the medicine ball has a mass M and a velocity V. If its mass is 10 pounds and its velocity 10 feet per second, its momentum, MV, would be 100 pound-feet per second. The subject has a mass of 190 pounds; the total mass of subject and medicine ball is 200 pounds. To have a momentum of 100 pound-feet per second he should roll backward at a speed of about $\frac{1}{2}$ foot per second. This will happen if he absorbs the momentum of the medicine ball in a sufficiently short time so that the acting force is much larger than the force of friction of his roller skates, which tends to oppose his motion. If he catches the medicine ball so that it slows down relatively slowly (by catching it at arms' length and reducing its speed to zero by the time it has reached his body), the time involved is perhaps half a second. Since the change of momentum is given by the product of force and time, and the change of momentum is 100 pound-feet per second, the force is only 200 poundals. If this force, acting for half a second, is less than the force of friction which must be overcome to set the skates rolling, then the subject will not roll backward at all. But how can the momentum of the medicine ball be reduced to zero without violating the principle of the conservation of momentum? Here the effective mass of the recipient is not just his 190 pounds, but also the mass of the floor on which he is standing, the foundations upon which this is built and, in fact, of the whole earth. The change of momentum of the earth is equal and opposite to the change of momentum of the medicine ball, but because the mass of the earth is so large, its change of velocity is negligibly small.

It is worthwhile to point out that the conservation of momentum is not an approximate law, but an absolutely rigorous one. It depends upon two facts: (1) A force cannot be applied to only one object; it is always applied equally to two objects. (2) An object acted upon by a net or resultant force moves with an acceleration equal to the force divided by the mass. How do these facts apply to a ball that is thrown upward and then falls to earth? Initially the momentum of the ball is directed upward; the ball then comes to rest at the top of its trajectory, and eventually it strikes the ground with a velocity equal to that at which it was thrown. The force that changes the momentum of the ball is the gravitational attraction between the ball and the earth. The earth undergoes a change of momentum equal and opposite to that of the ball, but this causes only a negligibly small change in the earth's motion.

Angular Momentum The momentum of a rotating object must be considered somewhat differently than that of an object moving in a straight line. *Moment* or *torque* must be substituted for force, and *moment of inertia* for mass. The product of angular velocity and moment of inertia gives the *angular momentum*, which is also given by the product of the torque and the time during which it acts. This is completely analogous to linear momentum, which is equal to mass multiplied by velocity or force multiplied by time. It follows that angular momentum can only be changed by applying a torque, to which there is always an equal and opposite reaction. Thus, angular momentum is conserved, and a rotating object continues to rotate, unless its momentum is transferred to something else. When a flywheel slows to a stop, its angular momentum is transferred because of friction in the bearings and with the surrounding air; but the total momentum is conserved. Angular momentum and ordinary momentum are really analogous, since the angular momentum of a rotating object is the summation of the linear momentums of all the various parts which do not, of course, all move at the same speed. Angular momentum can be converted to linear momentum, and *vice versa*. They are measured in the same units and are, in a sense, interchangeable. In the case of a windmill, for example, some of the momentum of the air moving against and past the sails of the windmill is converted to angular momentum. A good example of the conservation of angular momentum is seen when a pirouetting ice skater moves his arms further from or closer to his "axis of rotation," thereby increasing or decreasing his moment of inertia. If he starts rotating with his arms outstretched and then brings them close to his sides, his speed of rotation is greatly increased. This is because his angular momentum is constant but his moment of inertia is decreased by concentrating a greater proportion of his mass near his axis of rotation, that is, his own vertical axis. He can slow down again by stretching out his arms and he can repeat the whole process several times before the friction between the ice and his skates stops him.

Reaction Propulsion: Rockets   One of the most important applications of the conservation of momentum is rocket propulsion. In a rocket (see Fig. 3.5), combustion of the fuel causes part of the mass of the rocket to be ejected backward at very high speed; because the momentum of the whole system must be conserved, the rocket moves forward. The same force

Fig. 3.5. Rocket motor.

that ejects the gas backward pushes the rocket forward. For this reason rocket propulsion is at least as effective in outer space as it is in the earth's atmosphere.

The complete mathematical analysis of the motion of a rocket is extremely complicated for several reasons. One is that the mass of the rocket decreases continuously as the fuel is burned; a second is that as a rocket moves further from the center of the earth the force of gravity decreases; and a third is that the rotation of the earth itself, initially shared by the rocket, must also be taken into account.

Let us carry out this calculation in a simplified form. The performance of a rocket motor is given by the thrust multiplied by the time during which that thrust acts; the initial mass of a Titan II rocket is 300,000 pounds and its thrust, 430,000 pounds-weight. First we calculate its vertical acceleration. The net force on the rocket, in an upward direction, is the thrust minus the initial weight of the rocket, that is, $390,000 - 244,000$ or 130,000 pounds-weight. Expressed as a force, this is $130,000 \times 32$ poundals; this is equal to the mass times the acceleration: in this case, 300,000 times the acceleration.

Thus $130,000 \times 32 = 300,000 \times A$, and $A = 13.9$ feet/second². Using the formula $V = U + AT$, we calculate that after 1 minute (assuming that the motor operates for 1 minute), the vertical speed is 568 miles per hour, and the rocket will have risen to a height of 25,000 feet. Here we have neglected the complications due to change of gravity, change of mass, and the resistance of the air, so the calculation is not strictly accurate. The thrust of a rocket depends upon the rate at which gas is ejected from it and the velocity with which that gas moves. The blast velocity of a high performance rocket would be 10,000 feet per second.

Jet Propulsion   All methods of propulsion, from walking to flying, involve reaction. The reaction may be against the ground, as in a car; or against water, as in an outboard motor, whose propeller pushes the surrounding water backward, and the boat forward. In propeller-driven aircraft, the air pushed backward by the propeller is

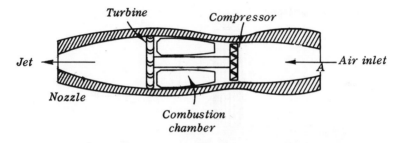

Fig. 3.6. Jet engine.

the reacting mass; in the rocket, the reacting mass is the expelled products of combustion. The jet engine combines the principles of the propeller and the rocket. It draws in air at the front, greatly increases the air's velocity, and ejects it at the rear. The change in momentum of the air passing through the engine accounts for the engine's thrust. The change of velocity results from a very rapid increase in volume caused by the combustion of fuel, which raises the temperature of the air very rapidly.

The main components of a jet engine are shown in Fig. 3.6. Air enters at A, passes through the compressor and into the combustion chambers. Here fuel is injected and burned, causing the air and the combustion products to expand very rapidly. Passing through the turbine, these gases cause it to rotate, and in doing so, lose some of their momentum. (The purpose of the turbine is to drive the compressor.) After passing through the turbine the gas, still traveling at a very high velocity, is ejected from the nozzle to form the jet. In a turboprop engine, the turbine is designed to reduce greatly the momentum of the escaping gases, and thereby to acquire sufficient momentum to drive both the compressor and the propeller. Some turboprop engines use two turbines, one to drive the compressor and another to drive the propeller. The forward thrust developed by the propellers corresponds to the momentum of the air that they drive backward.

Reaction propulsion can be demonstrated in a simple experiment with a carbon dioxide fire extinguisher. Compressed to a pressure 50 to 60 times greater than that of the atmosphere, carbon dioxide becomes liquid, making it possible to store a considerable amount of it in a relatively small volume. When the pressure is released—in other words, when the valve is opened—the liquid carbon dioxide again becomes a gas with a pressure of 50 to 60 atmospheres. When the valve of a fire extinguisher that holds 15 pounds of liquid carbon dioxide is opened, the carbon dioxide spurts out as a jet of gas with considerable velocity. The velocity was measured by mounting the carbon dioxide cylinder on a trolley (see Fig. 3.7). At first the trolley is fixed

CO$_2$ Fire extinguisher

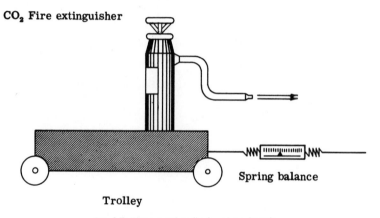

Spring balance

Trolley

Fig. 3.7. "Jet propulsion" of carbon dioxide.

to a spring balance to measure the thrust. In one such experiment the thrust was 25 pounds or $25 \times 32 = 800$ poundals. If the extinguisher delivers this thrust for 3 minutes, the momentum is equal to force times time, and the momentum of the carbon dioxide gas leaving the extinguisher is, therefore, equal to the thrust (800 poundals) multiplied by the time (180 seconds), or about 150,000 poundal-seconds. This is equal to the mass of the gas (15 pounds) times the velocity (in feet per second), which gives a result of 10,000 feet per second for the velocity of the carbon dioxide gas spurting from the extinguisher.

If the experimenter climbs aboard and the trolley is uncoupled from the spring balance, the thrust of the escaping gas will propel him and the trolley across the floor. Assuming that the total weight of the trolley and rider is 200 pounds, we can calculate their acceleration using the equation

$$F = MA,$$

where $F = 800$, and $M = 200$; thus

$$A = \frac{F}{M} = \frac{800}{200} = 4 \text{ ft/sec/sec.}$$

Problems

3.1 Does the "conservation of momentum" apply when a ball, initially at rest, falls (under the influence of gravity) and bounces when it hits the floor?

3.2 A gun weighing 2000 lb fires a shot weighing 10 lb at a velocity of 2000 ft/sec. Calculate the initial recoil velocity of the gun.

3.3 A rocket is put into orbit at a height of 500 miles. Does this affect the length of the day? If so, how would you calculate the amount?

3.4 A car, weighing 3000 lb is traveling at 60 miles/hr on a level road. If it is shifted into neutral, and travels $\frac{1}{2}$ mile before coming to rest, (a) how long would it take to come to rest, (b) what force acted upon it, and (c) what is its acceleration? (d) How is its momentum conserved?

3.5 A birdcage containing a bird is suspended from a balance, so that its weight can be observed. Is its weight greater if the bird flies around in the cage, or if it rests on the bottom of the cage?

3.6 The occupant of a rowboat has lost his oars. Can he propel the boat by moving about in the boat in any way?

3.7 Can the orbit or the attitude of a spaceship be affected by moving objects within it?

3.8 A 5-ton spaceship approaches the moon at a speed of 1 mile/sec; it is to be slowed down just before landing by means of a "retrorocket." (a) If the blast leaves the retrorocket at a speed of 10,000 ft/sec, what mass of blast would be required? (b) At what height above the moon's surface should the rocket be started if the acceleration is not to exceed $5g$?

Chapter 4

WORK, KINETIC ENERGY, AND POTENTIAL ENERGY

When a force is applied to an object, which it causes to move, the effort expended depends upon the distance through which the object is moved and the ease or difficulty with which it is moved. The effort expended is called the work done; it is calculated as the product of the force acting and the distance through which it acts, or, more briefly: *work equals force times distance.* Because there are various units of force and distance, there are also various units for measuring work. Some of these are shown in Table 4.1.

TABLE 4.1
THE UNITS OF FORCE, DISTANCE, AND WORK

Force	Distance	Work
Newton	Meter	Joule
Dyne	Centimeter	Erg
Poundal	Foot	Foot-poundal
Pound (weight)	Foot	Foot-pound

We can calculate the approximate relationship between two of these units; the foot-pound and the joule. One foot equals about 30 centimeters or 0.3 meter, and 1 pound equals about 0.45 kilogram or about 0.045 times 10 newtons. Therefore 1 foot-pound = $0.30 \times 0.45 \times 10 \cong 1.4$ joules.

We have already seen that when a force is applied to an object there is an equal and opposite reaction. The opposing force may originate in a variety of ways. For example, the lifting of a weight is opposed by the force of gravity. If a 1-pound weight is raised 1 foot, the work done is equal to 1 foot-pound; to lift 10 pounds 5 feet would require an amount of work equal to 50 foot-pounds, or 50×32 foot-poundals. Work may also be done against an opposing force of friction. In the case of a chair being pushed across a floor, the opposing force of friction must be measured to determine how much work is done. This measurement can be made by applying the force to the chair through a device such as a spring balance (see Fig. 4.1). The spring balance might read 2 pounds when the chair is sliding across the floor. This means that the force would be 2 pounds or 2 × 32 poundals; the work done in moving the chair is equal to this force times the distance the chair moves.

Another type of opposing force against which work can be done is exemplified by the stretching of a coiled spring. Here it is slightly more difficult to calculate the work done because the force required to stretch the spring

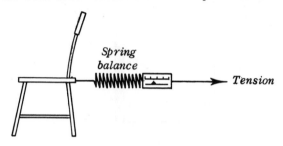

Fig. 4.1. Measurement of friction force.

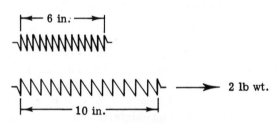

Fig. 4.2. Stretching a spring.

increases as the spring stretches, and therefore is not constant. Starting at zero, the force gradually increases to some maximum value (see Fig. 4.2). The spring shown here is originally 6 inches long; when stretched, its length is 10 inches. It requires a force equal to a weight of 2 pounds to stretch the spring by 4 inches. But the work done in stretching the spring is not simply 4 × 2 inch-pounds, because the force was not constant. Initially the force was zero; when the spring was stretched, the force was 2 pounds. The average force was therefore 1 pound. This is illustrated in Fig. 4.3, a graph of the force and the distance moved. The work being done at any particular stage of the stretching of the spring is equal to the force applied at that time multiplied by the amount of stretch during that time. This product is given for the short period *AB* by the area of the shaded region below *AB*. The total work done going from *P* to *Q* is equal to the area under the line *PQ*. The area of this triangle is equal to one-half the base (4 inches) times the height (2 pounds), that is, 4 inch-pounds or $\frac{1}{3}$ foot-pound.

Still another type of opposing force occurs during acceleration. If an object is accelerated by the application of a force, the work done is still equal to the force times the distance. The work must be done to overcome the *inertia* of the object. In other words, the force must be applied to the object to accelerate it at the required rate.

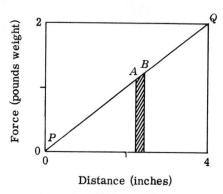

Fig. 4.3. Work done in stretching a spring. Work = force × distance.

Energy, the Capacity to Do Work   Is there any way of telling whether work has been done? Or does it disappear without leaving any trace? If we lift a weight against the force of gravity, or stretch a spring by means of a force, the mass that has been moved will return to its original position if it is released. Each of these systems can do just as much work as had previously been put into it. The weight, in descending, can do an amount of work equal to the number of foot-pounds done on it in raising it, and the spring can do the amount of work which had been done on it. The work done is recoverable. The capacity of these systems to do work is called *potential energy*. It is measured in exactly the same units as the work done, that is, in foot-pounds, foot-poundals, ergs, or joules.

Work may also be converted into kinetic energy (the energy of motion). This occurs when the work causes motion. We can calculate the motion resulting from an amount of work, $F \times D$, applied to an object of mass M. A force F applied to a mass M gives an acceleration F/M. This follows from the equation $F = MA$. If this force is applied through a distance D so that the work done is equal to $F \times D$, the velocity acquired is calculated from the formula $V^2 - U^2 = 2AD$. Assuming that the object starts from rest, $U = 0$, therefore, $V^2 = 2AD$ or $V^2 = 2FD/M$, from which $FD = \frac{1}{2}MV^2$. This quantity, $\frac{1}{2}MV^2$, is the *kinetic energy* resulting from the expenditure of an amount of work equal to FD.

When an object, falls under the influence of gravity, the potential energy which it loses is exactly equal to the kinetic energy which it gains. To raise an object weighing 1 pound to a height of 10 feet requires 10 foot-pounds or 320 foot-poundals of work. If the object falls the same distance, it acquires a velocity given by $V^2 = 2AD$, from which $V^2 = 640$. Its kinetic energy,

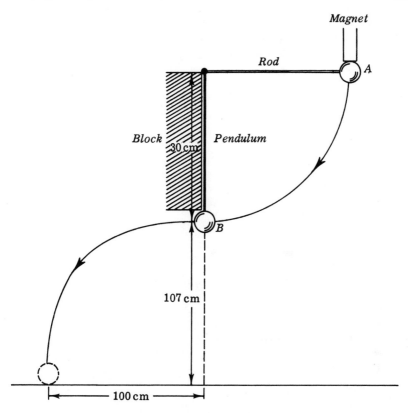

Fig. 4.4. Measurement of kinetic energy of pendulum.

$\frac{1}{2}MV^2$, therefore, equals 320, the number of foot-poundals of work done in raising the object.

A familiar example of the conversion between potential energy and kinetic energy is that of a swinging pendulum. At the end of its swing the pendulum is motionless (and so has zero kinetic energy), but it is higher above the ground than at the start of its swing (and so has a certain amount of potential energy). The potential energy and the kinetic energy of a pendulum were measured in an actual experiment as follows: Figure 4.4 shows a pendulum consisting of a rod pivoted at one end. At the end of the rod a steel ball is supported in such a way that it separates from the rod when the pendulum swings from the horizontal to the vertical position. After swinging into the vertical position, the pendulum is stopped by striking a block, but the ball continues to fall. It follows the trajectory shown in the illustration. In the experiment illustrated here, the horizontal distance traveled by the ball was 100 centimeters.

We can calculate the kinetic energy of the ball at the instant it separated from the pendulum, and compare this with the potential energy which the ball acquires when it is lifted from the point B to the point of release A. First we find the time taken by the ball to travel from the point B to the floor;

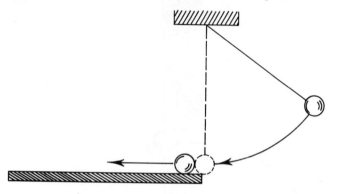

Fig. 4.5. Measurement of kinetic energy of pendulum by the recoil method.

knowing the height, 1.07 meters, we use the formula $\frac{1}{2}AT^2 = D$. Here, $\frac{1}{2}T^2 = 1.07$, and the time $T = 0.45$ second. During that period the ball traveled a horizontal distance of 1 meter. Its horizontal velocity was therefore 2.22 meters per second at the instant it left the pendulum. We assume that this remained constant (air resistance can be ignored). The kinetic energy, which is equal to $\frac{1}{2}MV^2$, is 2.47 × M joules, where M is the mass of the ball. The potential energy, also in joules, is given by the force required to raise the ball multiplied by the height to which it was raised. The force is its mass times 10 and the height is 0.30 meter. The potential energy is therefore 2.94 × M joules.

These results do not quite agree. There is an apparent loss of about 16 per cent of the potential energy. It does not reappear as kinetic energy because the experiment is not perfect. This experimental error has three main causes: there is some friction at the pivot of the pendulum; the ball must do some work to free itself from the device which holds it in place while the pendulum is falling; and there is some air resistance.

In a similar experiment, a pendulum strikes a ball which is free to run along a horizontal track (see Fig. 4.5). The velocity of the ball after it is struck by the pendulum is measured by a simple electrical timing device. Here again the potential energy of the pendulum is calculated from the mass and the height through which it had to be raised. The kinetic energy on reaching its lowest point is calculated from the kinetic energy of the ball which is set in motion by it. The pendulum comes to rest and therefore all of its kinetic energy is transferred to the ball. When this experiment was performed, nearly one-half of the potential energy was apparently lost. A large part of this discrepancy is explained by the fact that the ball is not only set in motion horizontally but it is also set in rotation. Some of the potential energy of the pendulum is converted into the ball's rotational kinetic energy and the remainder is converted into the ball's linear motion, or translational kinetic energy.

It is necessary to distinguish between rotational and translational kinetic energy. An interesting example of both is found in the yo-yo. A yo-yo can be made to spin at the end of the string for a time and then made to climb the string. While it is spinning at the end of the string the yo-yo's energy is entirely kinetic energy of rotation. When it starts climbing the string, this kinetic energy is converted partly into kinetic energy of motion in the vertical direction and partly into potential energy; when it comes to rest at the top of the string, all of the kinetic energy, both rotational and translational, has been converted into potential energy. If it is allowed to fall again, this is reconverted into kinetic energy of rotation and, while the yo-yo is descending, kinetic energy of vertical motion.

Three cases in which work is done on an object have now been discussed; in a fourth case, work done against friction, the work apparently disappears. It is not present either as potential energy or as kinetic energy and therefore is "lost" as mechanical energy. But in Chapter 5 it will be shown that the work is converted to heat energy.

The Conservation of Energy We have seen that mechanical energy may take either of two forms: potential energy or kinetic energy. Energy can be converted from one to the other without loss. Any apparent loss of energy can be explained as the conversion of energy into some other form. That energy is always converted and never lost or gained is known as the principle of the *conservation of energy*. It is sometimes stated: energy can be neither created nor destroyed.

Machines Machines can be considered from the point of view of the work they do and the work done on them. Consider the lever in Fig. 4.6. A large weight W is lifted by the lever, which is pivoted at the point P. A smaller downward force applied at the point A raises the weight. We have already seen that when the lever is balanced the force F times the distance A equals the weight W times the distance B; a

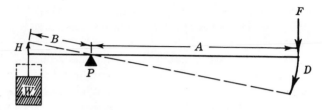

Fig. 4.6. Work done on and by a lever.

slightly greater force suffices to raise the weight. If the lever is tilted to the position shown by the broken line, the work done is equal to the force F times the distance D. The work done in lifting the weight is equal to the weight W times the height H through which it has been lifted; $F \times D$ is equal to $H \times W$, since F/W equals B/A. Thus, the work done on the lever is equal to the work done by the lever, provided that there is no loss due to friction at the pivot. Assuming no friction, we find that the mechanical advantage, W/F, is equal to the ratio of H to D: the ratio of the height (through which the weight is lifted), to the distance (through which the force F is applied). It is impossible to get more work out of the machine than is put into it; this is another example of the principle of the conservation of energy.

"Perpetual Motion" Machines   Many ingenious inventors have designed machines which they thought would provide a perpetual source of work or energy. One such machine is illustrated in Fig. 4.7. It consists of a smooth ramp with two slopes, one steeper than the other. A continuous chain of smooth spheres connected by a flexible string rests partly on the two slopes and hangs below them. Because there are four spheres on the gentle slope and only two on the steep one, the inventor claimed that the four spheres, which are heavier than the two, will pull the chain downward to the left. But there is a fallacy in this argument. The only force that tends

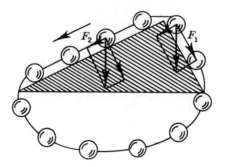

Fig. 4.7. A "perpetual motion" machine.

to move the spheres is the force parallel to the slope on which they rest. The weight of each sphere which rests on a plane can be divided into two components, one parallel to the plane and one perpendicular to it. The relative values of these forces are shown by two graphical constructions. The spheres in contact with the steep slope have a larger component of force (F_1) parallel to the slope than those which are in contact with the gentle slope (F_2); the total force acting parallel to one slope is equal to the total force acting parallel

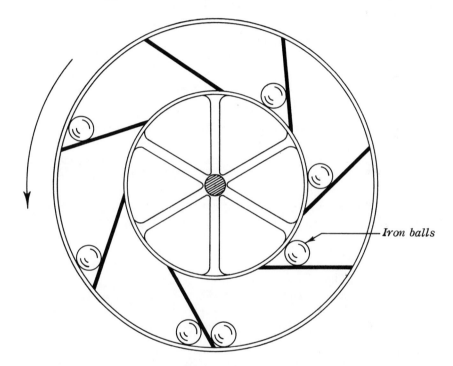

Iron balls

Fig. 4.8. Another perpetual motion machine.

to the other. These forces act in opposite directions (down the slope) and they balance each other. Therefore the chain would not move indefinitely and could not do work indefinitely.

Another perpetual motion machine is shown in Fig. 4.8. It consists of a hollow wheel free to rotate about its axis. The wheel is partitioned into several compartments, each of which contains a heavy iron sphere; a sphere can occupy any position within its own compartment. The distribution of the spheres tends to turn the wheel counterclockwise. It would seem that as the wheel rotates the spheres will roll outward to the left and maintain the rotation. It is left to the reader to discover the fallacy in this argument.

Water Power One of the ways in which energy is available to man is in the form of the potential energy of the rain that falls upon mountains or high land. If the water is allowed to run off into the oceans, its energy becomes unavailable; therefore it is necessary to store the energy until it can be converted into a form in which it is useful. To do this, natural valleys are closed off by dams that confine a large amount of water. In this way a considerable amount of energy can be stored, for example, in a small lake 100 feet wide, 50 feet long, and 20 feet deep. This lake contains $100 \times 50 \times 20 = 10^5$ cubic feet of water. Since 1 cubic foot of water weighs about 62 pounds, the total mass of the water is about 6,200,000 or 6.2×10^6 pounds. If this water is stored 1000 feet above a power station, the potential energy of the water is 6.2×10^6 pounds times 1000 feet, or 6.2×10^9 foot-pounds. This amount of energy will be compared later with that available in other ways.

Tidal Power Energy is also available from tides. One method of harnessing this energy is to enclose an area which fills at high tide; the water flows out of this enclosure through a water mill, which converts the potential energy of the water into the kinetic energy of rotation of the mill. The volume of water enclosed in an area of 1 square mile, if the tide is 10 feet, is about 3×10^8 cubic feet, or about 2×10^{10} pounds. This water would descend an average distance of 5 feet as the tide ebbs. The amount of energy available would therefore be about 10^{11} foot-pounds.

Power The term *power* is used in a technical sense to represent the rate at which work is done or energy is made available. Power can therefore be expressed as the work or energy that is expended or made available per unit of time. A simple unit of power would be 1 foot-pound per second, since the foot-pound is a unit of work and a second is a unit of time. Similarly, 1 joule per second is also a unit of power. The foot-pound per second is too small for general use; the customary units are the *horsepower* (550 foot-pounds per second), the *watt* (1 joule per second), and the *kilowatt* (1000 watts). Power, expressed in horsepower, can be easily converted into watts. One horsepower is equal to 550 foot-pounds per second; 1 foot is approximately 0.30 meter, and 1 pound is about 0.45 kilogram. Therefore, 550 foot-pounds equals approximately $550 \times 0.30 \times 0.45$ kilogram-meters; but 1 kilogram-meter is equal to 9.81 newton-meters or joules. Therefore, 550 foot-pounds per second equals $550 \times 0.30 \times 0.45 \times 9.81$ joules per second. This is approximately equal to 7.5×10^2 joules per second, 750 watts, or $\frac{3}{4}$ kilowatt. Very roughly the horsepower and the kilowatt are of comparable magnitude. More precisely, a kilowatt is equal to three quarters of a horsepower.

We can use several examples to gain some idea of the amount of power in 1 horsepower. First, what horsepower is required to raise an elevator weighing 1000 pounds to a height of 250 feet in 1 minute? The work done per minute is equal to 250 × 1000 foot-pounds; the rate of working is 250 × 1000, or 2.5 × 10⁵ foot-pounds per minute, or

$$2.5 \times 10^5/60 = 4.2 \times 10^3 \text{ foot-pounds per second.}$$

Since 550 foot-pounds per second is 1 horsepower, the rate of working is $4.2 \times 10^3/5.5 \times 10^2 = 7.6$ horsepower. We assume that the only work done was that required to raise the elevator against the force of gravity, and that all of the work done was converted into potential energy. This neglects any work consumed in other ways, such as overcoming friction.

Let us consider another problem; what horsepower is exerted by a man weighing 150 pounds if he runs up a staircase at the rate of 3 feet of vertical climb per second? Here the rate of work is equal to 3 × 150 foot-pounds per second. The horsepower is equal to $\frac{450}{550}$, that is, 0.8 horsepower. This work is converted completely into potential energy; we have neglected the work done to overcome friction.

The horsepower that a human can exert can be measured by the method shown in Fig. 4.9. A shaft turned by a handle rotates in a bearing that can be tightened to any desired extent. The bearing is tightened until the shaft can barely be turned by hand; the force required to turn it is then measured by attaching a spring balance to the handle and measuring the pull on the spring balance when the handle just moves. In one test the tension recorded in the spring balance was 8 pounds. The subject turns the handle as fast as he can and he is timed, by stopwatch, for, say, 10 turns. The work done in that time is equal to the force applied (8 pounds) times the total distance traveled by the handle (10 times the circumference of the circle through which it travels). The handle is 1 foot from the shaft, and the circumference of the circle is therefore $3\frac{1}{7}$ feet; during 10 revolutions the handle moves through a distance of about 31 feet. The work done is therefore 8 × 31 foot-pounds or about 250 foot-pounds. It took one subject exactly 3 seconds to turn the handle 10 times; his rate of work, therefore, was $\frac{250}{3}$ foot-pounds per second = 83 foot-pounds per second. This is $\frac{83}{550}$ or 0.15 horsepower; in other words, between 1/6 and 1/7 horsepower.

Like the horsepower, the kilowatt is a measure of the rate of working. If a kilowatt of power is exerted for 1 hour, a definite amount of work is done or a definite quantity of energy is supplied or used. A quantity of energy corresponding to 1 kilowatt for 1 hour is the *kilowatt-hour* (KWH), a unit frequently associated with electrical energy. It should be recognized that 1 kilowatt-hour will be used not only if 1 kilowatt works for 1 hour but also if 10 kilowatts work for 1/10 of an hour, or if 1/100 of a kilowatt works for

100 hours; so long as the product of the number of kilowatts and the time in hours is equal to one, then 1 kilowatt-hour is consumed. The work in kilowatt-hours is equal to power (in kilowatts) times time (in hours). Since the kilowatt-hour is a unit of work or energy, we can express the same amount of energy in foot-pounds: 745 watts are equivalent to 1 horsepower or 550 foot-pounds per second, so 1 kilowatt is equal to $\frac{1000}{750} \times 550$ foot-pounds per

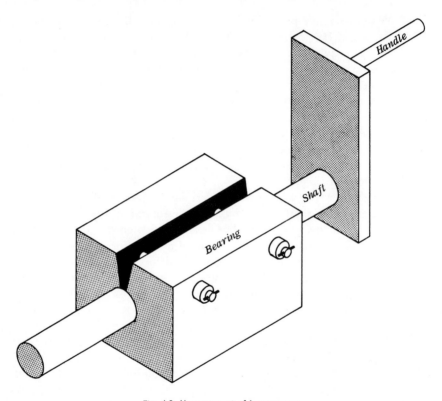

Fig. 4.9. Measurement of horsepower.

second, and 1 kilowatt-hour is equal to $11,000/15 \times 60 \times 60$ foot-pounds, or about 2.7×10^6 foot-pounds.

A somewhat similar unit of work is the horsepower-hour, which equals 1.34 kilowatt-hours. Using these units, let us consider the potential energy of stored water in terms of the power that it can yield. The lake that we considered earlier in this chapter has a water storage capacity of 10^5 cubic feet, with a potential energy of 6×10^9 foot-pounds. We shall now assume that the supply of water to this lake can fill it completely (starting empty) in 1 month. On this basis, one-thirtieth of the stored water can be used per day without lowering the level of the lake. Energy could be extracted continuously at the rate of

$$6 \times 10^9 \text{ ft-lb/month,}$$

or $\quad (6 \times 10^9)/(30 \times 24 \times 60 \times 60) \text{ ft-lb/sec} = 2.3 \times 10^3 \text{ ft-lb/sec,}$

or $\quad\quad\quad\quad (2.3 \times 10^3)/(5.5 \times 10^2) = 4.2 \text{ HP.}$

The potential energy of the tides was also discussed earlier in this chapter; we found that the energy available per tide (twice a day) in a particular tidal basin was about 10^{11} foot-pounds. If the water were released in 1 hour (at low water) the power available would be

$$10^{11}/3600 \text{ foot-pounds per second} = 2.8 \times 10^7 \text{ foot-pounds per second}$$
$$= 5 \times 10^4 \text{ horsepower for 1 hour;}$$

this would be available twice a day. If a continuous supply of power is required, then this 50,000 horsepower for 1 hour could in principle be used for pumping water into a higher lake from which it could be allowed to run continuously. Assuming no losses in pumping, the 50,000 horsepower for 1 hour would then be equivalent to 50,000/12 horsepower for 12 hours, and this would supply about 4000 horsepower continuously.

Elastic Energy One of the most important characteristics of potential energy is the fact that it is recoverable. In other words, it can be converted into work. Ideally, the amount of work that can be recovered is equal to the amount of work done (the potential energy). So far the discussion of potential energy has been mainly confined to cases in which work is done against gravity. We will now consider another major form of potential energy: the potential energy present because of the elastic distortion of a solid, a liquid, or a gas. We must begin by defining the term, "elastic." One of the main characteristics of a gas is that it will completely fill a container of any shape or size. No force is required to change the shape of a gas but a force is always required to reduce its volume, because a gas exerts a pressure on the walls of its container. In other words, if a gas is compressed, work is done upon it, and conversely, if a gas is allowed to expand, it can do work. Since the work done in compressing a gas is recoverable when the gas is allowed to expand again, the process is called *elastic* distortion. The only way in which a gas can be distorted so that it will subsequently return to its previous condition is by changing the pressure upon it; the only two variables that we need to consider are pressure and volume.

The case of a liquid is somewhat different. The volume of a liquid is much less affected by pressure. It will flow, that is, it will assume any shape without a force acting on it. The volume of a liquid can be changed slightly by compressing it, and so some recoverable work can be done upon it.

Solids differ from liquids and gases in that they always have a specific shape and volume and a force must be applied to change either of these. The change of shape may be either permanent (such as the flattening of a lump of putty) or elastic (such as the stretching of a rubber band). If the band does not break, it will snap back to its original length when the force stops acting upon it. Elastic deformation can be recovered upon removal of the force causing it. Since all solids can be deformed elastically to some extent, it follows that energy can be stored in them as potential energy of deformation.

Energy Stored To consider the energy stored in a compressed gas, we must
in a first calculate the work done in compressing it from its
Compressed Gas original volume (at atmospheric pressure) to some smaller volume (at increased pressure). The normal pressure of the atmosphere is about 15 pounds per square inch; we shall assume that a quantity of gas is

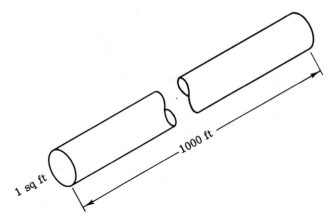

Fig. 4.10. Work done in compressing a gas.

to be compressed to 100 times this pressure, that is, to 1500 pounds per square inch or 100 atmospheres. When a gas such as air is compressed, its volume decreases so that the product of pressure and volume remains constant. Thus if the pressure is increased tenfold, the gas is compressed to one-tenth its previous volume. Similarly if the pressure is increased a hundredfold (as in this example), the gas is compressed to one-hundredth of its previous volume.

The energy stored in the compressed gas can be calculated in the following way. Figure 4.10 represents a pipe with a cross-sectional area of 1 square foot, and 1000 feet long. The air in the cylinder is compressed by a piston inside the pipe. The work done on the piston is equal to the energy stored in the gas, assuming that no energy is expended to overcome friction. We also

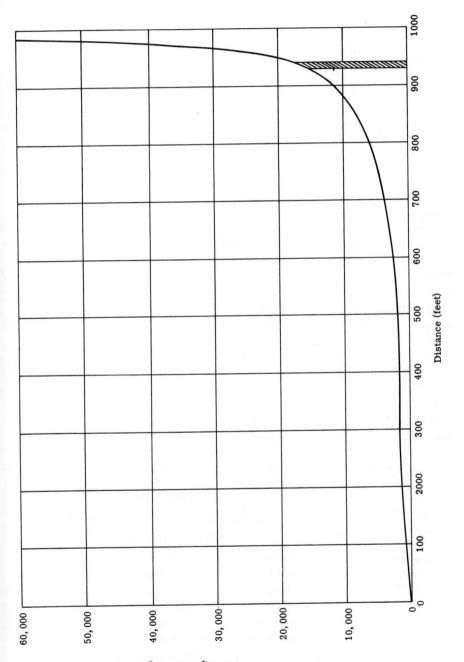

Distance (feet)

Force (pounds-weight)

60,000
50,000
40,000
30,000
20,000
10,000
0

0   100   2000   300   400   500   600   700   800   900   1000

assume that no air leaks past the piston (these assumptions would probably not be correct in an actual experiment). This method of compressing a gas is not practical, but the calculation gives the energy stored no matter how the air is compressed.

Initially the pressure of the atmosphere (15 pounds per square inch) acts upon both sides of the piston, and the force required to move it is zero. When the air is compressed to half its original volume (500 cubic feet) the pressure is doubled (30 pounds per square inch) and so the piston is opposed by a *net pressure* of 15 pounds per square inch, or a force of

$$15 \times 144 = 2160 \text{ pounds.}$$

When the volume is decreased to 100 cubic feet, the pressure is 150 pounds per square inch, and the force is 21,600 pounds. When the volume has reached its final value of 10 cubic feet, the pressure is 1500 pounds per square inch and the force is 216,000 pounds. The work done is found by plotting a graph of force and distance (Fig. 4.11). The force increases slowly at first and much more rapidly as the volume approaches the final value. Because the force changes continuously and at an increasing rate, the work cannot be computed by multiplying it by the distance; instead, the operation must be divided into parts that are so small that the force is almost constant in each of them. The shaded interval in the illustration is typical. In this interval the work done in compressing the gas is equal to the average force times the distance the piston moved; in other words, the area of the shaded rectangle. The total work done is equal to the area under the complete curve. If the graph is drawn on squared paper, the area can be estimated by counting squares. It is found to be equal in area to the rectangle at the right of the diagram, whose dimensions correspond to 100 feet by 100,000 pounds. The work done, and therefore, the stored energy, is approximately 100,000 $\times$ 100 or 10^7 foot-pounds.

If this amount of energy were used in 1 hour, the power would be 5.2 horsepower. The efficiency of storage, which in this case would be expressed as horsepower-hours per pound, would depend largely upon the weight of the container needed to store compressed air safely at the assumed pressure of 100 atmospheres, or 1500 pounds per square inch.

Energy Storage To calculate how much energy can be stored in the same **in a Compressed** volume of liquid at the same pressure, we must know how **Liquid** much the volume of the liquid changes for a given change of pressure. Unlike gases, liquids obey no simple law of volume-pressure relationships. But the compressibility of many liquids is known and is tabulated in various handbooks. The compressibility of water is given as 50×10^{-6} per atmosphere. This means that any volume of water will change by

50 × 10⁻⁶ of that volume if the pressure changes by 1 atmosphere. Ten cubic feet of water will therefore change by 10 × 50 × 10⁻⁶ × 100, or about 0.5 cubic foot, for a change of pressure of 100 atmospheres. The cylinder needed for this purpose would therefore be about 10.5 feet long compared with a 1000-foot cylinder in the case of the gas. The work done in compressing the liquid is equal to the average force (half the final force), or

$$1500 \times 144 = 1.1 \times 105 \text{ pounds}$$

multiplied by the distance through which this force works, which is 0.5 foot. This is 5 × 10⁴ foot-pounds. With the same pressure and the same volume, and therefore, with the same weight of container, it is only possible to store 5 × 10⁴ foot-pounds of energy in compressed water, compared with 10 million foot-pounds that can be stored with compressed air.

A simple experiment illustrates the difference in stored energy between a compressed gas and a liquid at the same pressure. If a small rubber balloon is blown up until it has reached a selected size, say a diameter of 8 inches, and is then burst by pricking it with a pin, it makes an appreciable noise and fragments of the balloon may be hurled a considerable distance. If a similar balloon is filled with water until its size (and therefore the pressure) is the same not much happens if it is pricked. This explains why the bursting of a gas storage tank causes more damage than the bursting of a similar container full of a liquid at the same pressure.

Energy Stored in an Elastic Solid Perhaps the most familiar example of energy storage in a solid is that of a spring. There are many different shapes and types of spring, but they all depend upon the elastic change of shape of the metal composing them. The change of shape is usually that of bending or twisting, and the maximum energy that can be stored in

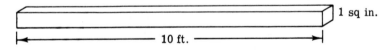

1 sq in.

|← 10 ft. →|

Fig. 4.12. Energy stored in a stretched steel bar.

the spring depends upon its material and upon its size and shape. We shall calculate the maximum energy that could be stored in a spring of the most efficient possible shape; we shall then compare this with the energy that can be stored in a spring of practical form.

Let us envision a spring consisting of a steel rod 1 square inch in cross section and 10 feet long (Fig. 4.12). We can do the greatest amount of work on this rod by stretching the entire spring to the limit of its elastic behavior. (In practice it is never possible to strain all of the material to its maximum extent, which is why this calculation will give an ideal rather than a real solution.) Let us assume that a force of 250,000 pounds per square inch can be applied to the steel before it ceases to behave elastically. From suitable handbooks we find that the amount by which steel stretches under stress is equal to one thirty-millionth of its length for each pound per square inch applied to it. The amount by which a 10-foot length would stretch is therefore equal to 260,000/30,000,000 × 10 feet; this is about equal to 0.1 foot, or a little more than 1 inch. The work done in stretching the spring by this amount is equal to half the maximum force times the amount of stretch. This is equal to 250,000 × 0.1/2, or about 12,000 foot-pounds. Calculating the energy available in the form of horsepower, we find that this is one horse-power for 24 seconds. As we mentioned earlier, the efficiency of energy

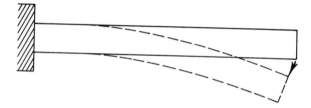

Fig. 4.13. Bent steel strip.

storage may be expressed in foot-pounds per pound of storage medium. In this case 12,000 foot-pounds are stored in about 35 pounds of steel. This is about 350 foot-pounds per pound of steel.

A much more common form of storage unit is a spring in which the metal is bent rather than stretched. If the steel consists of a strip which is bent to the position shown by the broken lines in Fig. 4.13, the upper part of the spring is stretched, the lower part is compressed, and the length of the center part is unchanged. The maximum force, 250,000 pounds per square inch, is applied only at the two surfaces; the force and the amount of stretch or compression become progressively less toward the center. In fact the average force is only half the maximum force and the average stretch or compression is only half the maximum stretch or compression; therefore the average work done is only one-quarter of the value calculated for the uniformly stretched bar. In other words, the material in the middle is not carrying its fair share of energy storage. It is difficult to see how this problem can be circumvented in a spring that bends. The same thing happens in a rod subjected to torsion, as shown in Fig. 4.14; the maximum energy storage is about the same as before, and if the rod is solid, the material near the center is stressed less and deformed less, and therefore stores less energy per unit volume or per unit mass. Torsion springs are often made as hollow cylinders. Here, most of the metal is concentrated near the periphery, and the energy storage is very much more efficient; in fact it might approach the theoretical value calculated earlier. When a coiled spring is compressed or stretched, the main deformation of the wire or rod forming it is by torsion.

A simple experiment illustrates the conversion of the elastic energy of a solid into kinetic energy. Figure 4.15 represents a rubber tube whose ends

Fig. 4.14. Energy stored in a rod with torsion.

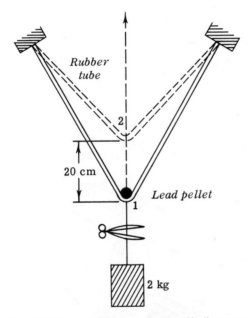

Fig. 4.15. Conversion of elastic energy to kinetic energy.

are attached to two fixed supports. Initially it is in the position shown by the broken lines; when a load of 2 kilograms is attached to it, it stretches to the position shown by the solid lines. The 2-kilogram load is then released by cutting the string which supports it, and the snapback of the tube propels a 90-gram lead pellet upward. The 2-kilogram load pulls the tube downward by 20 centimeters. The work done is equal to the average force (1 kilogram, or approximately 10 newtons) times the distance (0.20 meter); this works out to be about 2 joules. If this energy were completely converted into upward motion of the pellet, its kinetic energy (2 joules) would become its potential energy when it reached its maximum height. Knowing the potential energy and the mass of the pellet, we can calculate its maximum height.

Potential energy = *mgh*
$$2 \text{ joules} = 0.90 \times 10 \times h \qquad \text{(since mass of lead} = 0.090 \text{ kg)}$$
$$\text{thus} \qquad h = \frac{2}{0.090 \times 10} \text{ meters}$$
$$= 2.2 \text{ meters}$$

In one experiment the pellet reached a height of about 150 centimeters. Here less than 75 per cent of the potential energy stored in the stretched rubber tube was converted into the kinetic energy of the pellet and consequently into potential energy. Some energy is retained in the rubber tube as kinetic energy of vibration.

The Flywheel   Energy can also be stored as the kinetic energy of a rotating flywheel. To calculate the amount accurately we must consider the design of the flywheel and the maximum strength of its material. To simplify the problem, we shall consider the very simplest type of flywheel: a wheel consisting of a flat steel hoop fixed to a shaft by a thin web of negligible mass (see Fig. 4.16). If the hoop is so thin that all of its mass is effectively the same distance from the shaft, its kinetic

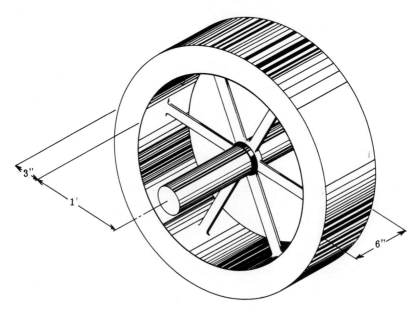

Fig. 4.16. Idealized flywheel.

energy is $\frac{1}{2}MV^2$, where M is its mass and V, its velocity along the arc of a circle.

Suppose the radius of the wheel is 1 foot, the thickness of the hoop is 3 inches, and its width is 6 inches. The mass of the hoop is calculated as follows. The circumference of the wheel is 2π times the radius, or approximately 6 feet; the width of the wheel is $\frac{1}{2}$ foot, and the thickness is $\frac{1}{4}$ foot. The volume of the wheel is $6 \times \frac{1}{4} \times \frac{1}{2}$, or $\frac{3}{4}$ cubic foot. The density of steel is about 420 pounds per cubic foot, so the mass of the wheel is about 315 pounds. We shall assume that the maximum strength of the steel is 200,000 pounds per square inch; the maximum speed of rotation of the wheel is calculated so that the centrifugal force in it does not exceed 200,000 pounds per square inch, that is, the centrifugal force on half of the wheel must not exceed the strength of the steel joining it to the other half. This corresponds to a total centrifugal force of 200,000 pounds weight or $200,000 \times 32$ poundals per square inch times 36 square inches, the cross section of the two sides of the hoop (because the force is divided between the two opposite sides of the rim). This number of poundals is equal to the centrifugal force MV^2/R, where R equals 1. Therefore $315V^2 = 200,000 \times 36 \times 32$ from which V^2 equals approximately 7×10^5 and V equals approximately 800 feet per second. This is equivalent to about 8000 revolutions per minute. The kinetic energy in foot-poundals is half the mass times the square of the velocity. The mass is already known (315 pounds), the velocity is 800 feet per second, and the kinetic energy is therefore about 2×10^8 foot-poundals. This is about 6×10^5 foot-poundals per pound and is equivalent to approximately 3 horsepower for 1 hour. This method of energy storage has been used experimentally for public transportation vehicles.

Problems

4.1 (a) What is the kinetic energy of a 2-ton car traveling at 60 miles/hr?

(b) What force would be needed to stop it in 250 ft?

(c) How far up a hill of 10 per cent slope would it go, assuming no friction, after stopping the engine?

4.2 Is kinetic energy a *directional* property? What is the change in kinetic energy when an elastic ball bounces on a hard floor?

4.3 How fast would a 3-ft pendulum swing through its lowest position if it swings through an arc of 20°? (Use a graphical method.)

4.4 (a) What is the kinetic energy of a 2-lb shell fired from a gun at 2000 ft/sec?

(b) What is the kinetic energy of the recoil of the gun, if it weighs 2 tons?

4.5 (a) What is the potential energy of the water in a lake of 10 square miles area, average depth 50 ft, at an elevation of 1500 ft?

(b) How fast must water be taken from the lake to provide energy at the rate of 10,000 kw?

(c) How much rainfall (per year) would be required, on a catchment area of 100 square miles, to keep it supplied?

4.6 Calculate the energy stored in the air in an automobile tire at a pressure of 30 pounds per square inch (psi). (Estimate dimensions of tire.)

4.7 Calculate the range of an arrow, of mass 2 oz, shot from a bow requiring a 60-lb pull; the arrow is pulled back by 2 ft when the 60 lb pull is applied.

4.8 A bicycle, traveling on a level road, freewheels to rest in 200 ft. Calculate the horsepower required to ride it at 10 miles/hr.

4.9 (a) What *thrust* would be required to accelerate a 2-ton car from rest to 60 miles/hr in 2 min?

(b) What is the horsepower at the beginning, in the middle, and at the end of this time?

4.10 Explain the action of the "Pogo Stick."

Chapter 5

THE NATURE OF HEAT

Temperature Temperature, in a qualitative sense, is familiar to everyone.
and The human body can sense that its environment is warm
Quantity of Heat or cold, or so neutral as to produce little, if any, sensation
of temperature. When the temperature stimulus is a mild one (i.e., not severe
enough to cause pain), discrimination is reasonably good among a variety
of temperature sensations ranging from very hot to very cold. But when the
stimulus becomes strong enough to cause pain, it is no longer possible to
make such qualitative distinctions, as anyone who has "burned" himself on
"dry ice" knows. With the advance of science and technology it has become
necessary to distinguish temperatures much more precisely; it has become
necessary to measure temperature instead of just estimating it. The physio-
logical and psychological responses of the human body are unable to make
measurements of the precision required and therefore other means are
needed.

Any property of a substance that depends upon temperature and can be
measured is available as a method of measuring temperature. In practice
only a few methods are commonly used. The best known of these, illustrated
by the ordinary mercury thermometer, depends upon the fact that the volume
of most liquids increases with temperature. Figure 5.1 shows the construction
of this type of thermometer. It consists of a narrow-bore glass tube attached
to a bulb filled with mercury, which also extends part of the way up the
tube. If the temperature is raised, the mercury expands and rises in the tube.
The glass of which the tube is made also expands, but much less than the
mercury. Consequently, the level of the mercury in the tube is an indication
of the temperature. But the device cannot be used to measure temperature
until units have been assigned. One way of doing this would be to construct
one thermometer, to be regarded as the standard, and to graduate it with
some arbitrary scale of units. Another thermometer could be calibrated from
this standard by putting both in water at various temperatures and marking
the second thermometer accordingly.

The tedious process of comparing each thermometer with a standard is avoided by choosing temperatures that are easily and accurately reproduced, called *fixed points*. If, for example, a thermometer is put into a mixture of ice and water, the mercury will come to a certain level such as L in Fig. 5.1. If the thermometer is taken out of this mixture and immersed in another ice-and-water mixture, the mercury will return to the same level, L, and will do so every time, whatever the proportion of ice and water in the mixture. This temperature can therefore be accurately described as fixed. Similarly, the boiling point of water is also fixed, though not quite as precisely, since this temperature depends to a minor extent upon atmospheric pressure. Any thermometer can now be marked at the points corresponding to these two temperatures. A scale of temperature is constructed by dividing the interval between the two temperatures into equal units, the number depending on the scale chosen.

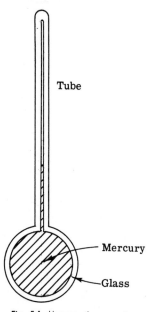

Fig. 5.1. Mercury thermometer.

Of the two scales in common use, the *centigrade* or *Celsius* scale divides the interval into 100 degrees, with the freezing point of water at zero degrees and the boiling point of water at 100 degrees. On the *Fahrenheit* scale the interval contains 180 degrees, with the freezing point of water at 32 degrees and the boiling point of water at 212 degrees. Thus an interval of 5 centigrade degrees is equal to an interval of 9 Fahrenheit degrees. This makes it possible to convert temperatures from one scale to another. The conversion of 15 degrees centigrade to degrees Fahrenheit involves a temperature which is 15 degrees above the freezing point on the centigrade scale and an unknown number of degrees above the freezing point on the Fahrenheit scale. The unknown interval on the Fahrenheit scale, F, is to 15 as 9 is to 5; that is, 15 centigrade degrees corresponds to $F/15 \times \frac{9}{5}$ or 27 Fahrenheit degrees. The Fahrenheit temperature is therefore 27 degrees above the freezing point (32 degrees Fahrenheit) and thus is $27 + 32$, which is 59 degrees Fahrenheit. The conversion of 72 degrees Fahrenheit to degrees centigrade, to use a different example, involves a temperature 40 degrees above the freezing point on the Fahrenheit scale and an unknown number of degrees above the freezing point on the centigrade scale. The unknown interval on the centigrade scale, C, is to 40 as 5 is to 9; that is, $C/40 \times \frac{5}{9}$ or approximately 22 centigrade degrees. The centigrade temperature is therefore 22 degrees above the freezing point (zero degrees centigrade) or 22 degrees centigrade.

Defined in this way, the temperature scales can be extended in either direction beyond the fixed points. The lower limit of the mercury thermometer is set by the fact that mercury freezes if it is cooled to too low a temperature (below about −40 degrees Fahrenheit) and, if the temperature is made too high, either the mercury would boil or the glass would soften. But there are many other methods by which temperatures can be measured, not all of them subject to the same limitations. For example, temperatures lower than −40 degrees Fahrenheit can be measured with a thermometer containing alcohol instead of mercury.

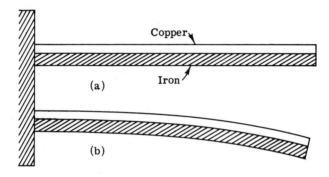

Fig. 5.2. Bimetal strip of copper and iron (a) bends when heated (b).

The expansion of solids, particularly of metals, with temperature may also be employed. All metals expand upon heating, some more than others. One common device for measuring temperatures is a bi-metal strip such as that shown in Fig. 5.2a. When the temperature is raised, the copper expands more than the iron, causing the strip to curve. If one end of the strip is fixed, the position of the other end can be used to indicate the temperature by moving a pointer on a dial.

Quantity of Heat If a quantity of water at a high temperature is mixed with a quantity of water at a low temperature, the final temperature of the mixture will be somewhere between the two extremes. This means that the temperature of part of the water has gone up and the temperature of the rest of it has gone down. An alternative statement is that some heat has been transferred from the part of the water that was originally hot to the part that was originally cold. The idea involved here is the obvious one that if heat is added to water its temperature rises and if heat is subtracted, its temperature falls. The Calorie (or kilocalorie), is defined as the quantity of heat that will raise the temperature of 1 kilogram of water 1 centigrade degree. Conversely, if 1 Calorie is removed from 1 kilogram of water, the temperature falls by 1 centigrade degree. The other familiar unit of heat is the quantity of heat required to raise the temperature of 1 pound of water by 1 Fahrenheit degree; that is, the British Thermal Unit (BTU). The mixing of hot and cold water can now be considered quantitatively. Suppose 1 kilogram of water at 80 degrees centigrade is mixed with 1 kilogram of water at 20 degrees centigrade. It can easily be seen that the final temperature of the mixture will be 50 degrees centigrade because the kilogram that started at 80 degrees and finished at 50 degrees will have lost 1.0×30 Calories to the water that started at 20 degrees, which in turn will have gained 1.0×30, or 30 Calories. It will be evident that the assumption has been made that the total quantity of heat remains unchanged. If this experiment is actually performed by putting 1 kilogram of water at 20 degrees centigrade into a metal container and pouring the 80-degree water into it, the final temperature will be, not 50 degrees, but perhaps 46 degrees centigrade. Since the heat lost by the hot water is greater than that gained by the cold water, it follows that some heat has gone into raising the temperature of the container and of the thermometer used to make the measurement. The next step is to calculate how much heat should have been taken up by the metal container. Suppose that the container, itself metal, also weighs 1 kilogram and has a temperature of 20 degrees centigrade. One kilogram of water at 80 degrees is now added to 1 kilogram of water at 20 degrees, and to the container, weighing 1 kilogram, also at 20 degrees. If it is assumed for the moment that the container behaves like the water in it, and that the total number of Calories gained by the water and the container is equal to the number of Calories lost by the water, the water and the container should all come to 40 degrees centigrade. The experiment shows that the temperature is 46 degrees centigrade and it must therefore be concluded that the metal container requires less heat for a given rise in temperature than was assumed. The experiment demonstrates that it does not require just 1 Calorie to raise the temperature of 1 kilogram of every substance by 1 centigrade degree.

The use of water in the definition of the Calorie is essential. Almost all other substances require less heat to raise their temperature by a given amount than does water, that is, it has a lower *specific heat*. The specific heat of a substance is the ratio of the heat required to raise the temperature of that substance a given amount to the heat required to raise the temperature of an equal mass of water by the same amount. The specific heat of a metal, for example, can be measured as follows. A quantity of water of known mass and temperature is placed in a thermos bottle. A piece of the metal to be studied is weighed and heated to a known temperature, for example, by immersing it in boiling water for a long enough time to reach 100 degrees centigrade. It is then placed in the water, which is at 20 degrees centigrade, and the temperature reached by the water and the metal is measured. The calculation is made on the basis that the heat lost by the metal is equal to the heat gained by the water and, for an accurate measurement, by the containing vessel. (The latter can be measured by an experiment of the type discussed previously, in which hot water is mixed with cold water and the heat taken up by the vessel is determined.) This experiment gives the number of Calories given up by each kilogram of the metal during each centigrade degree fall in temperature. Table 5.1 contains some figures for the specific heats of various substances. (It may be observed that the specific heat is a number with no units, because it is the ratio of the amount of heat required by, for example, copper to the amount of heat required by the same mass of water to change their temperatures by the same amount. This does not depend upon whether the measurements are made in kilograms or in pounds or whether the temperature is measured on the centigrade or the Fahrenheit scale.)

TABLE 5.1
SPECIFIC HEATS OF SOME SUBSTANCES

Substance	Specific heat	Substance	Specific heat
Aluminum	0.20	Salt	0.2
Mercury	0.33	Many organic substances	0.3–0.7
Copper	0.92	Hydrogen (gas)	3.39
Iron	0.11		
Lead	0.03		

It will be seen that most substances require less heat to raise the temperature of a given mass by 1 degree than is the case for water. The amount of heat required to raise the temperature of 1 liter or 1 cubic foot, by 1 degree, however, is in many cases very much closer to that of water. Copper, for example, has a density about 8 times that of water and therefore 1 liter of copper would weigh about 8 kilograms and it would therefore require 0.8 Calories to raise its temperature by 1 degree centigrade.

The amount of heat required to change the temperature of an actual object by a given amount depends upon the mass as well as the specific heat; the *heat capacity*, or thermal capacity, of an object is the amount of heat required to change its temperature by 1 degree. It is the specific heat multiplied by the mass, in Calories per centigrade degree or BTU per Fahrenheit degree. The amount of heat required to raise the temperature of a kettle containing water by 1 centigrade degree can be calculated as follows. Suppose that the kettle has a mass of 0.5 kilogram and a specific heat of 0.1, and that it contains 1 liter of water (i. e., 1 kilogram). The heat capacity of the water, then, is 1.0 Calorie per degree; the heat capacity of the kettle is its mass (0.5 kilogram) times its specific heat (0.1), or 0.05 Calorie per degree. Therefore the thermal capacity of the system, kettle plus water, is equal to 1.05 Calories per degree. If the temperature of the system is to be raised from 20 degrees centigrade to 80 degrees centigrade, it requires an amount of heat equal to the thermal capacity multiplied by the change in temperature, that is, 1.05 × 80, or 84 Calories.

Latent Heat   Suppose that the temperature of a kettle containing the water is measured continuously while it is being heated by means of a source of heat, either a gas burner or an electric hot plate. The temperature might, for example, rise at the rate of 10 degrees per minute. It would then take 8 minutes for the temperature to go up from 20 degrees to 100 degrees and the rate at which heat is supplied in Calories per minute can be calculated. It will be observed, however, that if heat is still supplied, at the same rate, the temperature no longer rises once the water begins to boil; it remains at 100 degrees centigrade. It must be concluded that although heat is continuously supplied, the temperature does not rise. It follows that producing a rise in temperature is not the only way in which heat can be used. In this case it will be evident that the heat is being used in the process of changing the water into steam. This is but one example of many in which heat is used not to produce a change in temperature, but to produce a *change of state*, as, for example, from liquid (water) to vapor (steam). Heat used in this way is referred to as *latent heat*. The heat required to change a substance from its liquid to its vapor state is the *latent heat of vaporization*. It is latent in that if the vapor is allowed to condense, the heat originally absorbed by the vapor becomes available again, and in fact must be removed for condensation to continue. A rough estimate of the latent heat of vaporization of water can be made by observing how long it takes for all the water in the kettle to boil away, assuming that the heat is supplied at a constant rate.

An accurate experiment of this kind would show that it requires about 540 Calories to evaporate or boil 1 kilogram of water. In other words, it takes more than 5 times as much heat to boil the water away once it has reached the boiling point than it takes to raise the temperature from the freezing point to the boiling point. A very similar situation exists in the conversion of ice to water. If ice at a temperature below the freezing point is heated, it is found that the temperature would rise until it reaches zero degrees centigrade. The specific heat of ice is about 0.5 and so it would heat up twice as quickly as an equal quantity of water. Latent heat of fusion would then be required in order to convert the ice to water. The temperature remains constant while the ice melts. The ice melts progressively, 1 kilogram for each 80 Calories of heat that is supplied. The sample consists, during this process, of a mixture of ice and water, as there is no intermediate state between ice and water. Once all the ice has melted, the temperature again starts to rise because the heat is now used for changing the temperature and not for melting the ice. Heat used in changing the temperature is sometimes referred to as *sensible heat*, since it can be sensed, to distinguish it from latent heat.

The latent heat of fusion of ice can readily be measured in the following way. Suppose that 1 kilogram of water at 30 degrees centigrade is placed in a thermos vessel and 0.1 kilogram of ice at zero degrees centigrade is added to it. The ice and the water reach a temperature of 20 degrees centigrade. The heat lost by the water is 10 Calories (1.0 kilogram × 10 degrees). The heat gained by the ice is equal to its mass (0.1 kilogram) times the latent heat, *L*, plus the heat required to raise the temperature of the resulting water from 0 to 20 degrees, which is 2 Calories (0.1 kilogram × 20 degrees). Since the heat lost by the water equals that gained by the ice,

$$10 \text{ Cal} = 0.1L + 2$$
$$L = 80 \text{ Cal/kg.}$$

The latent heat of fusion of ice is therefore 80 Calories per kilogram. Another interpretation of this quantity is that in order to freeze a quantity of water once it has reached the freezing point, it is necessary to remove from it as much heat as was required to lower its temperature from 80 degrees centigrade to the freezing point. Many substances melt in the same abrupt fashion as water. Ice and water can exist together only at the freezing point; and there is no intermediate state. On the other hand, there are many substances that do not freeze or melt abruptly at a fixed temperature. Butter and glass are good examples of materials that gradually soften as the temperature is raised or gradually harden as the temperature is lowered. There is no quantity equivalent to the latent heat of fusion for a substance that behaves in this way.

The Nature of Heat   It has been shown that the term heat has a definite quantitative meaning; when heat is added to an object, either its temperature rises or it changes from solid to liquid or from liquid to vapor, and vice versa. So far we have been dealing with solids and liquids, but the nature of heat is more easily understood if it is considered in relation to matter in its simplest state, that is, the gaseous state.

The most important characteristic of a gas is that it always fills the vessel containing it. If the volume of the container increases, the gas expands to fill the additional space. The pressure of the gas, however, decreases. To demonstrate this, it is first necessary to measure the atmospheric pressure, that is, the pressure of the air around us, for which purpose a *barometer* is used. The simplest form of barometer is a glass tube closed at one end with the open

end immersed in a dish which also contains mercury (shown in Fig. 5.3).
The tube is filled so that it contains no air. If the tube is sufficiently tall, the
mercury does not fill it completely, but remains at a definite level, about
76 centimeters above that of the mercury in the dish. (The unfilled portion
above the mercury contains no air and may be considered to be a vacuum.)
The pressure of the air on the surface of the mercury in the dish is sufficient
to balance the pressure caused by the mercury column in the tube. To calculate this pressure, assume that the cross-section of the tube is 1 square centimeter. The pressure of the atmosphere, then, supports a column of mercury

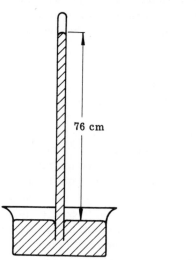

Fig. 5.3. Mercury barometer.

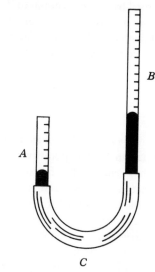

Fig. 5.4. Measurement of the effect of pressure
on the volume of a gas.

with a cross section of 1 square centimeter and a height of 76 centimeters.
That is 76 cubic centimeters of mercury. The density of mercury is 13.6 grams
per cubic centimeter; the mass of the mercury above the level of the dish is
therefore 76 × 13.6 grams, or about 1.034 kilograms. The pressure is therefore about 1.034 kilograms per square centimeter, or 14.7 pounds per square
inch; that is, equal to approximately 1.1×10^5 newtons per square meter,
or 1.1×10^6 dynes per square centimeter. The atmospheric pressure varies
according to meteorological conditions but it is almost always between 70 and
80 centimeters. For most calculations it is sufficiently accurate to regard the
atmospheric pressure as 15 pounds per square inch, 10^5 newtons per square
meter, or 10^6 dynes per square centimeter.

The height of a mercury column that can be supported by the pressure
of a gas is, therefore, a measure of that pressure, and can be used for studying

the effect of changes of pressure on the volume of a gas with an apparatus such as that shown in Fig. 5.4. The glass tube, A, closed at the top and graduated in cubic centimeters, is connected by a flexible rubber tube C to a second glass tube, B, similarly graduated, but open at the top. Mercury is added to the whole apparatus until it is visible in both tubes. The mercury level in A indicates the volume of gas (in this case the volume of air in the unfilled portion). The air pressure in A is equal to the pressure of the atmosphere plus the difference between the mercury levels in B and A if B is above A, or minus the difference if B is lower. Both the pressure and the volume of the gas in A can therefore be observed. Both of these may be changed either by adding or removing mercury or by raising or lowering tube B in order to change the effective volume in which the mercury is disposed. Specifically, if tube B is raised, both mercury levels are raised, the volume of air in A is decreased, but the pressure on it is increased. From Table 5.2, which

TABLE 5.2

EFFECT OF PRESSURE ON THE VOLUME OF A GAS

Volume (cm³)	Difference in pressure (cm Hg)	Pressure (cm Hg)	Pressure × volume
2	+116	192	384
3	+ 49	125	375
4	+ 19	95	380
5	0	76	380
6	− 13	63	378
7	− 21	55	385
8	− 29	47	376
9	− 34	42	378
10	− 38	38	380

shows the result of such an experiment, it will be seen that if the pressure and the volume are multiplied together, for each pair of observations, the result is practically constant. Thus, if the pressure is doubled, the volume is halved; and if the pressure is increased 10 times, the volume is reduced to 1/10. (This result was used in Chapter 4 to calculate the energy stored in a compressed gas.)

These observations can be explained in terms of what is known about the nature of gases. Any gas consists of an enormous number of extremely small particles, or molecules, which in a pure gas are all identical. The pressure of a gas arises from the fact that these particles are in motion and that they collide with and rebound from the walls of the containing vessel. Each molecule undergoes a change in momentum when it rebounds from a surface.

Since a change of momentum can be achieved only by the application of a force, it must be concluded that, at the moment of impact of a molecule on the containing vessel, a force is applied to both the molecule and the containing vessel. The sum of all these forces constitutes the pressure which the gas exerts on the container. The momentum of a molecule is equal to the product of its mass and its velocity. When it collides with a wall and rebounds from it, its mass is unchanged and its velocity is unchanged except in direction, which is reversed. The change in momentum is therefore equal to 2 × M × V, where M is the mass and V is the velocity of the molecule. The molecules are extremely small and there are relatively large spaces between them. At this point it will be assumed (not quite correctly) that the molecules do not collide with each other, but only with the walls of the vessel. The

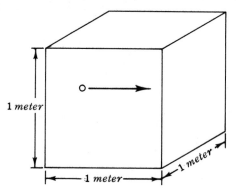

1 meter

1 meter

1 meter

Fig. 5.5. Motion of a molecule in a gas.

number of times per second that a particular molecule collides with a wall can be easily calculated for a containing vessel that is a cube (Fig. 5.5), 1 meter on a side. A molecule traveling with velocity of V meters per second in a direction perpendicular to one side of the cube collides with one of the walls $V/2$ times per second. Each collision corresponds to a change of momentum of $2MV$, for both the molecule and the wall. The total change of momentum of the wall per second is therefore $2MV \times V/2 = MV^2$. The opposite wall experiences an equal change of momentum in the opposite direction. It has been shown that the change in momentum is equivalent to the product of the force and the time. The force on the wall, then, is MV^2 divided by the time under consideration, 1 second, and is therefore equal to MV^2.

The effect of introducing large numbers of molecules does not make the problem of calculating the force more difficult; each molecule is assumed to behave independently; if there are a million molecules instead of one, the force is merely multiplied by 1 million. Therefore, the pressure is proportional to the mass of the molecules times the square of their velocity so long as the number of molecules in a given space remains unchanged. If the number of molecules in a given space is doubled, the pressure is also doubled, because twice the number of collisions with the wall will occur per unit of time. If, therefore, the volume is decreased to half its previous value (which is equivalent to doubling the number of molecules per unit volume), the pressure is doubled. This agrees with the experimental result shown in Table 5.2. The fact that the direction of travel of the molecules is random, and not perpendicular to one of the faces, reduces the pressure to one-third of that calculated above, but does not invalidate the argument.

Effect of Temperature and Pressure The effect of temperature upon the pressure of a gas if the volume remains constant can be studied with an apparatus like the one illustrated in Fig. 5.6. The glass bulb *A* is connected by a thin-bore glass tube to the flexible rubber tube *B* and to the glass tube *C*. Tubes *B* and *C* contain mercury. The glass bulb *A* is immersed in a vessel containing water at any selected temperature between zero and 100 degrees centigrade. The pressure of the air in *A*, as in the previous experiment, is the atmospheric pressure, plus or minus the difference between the mercury levels in the two tubes. The volume of air is kept constant by adjusting the

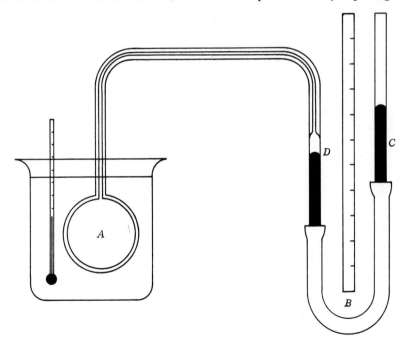

Fig. 5.6. Determination of the effect of temperature on the pressure of a gas.

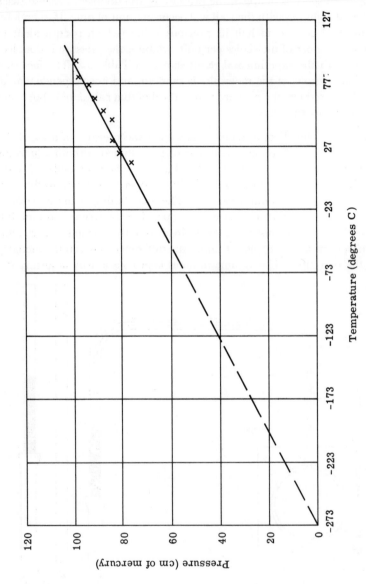

Fig. 5.7. Effect of temperature on the pressure of a gas at constant volume.

level *D* to the same position (by raising or lowering tube *C*) before taking a reading of the pressure difference. The procedure is to immerse the bulb in the water, allowing it to stand sufficiently long for the air in the bulb to reach the temperature recorded by the thermometer, and then to observe the pressure difference when the level at *D* has been brought to the standard position. When pressure variation is plotted against temperature, it will be seen that the pressure increases as the temperature rises, and that the graph relating these two variables is approximately a straight line (see Fig. 5.7). It is found that to a reasonably high degree of accuracy, it becomes closer to a straight line as the experiment becomes more precise. It may therefore be concluded that the effect of raising the temperature is to increase the pressure. The pressure is due to the change of momentum of the molecules; since the number of molecules does not change when the temperature is raised, the effect of increased temperature must be to increase the velocity of the molecules.

The Absolute If the straight line in Fig. 5.7 is extended in the direction of
Zero of decreasing pressure, a temperature is eventually reached at
Temperature which the pressure would become zero. The velocity of the molecules would also become zero at that temperature, which has been determined to be about −273 degrees centigrade. This is called the *absolute zero of temperature* because it is impossible for a gas to have a temperature lower than it has when all of its molecules are at rest. The line cannot be followed experimentally all the way down to absolute zero because all gases become liquid before this temperature is reached, and the straight-line relationship breaks down when the gas turns to liquid. The absolute zero of temperature has never been obtained experimentally, although it has been approached very closely indeed, and the evidence shows that as this temperature is approached it becomes increasingly difficult to lower the temperature any further.

In a somewhat similar experiment the pressure is kept constant and the volume allowed to vary. The result is shown in the graph in Fig. 5.8. It will be observed that again a straight-line relationship exists between volume and temperature, and that again the curve extrapolates to zero volume at −273 degrees centigrade. This follows from the fact that if the velocity of the molecules is increased, they must travel greater distances between collisions with the walls in order for the pressure to remain the same. Thus less volume is required as the temperature falls in order to maintain the same pressure.

Absolute Scale Calculations relating to the pressure, volume, and tempera-
of ture of gases become much simpler if all temperatures are
Temperature measured from absolute zero instead of from zero degrees centigrade. Thus zero degrees centigrade becomes 273 degrees absolute, and 100 degrees centigrade becomes 373 degrees absolute. On this scale, the *absolute scale of temperature*, the pressure of a gas is proportional to its temperature

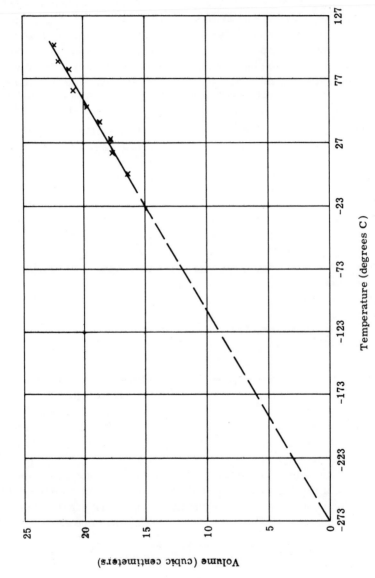

Fig. 5.8. Effect of temperature on the pressure of a gas at constant pressure.

72

if the volume is constant, and the volume of the gas is proportional to its temperature if the pressure is constant.

It now becomes possible to make calculations of pressure, volume, and temperature; for example, to calculate how the pressure of a tire increases as the temperature rises. Suppose that the air in a tire exerts a pressure of 30 pounds per square inch at a temperature of 15 degrees centigrade. To calculate the final pressure if the temperature is increased to 40 degrees centigrade, first assume that the volume of the tire remains unchanged. The absolute temperature corresponding to 15 degrees centigrade is 273 + 15, or 288 degrees absolute; 40 degrees centigrade is 313 degrees absolute. Since the pressure increases in direct proportion to the temperature, the unknown pressure divided by 313 is equal to 30 (the initial pressure) divided by 288. The unknown pressure is therefore 30 × $\frac{313}{288}$, or about 33 pounds per square inch.

If the volume of the tire had increased 5 per cent as the temperature rose, the pressure would be calculated as follows. The original pressure is 33 pounds per square inch, and the volume is taken as 100 per cent; the unknown pressure P corresponds to a volume of 105 per cent. It has been shown that the pressure multiplied by the volume is constant, and therefore $P \times 105 = 33 \times 100$, or $P = \frac{3300}{105}$, or approximately 31 pounds per square inch.

The three conclusions that have been drawn may be restated as follows:

(1) pressure times volume is constant at constant temperature;
(2) pressure divided by temperature is constant at constant volume;
(3) volume divided by temperature is constant at constant pressure.

The summary of this is that pressure times volume divided by temperature is constant for a given amount of a gas, or PV/T is constant.

Liquefaction of Gases   When a gas is subjected to very high pressures its volume decreases less than would be expected from the relationships that have been discussed. This is because the volume of the molecules themselves and the forces of attraction between them begin to play a significant role once the volume of the gas becomes small enough. The fact that many gases can be liquefied by compression is an indication of the attraction that exists between molecules forced sufficiently close together. This occurs when the volume is small, that is, at high pressure and low temperature. Those gases whose molecules have the least attraction for each other are the most difficult to liquefy. Helium is the extreme example. Helium molecules exert so little attraction for each other that the gas must be cooled to a temperature of 4 degrees absolute before it will liquefy.

Temperature as a Measure of Energy   It has been shown that for many gases the pressure is proportional to the absolute temperature if the volume is not allowed to change. It has also been shown that the pressure of a gas is proportional to the kinetic energy of its molecules. This is not an experimental observation but rather a deduction from the hypothesis that gas pressure is the result of molecules colliding with the wall of the containing vessel. From these two statements it follows that the *temperature of a gas is proportional to the kinetic energy of its molecules*. This leads to a definition of a temperature scale that has much more physical significance than the one based on the expansion of mercury. On this, the *Kelvin scale*, the *temperature is defined as being proportional to the kinetic energy of the molecules*. The same fixed points (freezing and boiling points of water) are used as for the centigrade scale, but all temperatures are measured from the absolute zero. For a "perfect" gas the pressure is proportional to the kinetic energy of its molecules and, therefore, to its temperature; but in real gases there are slight discrepancies that can readily be understood on the basis that the molecules of the gas do, in fact, collide with each other as well as with the walls of the container.

It follows that when different gases are at the same temperature, the molecules of each gas will have the same average kinetic energy, even if the molecules are of different masses. It is not necessary at this point to consider the individual molecule in detail, a subject that will be discussed in Chapter 9. It will suffice for the present to recognize that any pure gas consists of identical molecules (i.e., they all have the same mass) and that the mass of the molecule depends on the substance of which the gas is composed. It is usual to refer to the mass of the molecule of a substance by comparing it with the atomic weight of oxygen, which is taken as 16. On this basis, hydrogen (H_2) has a molecular weight of 2, oxygen (O_2) 32, water (H_2O) 18, helium (He) 4, and so on. It has been known for a long time that the density of any gas is directly proportional to its molecular weight. This means that at any given pressure the same number of molecules of any gas will occupy an equal volume. Putting the preceding statement in quantitative terms, we can say that 1 *mole* (i.e., the molecular weight of a substance expressed in grams) of any gas at zero degrees centigrade and 1 atmosphere pressure occupies a volume of 22.4 liters. Thus 1 mole of hydrogen (2 grams), helium (4 grams), or oxygen (32 grams) each occupies 22.4 liters. The mass of a gas in any given volume can now be calculated, once the molecular weight, the pressure and the volume are known; it is also possible to calculate how fast the molecules move at a given temperature. Consider the case of oxygen at zero degrees centigrade and 1 atmosphere pressure, in a volume of 1 cubic meter. Since 32 grams of oxygen occupy 22.4 liters (i.e., 22.4×0.001 cubic meter) 1 cubic meter contains $32/22.4 \times 1000$ grams, or 1.4 kilograms. Assuming that the container is a cube, the force on any one of its faces is equal to the change in momentum of all the molecules hitting it in 1 second. (It will also be assumed that one-third of all the molecules travel at right angles to each pair of opposite faces of the cube; there are three such pairs in a cube. The mass of these molecules is one-third of the total mass of the molecules present.) As each molecule collides with and rebounds from a wall, its momentum is changed by twice the product of its mass and velocity. The total change of momentum is therefore two-thirds of the mass of all the molecules in the gas multiplied by the velocity, on the assumption that each molecule hits the face of the cube only once. However, if the molecule travels V centimeters per second, it will hit each one of the pair of opposite faces $V/2$ times per second. The total change of momentum is therefore $2MV/3 \times V/2 = MV^2/3$ per second. The force exerted on an object changes its momentum by an amount equal to the product of the force and the period during which it acts. The force in the present example is the force on the square meter surface of the cube and that is the pressure exerted by the gas. It follows that $MV^2/3 = P$, where P is the pressure in newtons per square meter. Atmospheric pressure is about 10^5 newtons per square meter, and therefore

$$\frac{MV^2}{3} = 10^5 \text{ newtons/m}^2$$

or $\quad \dfrac{1.4 \times V^2}{3} = 10^5, \quad$ whence $V^2 = \dfrac{3 \times 10^5}{1.4} = 2.14 \times 10^5$

or $\quad V = 4.6 \times 100 = 460 \text{ m/sec} \quad$ or about 1000 miles/hr.

This calculation is for the case of oxygen but a similar calculation can easily be made for any other gas, such as hydrogen, which has a molecular weight of 2. The mass of the hydrogen molecule is one-sixteenth of that of the oxygen molecule. In order for it to have the same kinetic energy, the square of its velocity must be 16 times that of the oxygen molecule and so its velocity must be 4 times that of oxygen. The average velocity of the hydrogen molecule at zero degrees centigrade, then, will be about 1.6×1000 meters per second, or about 3600 miles per hour

The next question is how much kinetic energy a gas actually has. For example, the kinetic energy of the molecules in 1 cubic meter of oxygen at zero degrees centigrade and a pressure of 1 atmosphere is $\frac{1}{2} \times 1.4 \times 2.14 \times 10^5$ (since $V^2 = 2.14 \times 10^5$ and $M = 1.4$) which is 1.5×10^5 joules. It has only been necessary to know that 1 mole of any gas occupies 22.4 liters under the standard conditions of zero degrees centigrade and a pressure of 1 atmosphere.

Individual molecules must now be considered. A necessary result of the fact that the density of a gas is proportional to the mass of its molecules is that one mole of any gas at standard temperature and pressure always contains the same number of molecules as any other gas under the same conditions. This number, known as *Avogadro's number*, is about 6×10^{23} molecules per mole, from which the mass of a single molecule of any gas can be calculated. One mole of oxygen (32 grams), for example, contains 6×10^{23} molecules. The mass of one molecule is thus $32/(6 \times 10^{23})$, or about 5×10^{-23} grams or

5×10^{-26} kilograms. The kinetic energy of a molecule ($\frac{1}{2}MV^2$) is therefore, $\frac{1}{2}(5 \times 10^{-26})(2.14 \times 10^5) = 5 \times 10^{-21}$ joules. This is the average kinetic energy of a molecule of any gas at zero degrees centigrade. The kinetic energy of the molecule at any other temperature is directly proportional to the absolute temperature; thus the kinetic energy at 100 degrees centigrade is equal to $5 \times 10^{-21} \times \frac{373}{273} = 6.8 \times 10^{-21}$ joules.

The Distribution of Energy It has been implicitly assumed thus far that all the molecules travel at the same speed and that they collide only with the walls, never with each other. In fact, however, the molecules, though small, are sufficiently large to collide with each other from time to time and, consequently, to affect each other's velocities. Even if at one instant they all had the same velocity the situation would soon change, because the collisions between molecules affect their velocities in a number of ways. In

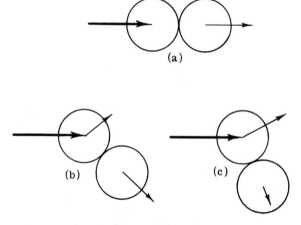

Fig. 5.9. Collisions between molecules.

any collision, momentum and kinetic energy must be conserved; but within these limitations the results may vary considerably, as the diagram of Fig. 5.9 suggests. In each of the three collisions depicted, it is assumed that the molecule on the left is in motion, and that the molecule it strikes is initially at rest. The velocities of the molecules are indicated by the lengths of the arrows (i.e., the longer the arrow, the greater the velocity).

In the first example (a) the right-hand molecule moves off with a velocity equal to the original velocity of the left-hand molecule, which has come to rest. In the second example (b) the left-hand molecule does not come to rest, but moves off with a much reduced velocity, having imparted a somewhat greater velocity to the other molecule. In the third (c) the velocity and direction of the left-hand molecule is affected only slightly by the collision; the other molecule moves off with a small velocity as shown. If a very large number of such random collisions occurs, it will obviously result in a wide range of molecular velocities. Nevertheless, it is possible to determine the average velocity and to plot the distribution of velocities about this average. The resulting *distribution curve* (see Fig. 5.10) is calculated in the following way: Assume that the individual velocities of a very large number of molecules are accurately known. The next step is to count the numbers of molecules that have velocities within given ranges (regardless of direction); for example, 400 to 410 meters per second, 410 to 420 meters per second, and so on, until all the molecules have been accounted for. It will be found that the greatest

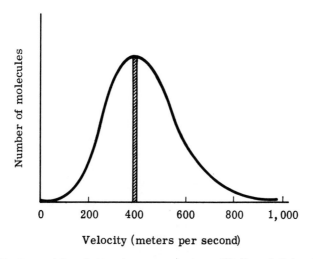

Fig. 5.10. Distribution of the velocities of oxygen molecules at 0°C. (From G. Holten, "Introduction to Concepts and Theories in Physical Science." Addison-Wesley, Reading, Massachusetts, 1952.)

number of molecules have velocities close to 400 meters per second. Progressively fewer molecules are found with velocities above or below this value, with very few molecules close to either zero or 1000 meters per second. The graph in Fig. 5.11 plots the distribution curves for a gas at a high and a low temperature. It can be seen that while the average velocity has decreased at the lower temperature there is still a wide range of velocities. It should not be concluded that an individual molecule has a high or low speed for any prolonged period. The collisions between molecules are extremely frequent and whenever a collision occurs, there is some redistribution of velocities.

The proportion of the volume of a gas actually occupied by the molecules can be estimated as follows. It is sufficiently accurate for an approximate calculation to assume that the radius of a molecule is 10^{-10} meters, its volume is $\frac{4}{3}\pi r^3$, or about 4×10^{-30} cubic meters. Since 22.4 liters contain 6×10^{23}

molecules, 1 liter contains $(6 \times 10^{23})/22.4$ and 1 cubic meter contains $(6 \times 10^{26})/22.4$ molecules, or approximately 3×10^{25} molecules. The volume available per molecule is therefore $1/(3 \times 10^{25})$ or about 3×10^{-26} cubic meters. The molecule itself occupies only 4×10^{-30} cubic meters; thus the molecules occupy roughly 10^{-4}, or one ten-thousandth of the total space. It is therefore concluded that the molecules travel freely most of the time but nevertheless they collide with each other quite frequently. They travel considerable distances between collisions, if these distances are measured on a molecular scale. At atmospheric pressure the *mean free path* between collisions is about 10^{-5} centimeters. In a vacuum this distance is greater because there are fewer

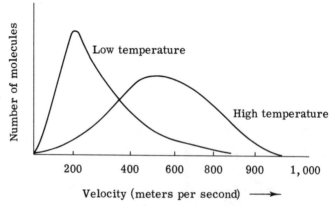

Fig. 5.11. Effect of temperature on the distribution of molecular velocities. (From G. Holten, "Introduction to Concepts and Theories in Physical Science." Addison-Wesley, Reading, Massachusetts, 1952.)

molecules; in a fairly good vacuum the mean free path would be about 10 centimeters.

The pressure of the atmosphere decreases with increasing height above the surface of the earth, because the pressure is due to the weight of the atmosphere itself, and only that part which is above any point contributes to the pressure there. At a height of 1000 kilometers above the earth, for example, the mean free path is many kilometers. At that height the escape velocity, that is, the velocity which an object must have in order to escape from the earth's gravitational attraction, is about 10^4 meters per second and, according to the distribution curve for velocity, some molecules at that altitude will have the escape velocity. Therefore, it is expected that the earth's atmosphere should lose some molecules to outer space. This will apply particularly to the lighter molecules such as hydrogen, because, for the same temperature, hydrogen molecules have a higher velocity than molecules of any other gas because of their lower mass. It is a fact that the earth's atmosphere contains a very small amount of hydrogen and it is possible that there was at one time a great deal more but that this has been lost by the process of escape from the outer confines of the atmosphere. A smaller planet, which has a smaller gravitational attraction, and therefore a lower escape velocity, would lose its molecules more rapidly; the smallest planet, Mercury, which is also hotter than the earth since it is nearer to the sun, does not have an atmosphere. The moon also has no atmosphere, perhaps because its gravitational effect is rather small on account of its small size and therefore the escape of molecules would be relatively easy. The larger and colder planets, on the other hand, do have atmospheres and this is readily accounted for on the basis that all the planets had atmospheres initially but that the hotter, smaller ones have lost their atmospheres in the course of time. It has been calculated that if the mean velocity is less than one-fifth of the escape velocity, then the loss of gas in this way will be extremely slow, even on an astronomical scale of time. On the other hand, if the mean velocity of the molecules is greater than one-quarter of the escape velocity, then loss will be relatively fast and can have an important influence on the atmospheres of the planets.

Temperature of Solids and Liquids The discussion so far has been confined to gases because it is much easier to make calculations about the motion of the molecules in gases than in liquids or in solids. The concepts of heat and temperature, however, also apply to liquids and to solids, but they must be modified slightly. Figure 5.12a is a diagrammatic representation of

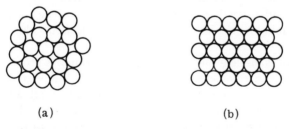

(a)   (b)

Fig. 5.12. Structure of a liquid (a) and a crystalline solid (b).

a liquid. The molecules are shown close together, almost in contact, and arranged in a random fashion, much in the way oranges would be if they were poured into a barrel. In the corresponding schematic diagram of a crystalline solid (Fig. 5.12b) the atoms are arranged as though they were oranges packed systematically so as to get the greatest possible number into a given volume. In both cases the mean free path between collisions is extremely small, much smaller, in fact, than the diameters of the atoms themselves.

The molecules and atoms in liquids and solids have some freedom to move because they are not rigid spheres pressed closely together; the heat of solids and liquids takes the form of vibrations of the atoms or molecules within the restricted space available between their neighbors. The energy of any sort of vibration alternates between kinetic and potential (as in the pendulum) and in this case the energy of each atom alternates between its kinetic energy of motion and its potential energy which increases, due to the repulsion between itself and its neighbor, as it slows down at each end of each vibration. As with a gas, the heat of a solid or liquid is the energy of motion of the atoms or molecules, and a measure of the temperature is the mean energy of the atomic or molecular vibrations. Again, there is a distribution of energies about an average value. The latent heat required to change liquid into vapor, or solid into liquid, is an additional quantity of energy that must be supplied to overcome the forces of attraction that hold the atoms or molecules together. (This attraction is not gravitational, but electrostatic, and will be discussed in Chapter 10.)

Evaporation   The process of evaporation can now be described in greater
and   detail. Water, for example, evaporates gradually and it is
Latent Heat   evident that few of the molecules have enough energy to
escape from the liquid; if they had, they would do so immediately and the liquid would at once become vapor or gas. Since the molecular energies are distributed over a wide range of values, however, there are always a few molecules with sufficient energy to escape from the surface. These molecules, if they happen to be at the surface and moving upward, may tear themselves away from the forces of attraction of the neighboring molecules. Because they escape with more than the average molecular energy, the average energy of the remaining molecules is reduced, thereby lowering the temperature of the liquid.

A familiar example of such cooling by evaporation is provided by the wet and dry bulb thermometer, which measures the amount of water vapor present in the atmosphere (i.e., the *humidity*). If water is allowed to evaporate in a closed space, an equilibrium between evaporation and condensation is eventually reached, so that as many molecules return to the surface of the water as leave it during any given period of time. The atmosphere is then said to be *saturated* and no more evaporation takes place. It follows that the drier the adjacent air, the faster the net rate of evaporation. As the adjacent air approaches saturation, evaporation slows down, stopping when the saturation point is reached. If a draught is introduced, then evaporation is maintained, because the air adjacent to the surface is continuously replaced by unsaturated air. The wet-and-dry-bulb thermometer consists of two thermometers, one of which has its bulb surrounded by a wick which is kept wet by dipping in water. Evaporation of water from the wick lowers the "wet-bulb" temperature below that of the atmosphere. When the air is drier, the rate of evaporation from the wick increases, lowering the temperature registered on the wet-bulb thermometer still further. The temperature difference between the two thermometers is an indication of the humidity of the atmosphere. To determine the relative humidity (i.e., the ratio of the actual humidity to the saturation value), tables of experimentally determined values must be used as there is no simple method of making the calculation.

Another example of cooling by evaporation is the way in which the human body maintains an optimum internal temperature. The human metabolism generates more heat than the body requires, and the removal of excess heat is achieved partly by the evaporation of perspiration. The rate of perspiration is adjusted by the mechanisms of the body so that the appropriate amount of evaporative cooling will take place. When the air is very humid, and evaporation therefore slow, the body has difficulty disposing of enough heat, and great discomfort is experienced under conditions of high temperature and high humidity.

Boiling of a Liquid   When a liquid boils, evaporation takes place not only from the surface of the liquid but also into bubbles that form in the interior. The vapor pressure within the bubbles must be sufficient to make them expand against the external pressure of the atmosphere. Boiling takes place mainly by the evaporation of water vapor into the bubbles, which expand, rise to the surface and burst, the vapor within them escaping from the liquid. The boiling point is therefore the temperature at which the vapor pressure is equal to the atmospheric pressure. Since the atmospheric pressure changes with weather conditions and with altitude, the boiling point of water is not a precisely fixed temperature. Table 5.3 shows the variation of the boiling point of water at various heights above sea level. It is interesting to note that, even with an oxygen mask, a human could not exist at altitudes much above

TABLE 5.3
BOILING POINT OF WATER

Altitude (feet above sea level)	Boiling point (°F)
0	212
1000	209
5000	202
10,000	194
20,000	176
40,000	141
60,000	110
80,000	76

60,000 feet except under pressurized conditions, because his blood and other body fluids would boil. Less drastically, it also follows that cooking of foods becomes difficult or impossible on high mountains, because of the reduced boiling point of water, unless a pressure cooker is used.

The Conversion As stated earlier, when heat is added to a substance it either
of causes the temperature to rise, thereby increasing the kinetic
Work into Heat energy of the molecules, or it melts or vaporizes the substance without raising the temperature. In the last two cases, the potential energy of the molecules is increased because the heat has been used to overcome, partially or completely, the mutual attraction between the molecules which causes them to adhere together in the form of a liquid or a solid. The Calorie, which is the amount of heat that will raise the temperature of 1 kilogram of water by 1 degree or melt 1/80 kilogram of ice, can also be expressed, in joules, as the amount of extra energy which the molecules acquire when their temperature is raised by this amount. Heat, then, is a form of energy that can be described and measured in units of work (e.g., ergs or joules or foot-pounds) as correctly as in units of heat. It is not difficult to demonstrate that work can be converted into heat by friction or by impact. Familiar examples are the heating of a saw as it cuts wood (friction) and of a nail as it is hammered (impact).

The Mechanical A rough but simple experiment to determine the relation-
Equivalent ship between heat and work can be made with a cardboard
of Heat mailing tube about 3 feet long, a cork to plug each end,
about half a pound of lead shot and a thermometer. The experiment consists of measuring the temperature of the lead shot, placing them in the cardboard tube, and closing the tube, then rapidly inverting the tube 100 times, say, so that the shot are raised to the top and allowed to fall to the bottom each time, and then measuring the final temperature of the shot. It will be found that the temperature has risen several degrees. The reason is that the potential energy imparted to the shot each time the tube is inverted is converted to kinetic energy while they fall and this in turn is converted to heat as a result of the impact on the end of the tube and on each other. The work done per unit of heat produced is called the *mechanical equivalent of heat*.

The calculation is made as follows. Figure 5.13 represents the tube. Let h be the distance through which the shot falls, M the mass of the shot, S the specific heat, and D the difference the temperature of the shot before and after the experiment. The work done on the shot, when they are raised once, is $M \times g \times h$, where "g" is the acceleration due to gravity, or 9.81 meters per second per second; therefore, the total work done on the shot is 100 Mgh joules. The heat capacity of the lead shot is $M \times S$ and the heat required to raise their temperature by D degrees is equal to $D \times M \times S$ Calories.

The following results were obtained in an experiment. The distance h was 0.77 meter; the work done on the shot was therefore

$$100 \times 9.81 \times 0.77 = 750 \text{ joules}$$

The temperature of the lead shot rose 1 centigrade degrees. The amount of heat acquired by the lead shot was therefore $4 \times M \times 0.031$ (the specific heat of lead), or $0.124M$ Calories. Thus, each kilogram of lead had an amount of work equal to 750 joules done on it, and this produced an amount

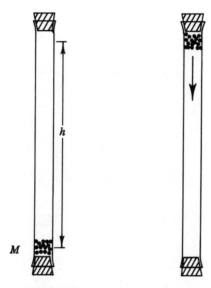

Fig. 5.13. Conversion of work into heat.

of heat equal to 0.124 Calorie. Thus 750 joules were required to produce 0.124 Calorie, or about 6000 joules of work were converted into 1 Calorie.

For a number of reasons this result is not accurate. In the first place, some of the heat generated leaves the lead shot, resulting in a temperature rise less than would be expected. Some of the work done by the shot is in the form of friction between the shot and the sides of the tube, heating the tube as well as the shot. Also the shot lose heat to the tube in their vicinity during the entire period of the experiment. The production of 1 Calorie of heat, then, should require fewer than 6000 joules.

The mechanical equivalent of heat can be determined much more accurately using an apparatus that consists of an insulated vessel filled with water and a paddle and vane arrangement for churning the water (see Fig.

5.14). The amount of heat generated when the water is agitated can be measured from the rise in temperature of the mass of water and the thermal capacity of the apparatus and the thermometer used. (This problem is identical in principle to the one discussed earlier (pages 62–63.) The work expended in churning the water must also be measured. This can be done by attaching weights to strings wound on pulley wheel *A*. The sum of these weights gives

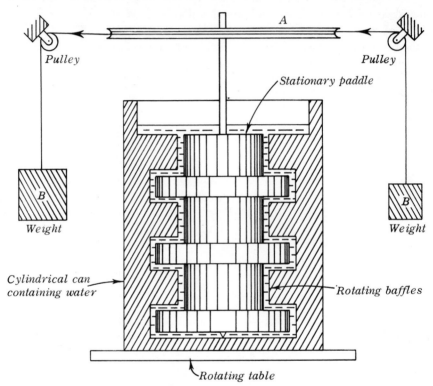

Fig. 5.14. Apparatus for determining the mechanical equivalent of heat.

the force applied to the paddle. Accurate experiments to determine the mechanical equivalent of heat give the result that 1 Calorie is equal to 4180 joules.

This relationship makes it possible to calculate the amount of heat generated when a moving object is brought to rest by friction. Suppose that a bicycle comes to rest from a speed of 5 meters per second (about 11 miles per hour) and that its mass, including the rider, is 80 kilograms (176 pounds). The kinetic energy of the moving bicycle is $\frac{1}{2}MV^2$, or 1000 joules. Since 4180 joules equals 1 Calorie, the heat generated is $\frac{1000}{4180}$, or about 0.24 Calorie.

Refrigeration and Air Conditioning When a gas is compressed both its pressure and its temperature increase. That is to say, some of the work done on it takes the form of heat; part of the work done in compressing a gas is used to increase the kinetic energy of its molecules. A molecule rebounding from a surface moving toward it rebounds with greater speed than it would from a stationary wall. Conversely, if the volume of a gas is increased by reducing the pressure, the temperature decreases. These facts may be applied to the problem of increasing the temperature of an object that

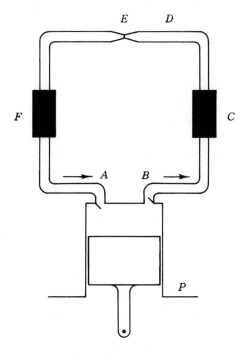

Fig. 5.15. Simplified refrigeration unit.

is already hotter than its surroundings, or lowering the temperature of an object that is cooler. These two problems are of great practical significance. The former is represented by the problem of heating a house in the winter, and the latter by the problems of refrigeration and of air conditioning. All three pose requirements contrary to the spontaneous behavior of matter, since the temperature of an object always changes spontaneously so as to reduce the difference in temperature between itself and its surroundings.

Figure 5.15 represents a mechanism that achieves the objective of increasing the difference in temperature between an object and its surroundings. It consists of a compressor pump P connected to a circuit of pipe, two heat exchangers C and F, and an expansion valve E. The function of the heat exchangers is to allow the air inside and outside the tube to equalize their temperatures by the transfer of heat through the exchangers. The valves are so arranged that the air in the circuit can enter only by the left-hand port A and can leave only by the right-hand port B. When the pump is operating, the flow of air around the circuit is counterclockwise. The pump compresses the air which enters the circuit at port B and is, because of compression, at a higher temperature than its surroundings. As it passes through heat exchanger C it loses heat to its surroundings; by the time it reaches D it is at the same temperature as its surroundings. In passing through the expansion valve E, the air passes from a high-pressure into a low-pressure area. Consequently, the air expands, its temperature drops, and it reaches the heat exchanger F at a temperature lower than that of the air outside the exchanger. As a result, heat flows from the surrounding air to the air inside the exchanger, thus lowering the temperature of the surroundings. By the time the air reaches A, it is at the temperature of the surroundings. It then enters the pump, is compressed and is ready to repeat the cycle. Heat has been given out at C, raising the temperature in this region slightly and heat has been taken in at F, lowering the temperature of the adjacent air. The net result is that heat has been pumped, so to speak, from the region around F where the temperature is now lower, to the region around C, where the temperature is now higher. If C is in a room and F inside a refrigerator the over-all result is to take heat from the interior of the refrigerator and put it into the room, the temperature of which must necessarily rise. This is the simplest example of a *heat pump*.

The system described above is in practice made much more efficient by the use of a fluid such as freon in the circuit instead of air. Freon has the property of becoming liquid at the high pressure developed by the pump, and returning to its vapor phase when it expands or passes through the expansion valve. The main part of the heat given out at C is the latent heat the freon must give up in changing from vapor to liquid, and the main part of the heat which it takes in at F is the latent heat that must be added to the liquid in order to convert it back into vapor. The heat exchangers also are somewhat more elaborate than the illustration suggests. To effect a rapid and virtually complete exchange of heat, a large area must be exposed, both to the freon in the circuit and to the surrounding air. In many cases, the heat transfer is also made more efficient by blowing air over the heat exchangers.

Air Conditioners An air conditioner works on exactly the same principle as the refrigerator (see Fig. 5.16). Again a compressor pump is used to increase the pressure and temperature of the fluid, usually freon. The resulting liquid freon is cooled in the heat exchanger C

(outside the room) and expanded at the valve E. It is then cold enough to take heat from the room at heat exchanger F (inside the room). A fan $B1$ circulates the air in the room over the heat exchanger F and another fan $B2$ circulates the external air over the heat exchanger C. Both the refrigerator

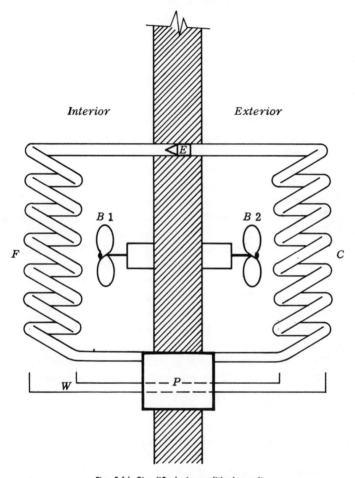

Fig. 5.16. Simplified air-conditioning unit.

and the air conditioner raise an additional problem. As the air is cooled, its capacity to retain water in the form of vapor decreases. If the temperature is lowered sufficiently, water vapor condenses on the heat exchanger. In the refrigerator this takes the form of ice; in the room air conditioner the temperature of the heat exchanger is usually higher and water forms. In the case of the refrigerator it is necessary to melt the ice from time to time; in some refrigerators the ice is melted by circulating heated "coolant" periodically, so that it can flow to the region heated by the external heat exchanger C, where it evaporates. The water in the air conditioner runs off the heat exchanger F into the pipe W which leads it to the vicinity of the heat exchanger C, where the air warmed by the heat exchanger causes it to evaporate. In this manner, water is transferred from inside the room, where a high humidity increases the discomfort caused by the high temperature, to the outside, where it evaporates into the atmosphere.

The Heat Pump A third application of the principles discussed in the two preceding sections is the *heat pump*. This is a device for taking heat from a heat source of relatively low temperature and delivering it to a region at a considerably higher temperature. The refrigerator and the air conditioner are both heat pumps within this definition. However, what is usually referred to as a heat pump is a device for raising the temperature of a house, say, above that of the atmosphere by using heat taken from a source at a considerably lower temperature. In one type of heat pump the heat source is a well containing water at a temperature of, say, 40 degrees Fahrenheit (see Fig. 5.17). It is required to maintain a house at a temperature of 70 degrees Fahrenheit, even when the surrounding atmosphere may drop to zero degrees Fahrenheit or lower. The installation, like the refrigeration and air conditioning units, consists of a compressor pump P, two heat exchangers C and F, and an expansion valve E. The working fluid can again be freon. The pump compresses the freon, raising its temperature. The freon is then supplied to heat exchanger F, which in this case would be the radiators in the house. After the hot (liquid) freon has been cooled by its passage through the radiators, it is allowed to expand; its temperature drops, to 10 degrees Fahrenheit perhaps, and it is then passed to the second heat exchanger C in the well, the temperature of which is 40 degrees. The freon is warmed from 10 to 40 degrees by taking heat from the water in the well. It returns to the pump, is compressed, its temperature rising to 90 degrees, and passes through another cycle. This process is continuous and represents a transfer of a large amount of heat from the well to the radiators. It is not necessary to use a well, although this is probably the most efficient device; it is possible to use ground heat, laying the external heat exchanger underground. It is also possible to use the external air as a heat source, although this fluctuates so much in temperature that the proper control of the installation becomes more difficult. The following statements are made regarding the heat pump as a heating unit for a house. A six-room house might require about 18^8 BTU per year. This heat can be generated electrically or by burning a fuel. The same amount of heat can be pumped from a heat source in the manner just described with an expenditure of from one-third to one-quarter of the amount of energy that would be required to generate the same amount of heat. It should be pointed out that the heat does not come from the electrical energy which is used to operate the pump; this is used for "pumping" heat from the low temperature source to the higher temperature at which it is utilized.

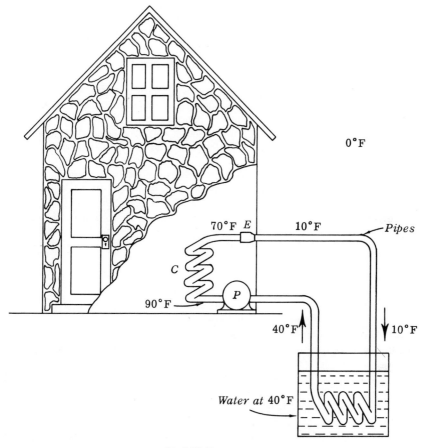

Fig. 5.17. Heat pump.

It will be noticed that in Fig. 5.17 the functions of the heat exchangers *C* and *F* have been reversed. In Fig. 5.15 the heat exchanger *F* is the one on which attention is concentrated, that is, the one which lowers the temperature of the room. In Fig. 5.17 the desired result is achieved by the heat exchanger *C*. That is because the requirement in this case is to produce a *rise* in temperature instead of a *fall* in temperature. One of the great advantages of the heat pump as a source of heat is that it can be reversed, by reversing the direction of flow. In the circuit in Fig. 5.17 heat would be pumped from *C* to *F* and the apparatus would then constitute an air conditioning rather than a heating unit. It is not appropriate here to discuss the economics of this type of heating and cooling system.

Problems

5.1 Construct a graph for the conversion between centigrade and Fahrenheit temperatures. From this graph determine (a) the centigrade equivalent of 0°F, (b) the centigrade equivalent to the normal body temperature (98.4°F), and (c) the temperature that is the same on both scales.

5.2 Calculate the number of Calories required to raise the temperature of 1 pint of water from 40°C to the boiling point.

5.3 Calculate the thermal capacity of a piece of copper 20 in.³ in volume, in British Thermal Units and in Calories; the specific heat of copper is 0.1, and the density of copper is 7.8 times that of water.

5.4 (a) An electric kettle is filled with water at 40°F. If it is heated so that it takes 5 minutes to reach the boiling point, how long will it take for all the water to boil away? Give your answer to the nearest minute.

(b) An ice tray filled with water at 40°F is put into a refrigerator. If it takes 10 minutes for the water to reach the freezing point, how long will it take for it all to freeze?

5.5 The specific heat of air at constant pressure is 0.24 Cal/kg and the density of air at atmospheric pressure is about 1.3 kg/m³. Calculate how much heat would be required to raise by 10°F the temperature of the air in a room of size 25 ft × 20 ft × 10 ft.

5.6 What is absolute zero on the Fahrenheit scale?

5.7 A tire is inflated to a pressure of 30 psi at a temperature of 32°F. What would its pressure be at 90°F, if the volume of the tire had increased by 10 per cent?

5.8 What is the density of air, assuming that it consists of a mixture of one part (by weight) of oxygen and four parts of nitrogen?

5.9 Calculate the average velocity of hydrogen molecules at 100°C and 1 atm pressure.

5.10 Does the velocity change with the pressure if the temperature is constant? (Give reasons.)

5.11 If the height of the mercury barometer is 76 cm of mercury, calculate the pressure of the atmosphere in pounds per square inch and in dynes per square centimeter. (The density of mercury is 13.6 gm/cm³.)

5.12 What would be the height of a water barometer?

5.13 Calculate the value of the mechanical equivalent of heat in British Thermal Units per foot-pound.

5.14 A car weighing 2 tons descends a hill of 10 per cent incline at a constant speed of 50 miles/hr. How many Calories per minute are generated in its brakes?

5.15 A large piece of copper is dropped from a height of 500 ft. If all the heat generated by the impact is used to raise the temperature of the copper, what is its change of temperature?

5.16 A river flows downhill without acceleration. If the level of the water falls by 100 ft/mile, how would the temperature of the water change, assuming that no heat is lost by the water?

5.17 In view of the law of conservation of momentum, how is it possible for a child sitting on a swing to set it swinging?

Chapter 6

HEAT TRANSFER

It is a common observation that an object which is originally hotter than its surroundings becomes cooler and conversely, that an object which is colder than its surroundings becomes warmer. To use a familiar example, suppose that a mercury thermometer at a temperature of 40 degrees Fahrenheit is dipped in water at a temperature of 100 degrees Fahrenheit.

The mercury will rise quickly (though not instantaneously), until it indicates the temperature of the water. The assumption in this statement—i.e., that the temperature of the thermometer will continue to change until it is equal to that of its surroundings—can be easily verified by experiment. It does not matter whether the thermometer was previously at a higher temperature than the water, or at a lower temperature. In either case, it will reach the same temperature, that of the water.

The conclusion that can be drawn from this kind of experiment is that in the collisions between the molecules at the adjoining surfaces of any two objects, some of the kinetic energy of the molecules of the hotter object is transferred to those of the cooler one; this increased kinetic energy, or heat, is transferred progressively throughout the colder material until the temperatures of the two objects, and therefore the average energies of thermal motion of their molecules, become equal.

It is usual to speak of the "flow of heat" as though heat were a fluid, like water. This is not the case, but it is nevertheless useful in describing the process of *heat transfer*, because the amount of heat lost by an object is always equal to the amount gained by its surroundings. The total amount of heat is conserved, unless there is some change, such as compression or expansion in which work is done.

The "movement" of heat, either within an object or from one object to another, takes place in several distinct ways, described as conduction, convection, radiation, and evaporation.

Conduction Conduction is the transfer of heat within an object, or from one object to another, at a surface where they are in contact, by the sharing of the energy of thermal motion. This process is described as the "flow" of heat from hotter to colder regions. Heat does not flow at the same rate through all substances; metals, for example, conduct heat very much faster than do nonmetallic substances such as wood, glass and plastics. The reason for this difference is that metals contain large numbers of electrons, whose nature will be discussed later, which are free to move, and which give metals their property of conducting electricity. These free electrons also play an important role in the conduction of heat. Some of the heat consists of the kinetic energy of electrons and these are responsible for a large part of the transfer of heat in substances such as metals which are good conductors of heat. Insulators such as glass, on the other hand, contain very few, if any, free electrons. These substances are poor conductors of heat.

Convection   The density of a liquid or a gas generally decreases as its temperature rises. Therefore, if part of a liquid or a gas is heated to a higher temperature than the rest of the material, the heated portion, because of decreased density, tends to rise, just as a cork immersed in water will rise and float to the surface. This type of heat transfer,

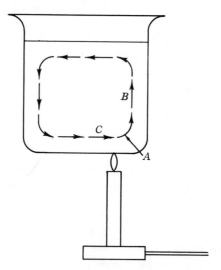

Fig. 6.1. Convection.

known as *convection*, can be demonstrated by heating a beaker of water as shown in Fig. 6.1. The immediate effect of the flame is to heat the glass at point A by conduction from the hot gases of the flame into the glass. This heat is then conducted through the glass and into the part of the water which is in immediate contact with the glass. The temperature of this water rises, its density decreases, and it starts to rise as shown by the arrow B. The water at C flows toward the region from which the water is rising. After a short time, the water circulates as shown by the arrows in the diagram. This pattern of circulation can be made visible by injecting a few drops of dye into the water. As a result of convection, the rise in temperature throughout the water is fairly uniform; if there were no convection, the water remote from the source of heat would be affected much more slowly. This can be demonstrated by heating a test tube containing water (see Fig. 6.2). If it is first heated near the top, then the water near the surface soon begins to boil, but the water at the bottom is scarcely affected; it can be held in the hand without discomfort. However, if the water is heated at the bottom, it will take longer before any boiling occurs, but then the whole of the water will be at the boiling point.

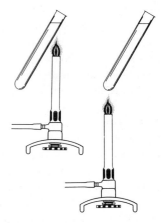

Exactly analogous processes take place in air. A "radiator" heats a room largely by setting up a similar circulation of air or *convection current*. The air close to the radiator is heated by contact with the radiator. This heat is conducted into the immediately adjacent air, and distributed around the room mainly by a convection current resulting from the rise of the heated air, and its replacement by cooler air.

The atmosphere is also moved by convection currents. All air motion, or wind, arises from convection currents caused by the heating of the earth's surface by the sun. Air always flows toward the regions of low pressure that are created under the upward-moving air. These currents are modified by the rotation of the

Fig. 6.2. Convection caused by heating at the bottom but not by heating at the top.

earth, and by the fact that heating due to the sun is very uneven. A thundercloud, for example, is produced by a rapidly rising air current above a local "hot spot" on the earth's surface; this current, subjected to a decreasing pressure as it rises, expands and its temperature falls. The water in the air then condenses into droplets which, after coalescence by a complicated process, may fall as rain.

Radiation A third type of heat transfer is by *radiation*, which is the subject of Chapter 8. For the moment let it suffice to point out that the heat of the sun reaches the earth, not by conduction or convection, since there is no continuous material between here and the sun, but in the form of radiation, which travels through empty space and is converted into heat when it is absorbed by an object such as the earth. All objects radiate heat, the amount depending upon the temperature and the nature of their surface.

Evaporation

A hot object, if it is liquid, may also lose heat by evaporation. Thus, boiling water loses 540 Calories for every kilogram that is turned into steam; even if the water is not hot enough to boil, evaporation occurs and the rate of loss of heat is still 540 Calories per kilogram; the rate of evaporation is, however much less when boiling does not occur.

Newton's Law of Cooling

A hot object may lose heat to its surroundings by any or all of four processes, namely, conduction, convection, radiation, and evaporation. These processes proceed at different rates, and the calculation of how fast an object will cool by any single one would in some cases be very complicated. However, it has been observed that, to a fairly good degree of approximation, an object loses heat to its surroundings at a rate which is proportional to the difference between its temperature and that of its surroundings.

This relationship, known as *Newton's law of cooling*, can be seen in Fig. 6.3, which plots the temperature of a cup of coffee (starting at a temperature of 160 degrees Fahrenheit) at half-minute intervals. The graph shows that the rate of fall of temperature decreases as the temperature drops. In order to calculate the rate of fall of temperature, a tangent may be drawn to the curve of Fig. 6.3 at any point. The tangent represents the instantaneous rate of change of temperature with time (i.e., the rate of cooling) at that point. It shows how far the temperature would have fallen in a selected time, such as 10 minutes, if the rate had remained constant. For example, the tangent drawn on the graph indicates that at a temperature of 120 degrees Fahrenheit, the coffee is cooling at a rate of about 5 degrees per minute. Table 6.1

TABLE 6.1
RATE OF COOLING

Temperature (°F)	Rate of cooling (degrees/min)	Temperature difference (Fahrenheit degrees)
155	10	85
145	8.8	75
135	7.7	65
125	6.5	55
115	5.3	45
105	4.1	35

shows how the rate of fall of temperature (calculated for a number of other points on the graph) varies with the difference between the temperature of the coffee and the room temperature, which was 70 degrees Fahrenheit.

Figure 6.4 is a graph for the rates of cooling at the temperatures shown plotted against the temperature difference; it will be seen that the points fall close to a straight line, showing that the rate of fall of temperature varies in proportion to the temperature difference.

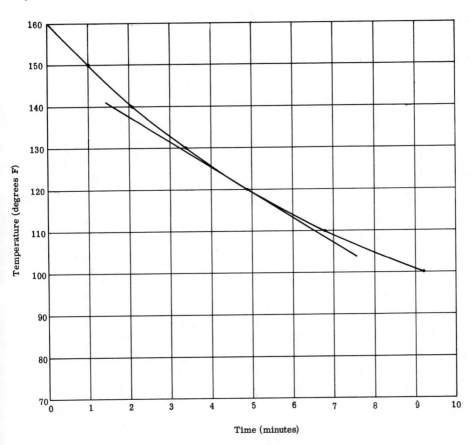

Fig. 6.3. The cooling of a cup of coffee.

Thermal Conductivity   The conduction of heat will now be considered in a more quantitative way. In order to compare the heat conduction properties of different substances, it is necessary to define this property in terms of a unit.

The unit generally used for this purpose is the amount of heat that would be transmitted per unit time through a centimeter cube of the substance if two opposite faces were held at temperatures 1 degree apart. The quantity of heat transmitted under these conditions is called the *thermal conductivity*,

Fig. 6.4. Variation in the rate of cooling with temperature difference.

Rate of cooling (degrees per minute)

Temperature difference (Fahrenheit degrees)

which varies from substance to substance. Some values for the thermal conductivity are given in Table 6.2.

The transmission of heat through a centimeter cube is not usually of much interest, but these values can be used to calculate the amount of heat transmitted through an object of any other size and shape. For example, how much heat would flow through a steel plate 5 centimeters thick and 30 centimeters square if the temperature difference between the two surfaces is 40 centigrade degrees? If the thermal conductivity is 10^{-4}, say, then 10^{-4} Calories will flow

TABLE 6.2

THERMAL CONDUCTIVITIES

(In Calories per centigrade degree
per second, for a centimeter cube)

Vacuum	0
Silver	1×10^{-3}
Copper	9×10^{-4}
Steel	1×10^{-4}
Aluminum	5×10^{-4}
Wood	2×10^{-6}
Ice	5×10^{-6}
Glass	2×10^{-6}
Snow	5×10^{-7}
Fiberglas	1×10^{-7}
Brick	$1-3 \times 10^{-6}$
Concrete	$3-5 \times 10^{-6}$
Air	5×10^{-8}

per second through a centimeter cube with a temperature difference of 1 degree. In this example, the temperature difference is 40 degrees over a thickness of 5 centimeters or 8 centigrade degrees per centimeter. The temperature difference is therefore 8 times as great as it would be in the standard case of 1 degree per centimeter. Therefore the heat transmitted through 1 square centimeter of the plate is 8×10^{-4} Calories per second. The total quantity of heat transmitted through the whole plate per second is 8×10^{-4} multiplied by the number of square centimeters, which is 900; that is, $900 \times 8 \times 10^{-4}$ Calories per second, or 0.720 Calorie per second. This method of describing the heat transmission depends upon the assumption that the actual surface temperatures of the two sides of the object are known and for many purposes this is a useful method of calculation.

Heat Transmission Coefficient: Domestic Heating For many other circumstances, such as the transmission of heat through the wall of a house or through the door of a refrigerator, the surface temperatures are not known, and they are not particularly important. The air temperatures on both sides, however, are known. For such calculations the *heat transmission coefficient* is used. The heat transmission coefficient is the amount of heat transmitted, in British Thermal Units per square foot per hour, for a temperature difference of 1 Fahrenheit degree between the opposite surfaces. (Some examples of heat transmission coefficients are given in Table 6.3.) The rate of loss of heat through, for example, the walls of a house can be calculated from these values if the temperature difference between the interior and the exterior is known. As an example, suppose that the external dimensions of a house are 50 feet by 20 feet and that the height of the walls is 10 feet, ignoring the

TABLE 6.3
HEAT TRANSMISSION COEFFICIENTS
(In BTU foot, degree Fahrenheit units)

Brick (4 inches)	0.36
Brick (with air space)	0.22
Brick (plastered)	0.16
Wood ($\frac{7}{8}$ inch thick)	0.55
Wood with air space	0.20
Window (single)	1.13
Window (double)	0.45
Window (triple)	0.28
Concrete (2 inches thick)	0.78
Concrete (6 inches thick)	0.56

roof at this point. Then, if the internal temperature is 70 degrees Fahrenheit and the external temperature is 20 degrees Fahrenheit, the rate of loss of heat is the total wall area (1400 square feet), multiplied by the temperature difference (50 degrees), multiplied by the heat transmission coefficient, which will be taken as 0.2, on the basis of wood with an air space. This gives a heat loss of 14,000 BTU per hour. If the average external temperature for 24 hours is 20 degrees Fahrenheit, then the total heat required during that period is 14,000 × 24, or 336,000 BTU.

To calculate the amount of heat required for the whole winter, it would be necessary to know either the expected average temperature for each day or an average value for this quantity. For this purpose a unit known as the *degree day* has been devised. The number of degrees by which the average temperature for 1 day is below 65 degrees is the number of degree days for that day; when this is totaled for the whole winter the total number of degree days can be used to calculate the total amount of heating which will be required. The assumption is made that heating is not required unless the temperature falls below 65 degrees, and that if it does, the amount of heating required is proportional to the amount by which the temperature is below this value. Some figures of the number of degree days in the average winter in various localities are given in Table 6.4. The house considered previously would require a minimum of 1400 × 0.2 × 24 BTU for each degree day, since this is the number of BTU's required over 24 hours for a temperature difference of 1 degree. The total heating required as a result of heat loss through the walls, for the Massachusetts winter, would be 1400 × 0.2 × 24 × 5800, or roughly 4 × 10⁷ BTU. This value is a little less than half the actual heating requirement for a house of the size assumed. The heat loss through the roof was ignored, as was the heat loss through the windows and by movement of air through the doors and around the windows. The appro-

TABLE 6.4

NUMBER OF DEGREE DAYS IN AN
AVERAGE HEATING SEASON

Massachusetts	5800
Florida	1160
District of Columbia	4582
San Francisco	1161

priate corrections for these heat losses can be found in the handbooks used by heating engineers.

Heat Insulation In the table of thermal conductivities (Table 6.2), it was shown that the thermal conductivity of air is 10^{-8} and that of a vacuum is zero. Both are obviously effective as thermal insulators. Using a vacuum as a thermal insulator on a large scale would involve great mechanical difficulties and it would be extremely expensive to maintain (between the inner and outer parts of the walls of a house, for example). On the other hand, it is not difficult to maintain a very good vacuum in a small space such as that between the walls of a vacuum or thermos flask, which is an extremely effective insulating device.

The use of air as a thermal insulator is made difficult by the fact that heat is transmitted through air not only by conduction but also by convection, the latter being by far the more significant. Therefore, in order to use air for thermal insulation, convection must be prevented and this requires that the motion of the air be obstructed. All ordinary thermal insulators consist of fibrous or cellular material in which a great deal of air is entrapped in small pockets between the fibers or particles. These small air pockets are poor thermal conductors, and they are not large enough to permit the kind of air movement needed for a convection current. For a good insulator it is necessary that the fibrous material itself should have a low thermal conductivity. The difference between the thermal conductivity of ice and snow is a good example of the effect of entrapped air. They consist of the same material, but snow when loosely packed contains a great deal of air; approximately one-tenth of its volume is ice and the other nine-tenths is air, and the heat conduction is only one-tenth of the value for ice in bulk form. Fiberglas insulation is another example, in which glass, a fairly good insulator, is used in the form of extremely thin filaments, which are distributed in a random fashion so that air is trapped and cannot set up convention currents.

As noted in Chapter 5, the sensation of touch is highly unreliable in estimating the temperature of an object. If, on a hot day in the summer, one touches a piece of wood and a piece of metal that are both at same temperature, the metal feels very much hotter than the wood. The reverse occurs when the temperature is low; that is, the metal seems much colder than the wood or other poorly conducting material. The reason is that the sensation of heat or cold arises from the conduction of heat to or from the skin and this depends upon the thermal conductivity of the object which is being touched. If it is a very poor thermal conductor, heat is conducted through its own surface layers to the skin very slowly and the sensory nerves just below the skin receive a weak stimulus because their temperature does not rise much. On the other hand, if heat is conducted rapidly through the surface layers of the object being touched, then sensory nerves receive heat rapidly, their temperature rises appreciably, and the sensation is strong.

Aerodynamic Heating   In high-speed flight the air just ahead of the moving object, such as the wing of an aircraft or the nose of a rocket, is compressed. To a lesser extent this is also true at lower speeds, but above the speed of sound, the compression is much more severe and much more concentrated in the region immediately ahead of the moving object. The reason is that the air in front does not have time to flow smoothly out of the way; instead it is compressed violently and forced out of the way. The well-known noise produced when an aircraft "penetrates the sound barrier" is a result. The rise in temperature resulting from this rapid compression of air causes a major problem in ultra-high-speed flight and in the return of rockets and spaceships into the atmosphere. The same heating effect causes meteorites to glow and meteors to burn completely as they travel through the atmosphere. It should be made clear that the major part of the heating that occurs during high-speed flight is not caused by the friction of the air passing over the surface of the moving object but rather by the compression of the air immediately ahead of the leading surface. This is shown by the fact that the maximum amount of heating occurs in the very front, where the air flow is least, and is much less in the region where the air flows over the wings or the surface of the rocket. Depending upon the speed of the moving object, the amount of heat generated varies from 50 to 10,000 BTU per square foot per second. In a flight of very short duration at high speed within the earth's atmosphere this heat can be absorbed by the nose cone or wings; if the quantity of heat to be disposed of in this way is small enough, the increased temperature will not damage or unduly weaken the structure. On the other hand, for longer flights the amount of heat becomes too great to be stored within the moving object and the surface may therefore be heated up to an increasing extent. Figure 6.5 shows the combination of speed and altitude at which various temperatures would be reached if

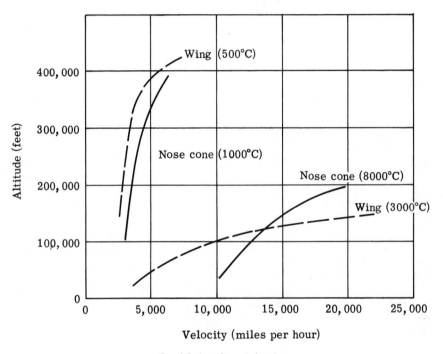

Fig. 6.5. Aerodynamic heating.

the only heat loss were by radiation. It will be seen that as the altitude increases higher speeds can be tolerated for any given temperature limitation. This is because the less dense atmosphere at high altitudes transfers less heat to the moving structure. Most of the temperatures shown on the graph are too high to be tolerable, and means other than radiation must be used to remove the heat. One of the most widely used methods is that of *ablation*. In ablation the surface of a nose cone, for example, is partly melted and partly evaporated; this removes a very large amount of heat. Ablation is obviously permissible only when the duration of the high-speed flight in the atmosphere is to be short, as in the case of the re-entry of a nose cone. The other methods that are useful in particular circumstances are a liquid coolant that can be circulated in order to limit the temperature of the most critical region; the use of construction materials with a high heat capacity, so that the additional heat goes to raising the temperature of the material, and the boiling of a liquid with a high latent heat of vaporization.

Problems

6.1 You have a cup of coffee that is too hot to drink and a small jug of cream. In order to cool the coffee as quickly as possible, should you put the cream into the coffee immediately, or should you wait until the coffee has partly cooled before you add the cream?

6.2 How much heat would be conducted per minute through a plate of copper, 10 cm² in area and $\frac{1}{2}$ cm thick, if it is held at 100°C, by means of boiling water, on one side, and at 0°C, by means of ice on the other?

6.3 How many foot-pounds of energy would it take to melt 1 lb of ice?

6.4 A room air conditioner has a capacity of 7000 BTU/hr. Would this be sufficient to maintain a wooden hut (20 ft × 20 ft × 10 ft) at 70°F when the external temperature is 90°F? (Assume heat transfer coefficient of the walls and roof to be 0.55 BTU/ft²/°F/hr.)

6.5 Does an escalator do more or less work if you walk up it than if you stand on it?

6.6 A human being at rest gives off heat at the rate of about 300 BTU/hr. How fast would the temperature of the air in a room 20 ft × 10 ft × 10 ft rise if there were 20 people in it? (Assume no loss of heat to the walls and no ventilation!) Specific heat of air = 0.24.

6.7 Compare the amounts of energy required (a) to melt snow and (b) to lift it to an average height of 8 ft onto a truck.

6.8 How much heat would be required to melt a 10-in. snowfall on a driveway measuring 100 ft × 10 ft? (10 in. of snow is equivalent to 1 in. of rain.)

6.9 If the snow in the previous problem is to be melted at the rate of 3 in. of snow per hour, at what rate, in kilowatts, must energy be supplied?

6.10 Calculate the heat loss per hour from an igloo of hemispherical shape of internal radius 8 ft and thickness 2 ft. The heat transmission coefficient for 2 ft of snow is 0.03 BTU/ft²/hr/°F. Internal and external temperatures are 50°F and 0°F. (Approximate by using the area = $2\pi r^2$ and calculate as if for a flat slab.)

Chapter 7

THE CONVERSION OF
HEAT INTO WORK

A very large proportion of the world's work, in the mechanical sense, is now done by machines, which can be divided into two broad categories: those, such as automobiles, aircraft, ships, that draw their energy directly from the heat generated by the combustion of a fuel (coal, oil, or gasoline), and those that are operated by electricity. However, a large proportion of the electricity used in this way is in turn derived from fuel-burning machines; therefore the whole process depends, in both cases, upon the conversion of the heat, resulting from combustion, into work, which is used directly or to generate electricity. The nature and use of electrical energy will be discussed in Chapter 10.

Heat Engines Any device for transforming heat into mechanical work is called a *heat engine;* all heat engines are subject to certain general principles which show that only a limited proportion of the heat put into the engine can be converted into work. The balance remains in the form of heat but is no longer available for conversion into work. It will be appreciated that the conversion of *work* to *heat* is not subject to this limitation; it can be complete. The consideration of heat engines will start with a very simple, but quite impracticable type of engine. The purpose is to expose the principles that are inherent in *all* heat engines. The simplest possible heat engine (see Fig. 7.1) consists of a cylinder (*A*) closed at one end and a piston (*B*) that is free to move within the cylinder but fits closely enough so that, ideally, there is no leakage of air past the piston. The piston is attached to a piston rod (*C*) which in turn is attached by means of a pivoted joint to the connecting rod (*D*) which is connected, also by a pivoted joint, to the crank *E*. The crank is attached rigidly to the shaft (*F*), which can rotate on its axis. If the piston moves back and forth through the appropriate distance, the shaft will rotate. If sufficient force is applied to the piston to move it, work can be done by the rotation of the shaft *F*. It is necessary to apply force to the piston for only part of each complete cycle because a flywheel attached to the shaft will cause it to continue to rotate even when no force is being applied.

This simple type of heat engine is operated by alternate heating and cooling of the air in the cylinder. When the air is heated, the pressure it exerts increases, driving the piston to the right (see illustration); when cooled, its pressure decreases, allowing the pressure of the atmosphere to push the piston to the left. At the completion of the cycle, the piston has returned to its original position and the air to its original temperature and pressure. Some of the energy supplied in the form of heat has been converted into work. The cycle can then be repeated. The amount of heat which is put into the air of

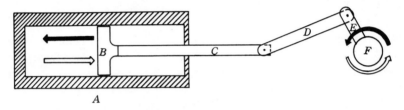

Fig. 7.1. Simple heat engine.

the cylinder is equivalent to an amount of energy that can be calculated from the mechanical equivalent of heat. However, it will be apparent that the whole of the heat that has been supplied to the air in the piston is not converted into the form of work because some of the heat that was initially put in is subsequently withdrawn when the air is cooled. The important point is that it is impossible, by any means whatever, to convert the whole of the heat supplied into mechanical work.

Efficiency

The meaning of the preceding statement—and its importance—will become clearer if we consider the *efficiency* of heat engines. The efficiency of a heat engine is a measure of the proportion of the heat input that is converted into useful work. There is a fundamental limitation to the proportion that can be converted (i.e., to the efficiency), because some heat is necessarily removed from the heated air in order to bring it back to its original temperature and pressure so that the cycle can be repeated. The only alternative would be to reject the heated air after it has expanded and has caused the piston to move, and to replace it by a fresh supply of air at the starting temperature. Here again, the heat rejected in the hot air would not be converted into work and would therefore limit the efficiency of the machine. None of the energy is completely lost but only a part of it can be converted into useful work.

In more formal terms, any heat engine must work between two temperatures, the upper temperature being that of the *heat source* from which heat is supplied to the cylinder, and the lower temperature that of the *heat sink*, to which heat is conducted from the cylinder in the return half of the cycle. Without this heat sink (i.e., without a temperature difference), there would be no heat flow and thus no work. Once heat energy has been transferred to the heat sink, it is no longer available to do work, because it can no longer be conducted into the gas in the cylinder, which is necessarily at a higher temperature. Heat will *never* flow spontaneously from a cooler to a hotter object; that is, from the heat sink to the gas. Another way of stating this is that heat will not flow "uphill," or, to be more precise, up a temperature gradient. This basic principle, though it may appear obvious, is of great

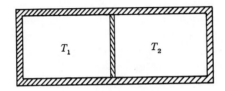

Fig. 7.2. Mixing of gases at different temperatures.

importance. In the case under discussion, it explains why the utilization of heat energy is apparently inefficient; why some heat is always rejected and not converted into work. This principle must be examined more closely. It states that if two objects, at different temperatures, are in contact with each other, heat flows from the hotter to the colder, and never from the colder to the hotter. That is, the temperatures tend to become more nearly equal and finally will become equal; the temperature difference never increases spontaneously. A simple example of this principle is a gas-filled vessel (insulated so that heat cannot enter or leave it) that is divided into two compartments by an insulating partition (Fig. 7.2). The gas in the left-hand compartment is initially the temperature at T_1, and that on the right is at T_2. Both are at the same pressure. When the partition is removed the gas at the higher temperature T_1 comes into contact with the gas at the lower temperature T_2; the molecules of the hotter gas give up some of their kinetic energy to those molecules of the colder gas with which they collide. The kinetic energy, and therefore the temperature, of the latter increases. This process will continue by random collision until all the molecules have the same average kinetic energy. The number of molecules involved in such a process is enormous; it is thus inconceivable that at any moment all those molecules with higher-than-average energies should move in one direction, and all those with lower than average energies move in the opposite direction. It is therefore inconceivable that different parts of the gas should spontaneously establish different temperatures and it follows that it is impossible for heat to flow "uphill."

To use "inconceivable" and "impossible" in referring to the spontaneous flow of heat "uphill" may seem contradictory. The probability of such an event, however, may be looked at in the following way. Suppose a deck of cards is shuffled and dealt into four hands (as in bridge, for example). It is extremely improbable, though possible, that each hand will consist of one complete suit. The probability is less than one chance in 10^{27}, a very small probability indeed. If two tables played simultaneously, would each have the same chance (10^{-27}) of dealing four separate suits; but the probability of both tables doing this at the same time is so small (10^{-54}) that it has probably never happened. It is even more certain that four separate suits would never be dealt at each of 100 tables simultaneously, although this would be a possible chance arrangement of only 5200 cards.

The chance arrangement of 5200 cards into separate suits is, in a sense, analogous to the spontaneous establishment of a temperature difference among the molecules in the insulated vessel. The number of molecules in a sample of gas or solid of observable size is, however, vastly greater, being at least 10^{22} (as compared to 5200 cards). The actual probability of such an unlikely event occurring becomes astonishingly small even for a few thousand individuals; for vastly greater numbers this event is so improbable that "impossible" becomes a reasonable description. It is sometimes stated, for example, that it is theoretically possible for a kettle of water placed on a hot plate to become cooler and for the hot plate to be heated by the heat which leaves the water. This would be equivalent to the spontaneous separation of the gas in Fig. 7.2 into a hot portion at one end and a cold portion at the other end after it had been allowed to mix. It is inconceivably improbable that a very large proportion of the molecules at the bottom of the kettle should suddenly move downward with energies above average and therefore impart a large amount of energy to the molecules with which they are in contact on the surface of the hot plate. Certainly, some molecules of above-average energy on the bottom of the kettle will transfer energy to the hot plate; but if the hot plate is hotter than the kettle, far more molecules from the hot plate will transfer energy to the kettle. Therefore, the probability is overwhelming that heat will be transferred from the hotter to the colder object. Inevitably, then, some of the input of a heat engine will flow to a heat sink at a lower temperature; this energy is no longer available to do work, unless it can flow to another sink at a still lower temperature. Thus we return to the statement made earlier that there is a fundamental limitation to the efficiency of a heat engine. Assuming that all the input (except the portion which *must* flow to the heat sink) is converted into work, the efficiency can be calculated from the equation

$$\text{Efficiency} = \frac{T_1 - T_2}{T_1}$$

where T_1 and T_2 are the absolute temperatures of the heat source and heat sink respectively. The efficiency can never be 100 per cent unless the lower temperature (T_2) is absolute zero, as is clear from the above equation. Moreover, since temperatures below absolute zero are impossible, it is impossible for a heat engine to have an efficiency of greater than 100 per cent. It follows that whenever a heat engine is operated, part of the heat which is supplied to the engine is converted into mechanical work and part of it is rejected to a heat sink at a lower temperature. This means that part of the heat initially supplied becomes unavailable; this is the fate of all the energy that we utilize or fail to utilize. There is a continuous, progressive trend towards the degradation of energy in the sense that energy in the form of heat is available for conversion to work only if the substance in which the heat resides is at a higher temperature than an available heat sink. If all the heat were "at the same temperature," no heat engine could be made to operate, and although the energy would still be present it would be unavailable for doing work. Any moving object will eventually be slowed down and stopped by friction, its kinetic energy thereby being transformed into heat; and although energy is never lost in this process it can cease to be useful. This process is happening all the time and will always continue to happen in the future.

As an addendum to the principle of the conservation of energy, therefore, it must be recognized that the *availability* of energy is *not* conserved. It decreases spontaneously wherever heat flows from a hotter to a colder body; that is, whenever kinetic energy becomes less "organized" or more random. The kinetic energy of a moving object is highly organized, in the sense that all of its molecules move in the same direction and with the same speed. When some of this energy is converted into heat (by friction) the molecules in the regions that are heated have their kinetic energy increased, but only by increasing their random vibrations. Similarly, the gas molecules of the gases at temperatures T_1 and T_2 in Fig. 7.2 have some organization, or "nonrandomness," because the molecules in one compartment have, on the average, greater kinetic energy than those in the other. This "nonrandomness" disappears when the two gases mix, and the possibility of using them as source and sink for a heat engine is lost. An alternative form of the statement is that the *free energy* has decreased.

Types of Heat Engines The foregoing discussion of the conversion of heat energy into mechanical work has been in terms of an idealized but completely impractical type of engine. The same principles apply to the practical types of engines in which the heat resulting from the combustion of a fuel is converted into mechanical work. The underlying principle of all these types of engines is, therefore, that when the working substance is heated its pressure and volume increase, causing it to exert a force on the surrounding parts of the machine. The motion produced by this force is converted mechanically into the rotation of a shaft from which the output of work is taken.

All heat engines can be conveniently classified according to the location of the combustion chamber and according to the way the force exerted by the working substance is applied. In many engines, fuel is burned and the resulting heat is used to convert water into steam at high pressure. The steam is then conveyed from the boiler into the engine proper, where it does mechanical work. Such *external combustion engines* are to be distinguished from *internal combustion engines* in which combustion takes place within the engine itself. The second classification depends on whether the force is applied intermittently to a piston which moves to and fro in a cylinder, or continuously to vanes on a wheel, causing it to rotate. These two types are known as *reciprocating* and *turbine* engines.

Reciprocating Steam Engine   In the reciprocating steam engine, a boiler *A* (Fig. 7.3) is heated as a result of the combustion of a fuel. Steam from the boiler is led to the engine proper, part *B* of Fig. 7.3. The cylinder contains a piston *P* connected to a piston rod which can move to and fro. The piston fits closely within the cylinder in order that steam cannot pass around it from one part of the cylinder to another. The cylinder is connected by two openings (*R* and *S*) to the valve chamber. The valve chamber contains the slide valve (*T*) and exhaust port (*E*). The slide valve alternates between two positions. In the position shown steam from the boiler is admitted to the left-hand end of the cylinder and therefore it forces the piston (*P*) to the right. In this position of the valve, exhaust steam from the right-hand end of the cylinder escapes through *S* to the exhaust port. The function of the slide valve is to admit steam at high pressure to each end of the cylinder alternately, and to prevent it from reaching the exhaust port until it has expanded in the cylinder. In the other position of the slide valve, high-pressure steam is admitted at *S* and steam escaping at *R* is allowed to reach the exhaust port. The slide valve is driven by a rod connected to a crank which in turn is driven by the shaft that is activated by the piston. The high pressure steam is therefore admitted alternately to the left and the right-hand ends of the piston, the other end of the cylinder being connected to the exhaust and therefore at low pressure.

There is always a higher pressure of steam on one side of the piston than on other side and therefore a force is exerted on it. It is this force which moves the piston, causes the crank shaft to rotate, and enables the engine to do external work. The steam which is admitted to the cylinder expands and does work on the piston; its heat content is reduced by the amount of energy extracted as work, and its temperature falls; by the time it is allowed to escape through the exhaust system, it has given up some of its heat energy and this has been converted into work. However, the exhaust steam still retains part of its heat energy because work would have to be done on it to cool it down to its initial temperature. Therefore some of the heat which was supplied to the water in the boiler remains in the steam when it is rejected as exhaust. It is concluded that this, like any other heat engine, is less than 100 per cent efficient in converting heat into work. The ideal and the actual efficiencies of engines of this type are as follows. If the steam temperature were 120 degrees centigrade and the lowest temperature reached by the steam when it is cooled down or condensed is 20 degrees centigrade, then the ideal efficiency would be given by $(T_1 - T_2)/T_1$, using absolute temperatures; this would be $\frac{100}{393}$, which is about 25 per cent. This means

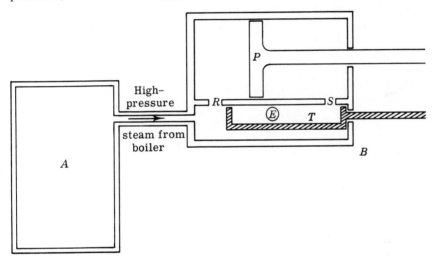

Fig. 7.3. Reciprocating steam engine.

that each Calorie supplied to the steam would produce only about 1000 joules of energy in the form of mechanical work, while its total energy content is equivalent to 4200 joules. If the steam temperature were raised to 300 degrees centigrade, which would involve quite a high boiler pressure, the ideal efficiency would be very close to 50 per cent. The ideal efficiency, however, is not realistic. It is based upon an ideal working substance, but steam, although extremely convenient to use, cannot give the ideal efficiency. It also requires that the engine be run extremely slowly, which would seriously limit its usefulness. The maximum *theoretical* efficiency (as distinct from the *ideal* efficiency) of a steam engine with a steam temperature of 300 degrees centigrade is between 30 and 35 per cent, depending on the pressure and on the temperature of the condenser. Since the theoretical efficiency is calculated upon the assumption that no heat is lost, the actual efficiency is always lower than the theoretical; conditions can never be made perfectly ideal and some heat is always lost. The actual efficiencies are usually 50 to 80 per cent of the theoretical value, although the efficiency of the steam loco- motive is only about 5 per cent. The actual efficiency can be made to ap- proach the theoretical efficiency more closely in larger installations than in smaller ones because the heat loss is relatively less important in a large than in a small unit. The over-all or actual efficiency is measured as the ratio of the output of mechanical work to the input of heat energy.

An alternative, and sometimes more useful, method of describing the efficiency of an engine, is to express it as the number of British Thermal Units required per horsepower-minute, or per kilowatt-hour. For example, a par- ticular steam engine is stated to have a performance of 200 BTU per horse- power-minute. One BTU is equivalent to 778 foot-pounds, so 200 BTU is equivalent to 155,600 foot-pounds. This would be the work performed if the efficiency were 100 per cent. In fact only 1 horsepower-minute (i.e., 33,000 foot-pounds) is produced. The efficiency is therefore 33,000/155,600, or 21 per cent. Similarly, for a steam-turbine plant with a performance of 10,000 BTU per kilowatt-hour, 1 BTU is equivalent to 778 foot-pounds, so 10,000 BTU is equivalent to 7,780,000 foot-pounds. Since 1 kilowatt-hour equals 60,000 watt-minutes, and 746 watts equal 1 horsepower (33,000 foot-pounds per minute), 60,000 watt-minutes equal 60,000/746 horsepower-minutes, or

$$\frac{60,000}{746} \times 33,000 \text{ ft-lb} = 2,600,000 \text{ ft-lb}.$$

The efficiency is, therefore,

$$\frac{2,600,000}{7,780,000} = 34 \text{ per cent.}$$

Steam The over-all efficiency of the most modern large steam
Turbines plants is about 40 per cent. Such plants use the *steam turbine* instead of the reciprocating steam engine. The steam turbine is illus- trated diagrammatically in Fig. 7.4. It consists of a boiler and an external combustion engine. The engine consists of an outer casing and a rotor (housed in an outer casing). The rotor consists of a series of disks (D_1, D_2, etc.), each carrying a large number of vanes at its periphery. The vanes are tilted so that steam moving past them causes the disk and thus the rotor to rotate. Steam is deflected against the rotor vanes by means of a series of fixed vanes (S_1, S_2, etc.) appropriately placed between the rotor disks. The diameter of the casing and of the rotor disks increases from the high-pressure end (at left in the illustration) to the low-pressure end (at right) because as the pressure of the steam decreases, its volume increases.

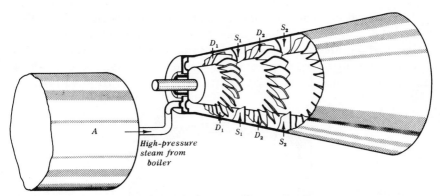

Fig. 7.4. Steam turbine.

Internal Combustion Engines   As noted earlier, the fuel of an internal combustion engine is burned within the engine itself. In the reciprocating type the cylinder (*A*) in Fig. 7.5 containing the piston has two valves (*Q* and *R*). The valves are opened and closed at appropriate times by means of a mechanical linkage with the crankshaft (*S*), which is turned by the connecting rod (*C*). In the typical *four-cycle engine* each cylinder, of which there may be many, is first filled with a fuel-air mixture, entering through the inlet valve (*Q*), which is open while the piston moves downward. The inlet valve then closes as the crankshaft continues to rotate and the piston moves upward, compressing the fuel-air mixture. When the piston reaches approximately its highest position, the fuel is ignited (in the gasoline engine) by means of a spark plug (*P*), causing the fuel to burn very rapidly. The pressure rises and pushes the piston downward. When the piston reaches its lowest position the exhaust valve (*R*) opens and as the piston moves upward, the burned fuel is ejected through the exhaust valve. At the top position the exhaust valve closes, the inlet valve opens and a new charge of fuel and air is drawn in from the carburetor. The complete cycle can then be repeated, indefinitely. There is one working stroke (the combustion part of the cycle) during each complete sequence of four traverses of the length of the cylinder by the piston. In a *diesel* engine the fuel ignites as a result of the high temperature reached during the compression of the fuel-air mixture by the piston, and a spark plug is not necessary.

One of the problems in the design of internal combustion engines is to prevent the temperature of the cylinder and piston from rising to such a level that the metal would be weakened or the fuel mixture would ignite prematurely. Air cooling and water cooling are used for this purpose, and it is clear that some of the heat generated by the fuel is removed by the coolant and does not contribute to the useful work done by the engine. Some heat is also carried away in the exhaust.

The over-all efficiency of internal combustion engines depends on their design and their size. An engine designed for maximum efficiency is usually heavy, and for aircraft purposes this is obviously a great disadvantage. The figures quoted for various types of internal combustion engines are as follows: automobile engines, 17 to 23 per cent; aircraft engines, 20 to 33 per cent;

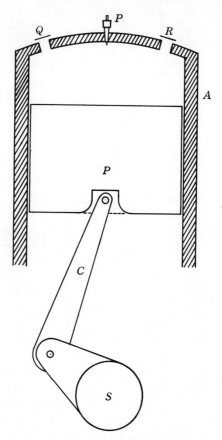

Fig. 7.5. One-cylinder internal combustion engine.

diesel engines, 26 to 38 per cent; and marine engines, 30 to 35 per cent. These over-all efficiencies are comparable to the 40 per cent efficiency of a large steam turbine plant.

Gas Turbines   The fourth category of engine is the *gas turbine*. This consists essentially of the following parts (Fig. 7.6): A shaft (*S*), a compressor (*C*), combustion chambers (*B*), and the turbine disk (*D*). The compressor draws air in at the inlet end of the engine and compresses it. It is then mixed with fuel in the combustion chamber (*B*), where it is burned. Its expansion causes it to move rapidly towards the turbine disk. Some of the momentum of the hot mixture of air and combustion products is transferred to the turbine blades, and becomes angular momentum of the moving parts of the engine (shaded in Fig. 7.6). Stationary vanes attached to the interior of the casing deflect the moving gas onto the blades of the disk. The detailed design depends upon the purpose of the engine. If it is to be used as a jet engine, then only enough energy to drive the compressor is extracted from the gas stream by the turbine. The remaining kinetic energy of the burned fuel-air mixture propels the aircraft. If the engine is to

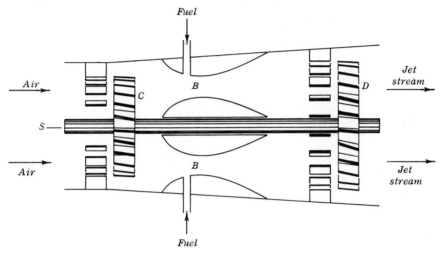

Fig. 7.6. Gas turbine (jet) engine.

drive a propeller, as in a "jet-prop" type of engine, then the turbine is designed to extract a much higher proportion of the energy from the moving gas or, alternatively, a second turbine is used to drive the propeller. The efficiency that could be achieved in gas-turbine engines in the earlier days of their development was seriously limited by the lack of materials that could withstand the extreme temperatures which the blades of the turbine must encounter if the efficiency is to be high. During the last 20 years great advances have been made in the development of materials for turbine disks and blades that can withstand very high temperatures without becoming too weak or oxidizing too rapidly.

As mentioned earlier, the weight of an engine is of crucial importance if it is to be used for aircraft purposes. One criterion for the usefulness of an engine from this standpoint is the comparison of the engine's weight with the thrust it is able to develop. Certain gas turbine engines, for example, develop 1 pound of thrust per pound of engine weight. It is much more realistic to describe the performance of a jet engine or rocket in terms of thrust than horsepower, because horsepower is a measure of the work done per unit time, and this depends not only on the force but also on the distance moved. This is determined by the speed, which in turn depends upon many other factors besides the performance of the engine. A rocket on a test bed, for example, would deliver no horsepower because it is not allowed to move; its thrust is the force that would be required to prevent it from moving.

Problems

7.1 (a) What is the ideal efficiency of a engine working between 100°C and 0°C?

(b) What rate of work, in horsepower, could be obtained from such an engine from 7000 BTU/hr, assuming the efficiency to be one-half of the ideal?

7.2 (a) How much heat in British Thermal Units must be supplied to run an internal combustion engine of $5\frac{1}{2}$ HP operating at 20 per cent efficiency for an hour?

(b) How much heat must be removed by the cooling system?

Chapter 8

RADIATION

The light that reaches us from the sun and the stars travels through space at a speed of about 186,000 miles per second, or 3×10^8 meters per second. If light consisted of solid matter, its momentum at this speed would be extremely large and it would exert enormous forces on any object upon which it fell. But light is not solid matter (though it does possess mass and does exert a pressure, both of which are negligible, for most purposes); it is, rather, a form of radiant energy. Light is described for many purposes as a type of wave motion traveling through space in a manner somewhat analogous to the way in which a ripple travels over the surface of water. When a ripple travels over a pond, the water itself moves only a very short distance but it does this rhythmically so that the movement is passed on from one region of the surface to another.

One of the characteristics of any wave motion is its wavelength: the distance between the crest (or trough), of one wave and the crest (or trough) of the next one (see Fig. 8.1). The wavelength of the ripples on a pond may be only a few inches; for waves on an ocean it may be many feet. Similarly light can be characterized by its wavelength. If light from a lamp or from the sun passes through a triangular glass prism (see Fig. 8.2), it undergoes several changes. In the first place, its direction changes as it passes from the air into the glass and again as it passes from glass back into air. This is because glass slows down the light somewhat, (i.e., the speed of light in glass is less than 186,000 miles per second). In addition, the prism divides the light into its component colors, producing a spectrum. This color spectrum is identical to that of a rainbow, which results from white light from the sun being split up by raindrops. Moreover, these colors, which always fall in the same sequence, can be recombined to form white light by interposing a second prism, (see Fig. 8.3), which exactly reverses the effect of the first.

Each color of the spectrum has a characteristic wavelength. For example, a color would be recognized as red if its wavelength were between 6.1 and 7.5×10^{-7} meters, the latter being the longest visible wavelength; Table 8.1 gives the wavelengths of the principal colors. The different colors are dis-

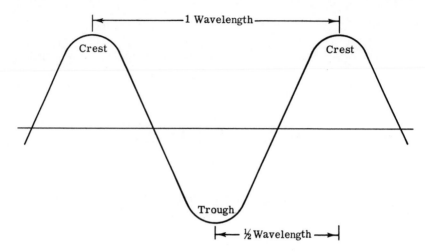

Fig. 8.1. Wavelength, defined as the distance between two successive crests or troughs.

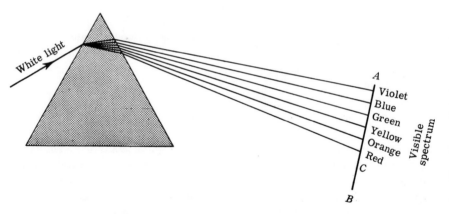

Fig. 8.2. White light divided into its component colors by a prism.

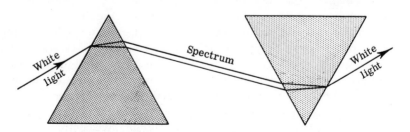

Fig. 8.3. Recombination of the color spectrum into white light.

tinguishable from one another because different wavelengths stimulate different parts of the detection mechanism in the eye. The whole spectrum of color is not required to produce the sensation of white light, since the same visual effect can be achieved, for example, by a suitable mixture of red,

TABLE 8.1
COLORS AND THEIR WAVELENGTHS

Color	Wavelength (meters)
Red	$6.1–7.5 \times 10^{-7}$
Orange	$5.9–6.1 \times 10^{-7}$
Yellow	$5.7–5.9 \times 10^{-7}$
Green	$5.0–5.7 \times 10^{-7}$
Blue	$4.5–5.0 \times 10^{-7}$
Violet	$3.8–4.5 \times 10^{-7}$

yellow, and blue light. All visible light, whatever its color, consists of a mixture of wavelengths within the range of 4×10^{-4} meters and 7×10^{-7} meters. These are the limits of the wavelengths to which the eye is sensitive.

Infrared Radiation These wavelengths, however, form but a very small part of the totality of wavelengths. For instance suppose that the spectrum produced by a prism were allowed to fall on a screen (*AB*, in Fig. 8.2). A heat detector placed just beyond the red end of the spectrum (*C*) would begin to heat up. That the heating is caused by radiation falling upon it, becomes clear because if the light is obstructed, or if the detector is moved from *C* towards *B*, heating immediately ceases. We can conclude then, that the part of the radiation beyond visible red light has the property of heating objects upon which it falls. For this reason, it is sometimes called radiant heat, but it is usually referred to as infrared radiation because of its position just beyond the red end of the visible spectrum.

Visible light and infrared are the only two kinds of radiation that can be detected directly by the senses; there are, however, many other kinds of radiation that can be detected by special methods (see Table 8.2). It will be observed that microwaves (used in radar) and radio waves, lie beyond the infrared end of the visible spectrum, while shorter wavelengths include ultraviolet radiation, which is invisible but has an effect on the pigmentation of the human skin, and on plant life; x-rays and gamma rays are found at even shorter wavelengths. These types of radiation have much in common. They all travel through space at the same speed; they can all be reflected from suitable surfaces and they can all be refracted, that is, they are slowed down, and usually change direction, when entering transparent substances.

Both of these properties of light are familiar. Furthermore, they all travel in straight lines through space and therefore produce shadows when opaque objects intervene. However, one important difference is the way in which the various kinds of radiation are transmitted or absorbed by different substances. For example, visible light passes very freely through glass, water, plexiglass, and gases, but is absorbed by most other substances; ultraviolet, if its wavelength is less than 3.5×10^{-7} meters, is absorbed by glass. One of the major uses of x-rays is in radiography, a technique that depends on

TABLE 8.2
ELECTROMAGNETIC SPECTRUM

Wavelength (meters)	Kind of radiation
10^2	
10	
1	Radio
10^{-1}	
10^{-2}	Microwave
10^{-3}	
10^{-4}	
10^{-5}	Infrared
10^{-6}	
10^{-7}	Visible light
10^{-8}	Ultraviolet
10^{-9}	
10^{-10}	
10^{-11}	X-rays
10^{-12}	
10^{-13}	
10^{-14}	Gamma rays
10^{-15}	

the fact that x-rays pass through substances that are opaque to ordinary light. Radio waves pass through the atmosphere readily but are absorbed by the ionosphere (a region in the upper atmosphere), the extent of absorption depending on the wavelength. Indeed, the extent to which radiation is absorbed by a substance depends very much upon the wavelength of the radiation. Sometimes the absorption is selective; when white light passes through a piece of green glass, the light that is transmitted is white light from which the red color has been subtracted.

The following demonstrations will show the similarity in the behavior of visible light, infrared radiation, and microwaves. Figure 8.4 shows a polished metal reflector (1), shaped so that light diverging from point A is reflected as a parallel beam. The reflector is similar in shape to, but larger than, the reflector of an automobile headlight, in which a parallel beam of light (the "high beam") is produced by placing the lamp at the *focal point*, (i.e., *A*) of the curved reflector. Very much more light reaches point *B* when the mirror is in place than when it is not. In the absence of the mirror, light from *A* spreads out in all directions, whereas when the mirror is correctly placed, the

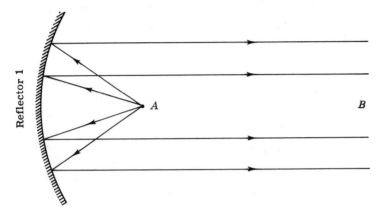

Fig. 8.4. Reflection of light, infrared radiation, or microwaves.

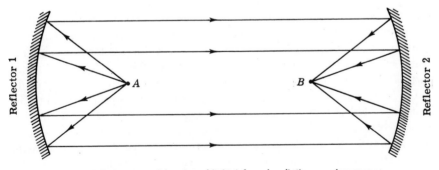

Fig. 8.5. Reflection and focusing of light, infrared radiation, or microwaves.

light is concentrated in the beam as shown (Fig. 8.5). A second reflector (2), in the path of the beam can be used to focus it at point *B*. Identical demonstrations can be made with light, which can be seen if a piece of paper is placed at *B*, with radiant heat, detected by a thermometer at *B* (or, with good reflectors, a match at *B* will light if the heat source at *A* is strong enough), or by a microwave transmitter at *A* and a receiver at *B*. A very simple microwave receiver is a neon tube, which glows visibly when subjected to microwave radiation. This demonstration shows that visible light, of wavelength averaging 5×10^{-7} meters, infrared radiation with a wavelength 10 times as great, and microwave radiation of several centimeters wavelength, all share the basic properties of being reflected and focused; many other properties of light are shared by the other forms of radiation. The only difference, but an important one, is in wavelength. For example, any reflector used for focusing radiation must be large compared with the wavelength of the radiation. This is why the reflectors for radio telescopes must be very large and the reflector in a headlight can be rather small. The wavelengths of the radiation picked up by radio telescopes fall in the microwave region of about 0.3 to 30 centimeters. Also the reflector should be as large as is feasible in order to collect as much radiation as possible.

Radiation A block of iron heated to high temperature will cool unless **of** heat is supplied to it continuously. It can be shown that **Energy** this cooling is not entirely due to convection and conduction. The rate of cooling decreases, but not very much, if the iron is placed in a vacuum instead of being surrounded by air. It follows that a hot object loses some of its heat energy as radiation, which is also a form of energy. The rate at which energy is radiated from a hot surface depends on three variables: the surface area of the object, the nature of the surface, and the temperature.

First, every square inch of surface area of a given material at the same temperature radiates at the same rate; therefore the rate at which energy is radiated is proportional to the total area of the surface. Second, a dull, black surface radiates far more than a bright and polished surface. The relevant property here is *emissivity*, which has the value *one* for a completely black and dull surface, and decreases to about 0.04 for a well-polished metal surface. An ideally bright and shiny surface, with an emissivity of zero, would not radiate at all. The rate at which energy is radiated is proportional to the emissivity. Third, temperature is a very important criterion in determining the rate of radiation. The amount of energy radiated per unit area per second increases with the fourth power of the absolute temperature; that is, with T^4, where T is the absolute temperature. The rate of radiation is given by $W = A \times E \times 5.3 \times 10^{-8} \times T^4$ watts, where W is the rate of emission of energy in joules per second (i.e. watts), A is the area in square meters, E is the emissivity, 5.3×10^{-8} is a constant, and T is the absolute temperature of the surface. Table 8.3 illustrates how fast the radiation increases with rising temperature. To take an example, suppose that a kettle has a surface area of 0.1 square meter, an emissivity of 0.1, and a temperature of 100 degrees centigrade. The rate of heat loss will be

$$W = A \times E \times 5.3 \times 10^{-8} \times T^4 \text{ watts}$$
$$= 0.1 \times 0.1 \times 5.3 \times 10^{-8} \times 373^4 \text{ watts}$$
$$= 10 \text{ watts (approximately)}.$$

An emissivity of 0.1 corresponds to a fairly bright, well-polished surface; if it were black, with an emissivity of 1, the rate of radiation would be 10 times as great, or about 100 watts.

Some of the radiation falling upon an object is reflected, some of it is absorbed, and, if the object is transparent to that radiation, some of it is transmitted. The emissivity indicates the proportion absorbed. If the emissivity is *one*, as for a black surface, then all the radiation reaching it is absorbed and turned into heat and none of it is reflected. If the emissivity is low, as for a bright shiny surface, a large proportion of the energy reaching it is reflected and not absorbed; thus a surface with an emissivity of 0.1 absorbs (and turns

TABLE 8.3

Energy Radiated from a Hot Surface with an Emissivity of 0.1

Temperature (°C)	Energy radiated (watts per square meter)
100	10^2
400	10^3
600	3×10^3
800	7×10^3
1000	1.3×10^4
1200	2.4×10^4

into heat) $\frac{1}{10}$ of the radiation it receives, and reflects the rest. Thus the same property, the emissivity, determines how much an object will radiate and how much it will absorb. A good radiator is a good absorber and a poor reflector. A hot object, such as the kettle just discussed, radiates heat, but it also receives radiation from its surroundings, the temperature of which determines how much radiation reaches its surface. The kettle, considered above, is in a room at 20 degrees centigrade, (68 degrees Fahrenheit), that is 293 degrees Kelvin. The amount of radiation absorbed (W') is given by the same formula,

$$W' = A \times E \times 5.3 \times 10^{-8} \times T^4$$

where T is now the absolute temperature of the surroundings. Thus,

$$W' = 0.1 \times 0.1 \times 5.3 \times 10^{-8} \times (293)^4 \text{ watts} = 3.5 \text{ watts.}$$

If E is 1, W' becomes 35 watts. The kettle would, therefore, radiate 10 watts and receive about 3.5 watts if its emissivity were 0.1, and it would radiate 100 watts and receive about 35 watts if its emissivity were 1.

The energy radiated by a hot surface is not restricted to a single wavelength. It always covers a considerable band of wavelengths; there is, nevertheless, a single wavelength where the energy is most concentrated. This can be represented graphically as in Fig. 8.6, in which the point *A* represents the wavelength of maximum energy. The total energy is found by adding together the energies at all the wavelengths. At low temperatures, the wavelength of maximum energy is long; as the temperature increases the wavelength of maximum energy decreases. At a temperature of 100 degrees

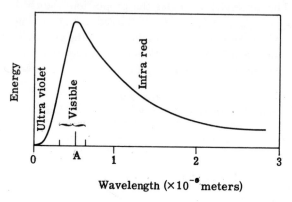

Fig. 8.6. Distribution of energy in the radiation from a hot surface (6000°K).

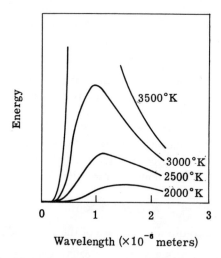

Fig. 8.7. Distribution of radiation at different temperatures.

centigrade the radiation that is given out cannot be seen but it can be sensed from its effect on the skin. It is, therefore, in the infrared region. As the temperature is raised, the wavelength of the maximum energy decreases and the total energy increases (see Fig. 8.7).

At temperatures above about 600 degrees centigrade an appreciable amount of radiation falls within the visible spectrum. An object at such temperatures is said to be red hot, since the visible radiation from it is predominantly at the red end of the spectrum. As the temperature increases further, the wavelength of maximum energy decreases still more until, at about 1200 to 1400 degrees centigrade, the energy is distributed throughout the visible spectrum and the surface appears white. This is the region of white heat. At higher temperatures, the wavelength of maximum energy becomes progressively shorter. The radiation we receive from the sun has its maximum in the yellow part of the spectrum, (i.e., about 5.8×10^{-7} meters). This wavelength, to which the eye is more sensitive than to any other, corresponds

TABLE 8.4
TEMPERATURES OF SOME SOURCES OF LIGHT

Source of light		Temperature (°K)
Candle or kerosene lamp		1900
Vacuum tungsten lamp		2360
Acetylene flame		2360
Gas-filled tungsten lamp:	50 watt	2770
	100 watt	2860
Photoflood lamp		3400
Clear flash bulb		3800
Sunlight		6000

to a temperature of about 6000 degrees Kelvin. However, only about one-sixth of the energy of the sun's radiation is in the form of visible light; the remainder is largely in the infrared part of the spectrum.

A radiating surface, therefore, has a characteristic *color temperature*. At higher temperatures the color is further towards the blue end of the spectrum. Table 8.4 shows the temperatures corresponding to some familiar types of light source. In the case of the candle or kerosene flame light is emitted by particles of carbon that are heated within the flame to a high enough temperature to radiate. When the purpose of heating an object is to produce light (e.g., the filament of an electric lamp), the temperature should be as high as possible because the maximum proportion of the radiated energy is then in the visible spectrum.

The size of an object has a great effect on its rate of cooling by radiation. To take a simple example, suppose that two copper blocks, one a 10-centimeter cube (Fig. 8.8), and the other a 1-centimeter cube, both having an emissivity of 0.5 were heated to an initial temperature of 1000 degrees absolute, (727 degrees centigrade). The total surface area of the large cube is

6×10^{-2} square meters and that of the small cube is 6×10^{-4} square meters. The rates of heat loss W_1 and W_2 of the two cubes are:

$$W_1 = 6 \times 10^{-2} \times 0.5 \times 5.3 \times 5.3 \times 10^{-5} \times 1000^4 \text{ watts}$$
$$= 1590 \text{ watts} = \tfrac{1590}{4200} \text{ Cal/sec} = 0.38 \text{ Cal/sec}$$
$$W_2 = 16 \text{ watts} = \tfrac{16}{4200} \text{ Cal/sec} = 0.0038 \text{ Cal/sec.}$$

The large cube, which has a surface area 100 times that of the smaller cube, loses heat 100 times as fast.

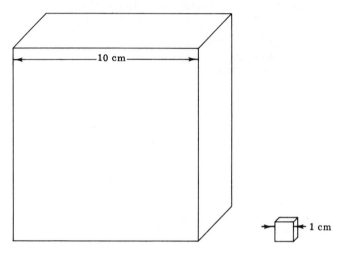

Fig. 8.8. Effect of size on the rate of cooling.

The rate of cooling also depends, however, on the heat capacity. The heat capacity is the mass times the specific heat; that is, volume times density times specific heat. The heat capacities H_1 and H_2 are

$$H_1 = V_1 \times D \times S = 10^{-3} \times 8 \times 10^3 \times 0.1^{-1} \text{ Cal/°C} = 0.8 \text{ Cal/°C}$$
$$H_2 = V_2 \times D \times S = 10^{-6} \times 8 \times 10^3 \times 0.1^{-1} \text{ Cal/°C} = 0.0008 \text{ Cal/°C}$$

where the density D is 8×10^3 kilograms per cubic meter, and the specific heat S is 0.1 Calorie per kilogram degree centigrade. Thus, the large cube requires 0.8 Calorie for a change of 1 degree centigrade, while the small cube only requires 0.0008 Calorie per degree centigrade. But the large cube loses 0.38 Calorie per second, so that its temperature falls 1 degree in approximately 0.5 second. The small cube loses 0.0038 Calorie per second but requires only 0.0008 Calorie per degree and therefore cools at the rate of about 5 degrees per second. The large cube, though radiating 100 times as much heat, cools at $\tfrac{1}{10}$ the rate of the small cube.

This result becomes more obvious if looked at in the following way. If the large cube were to be cut up into 1000 small cubes parallel to the three pairs of faces, it would require nine cuts parallel to each of the three pairs of faces and this would increase the surface area by a factor of 10. Thus the same amount of material, at the same temperature, will radiate 10 times as much heat in a given time, and its temperature will fall 10 times as fast. This result is quite general. For example, if the same calculation is made for two spheres, one having a radius three times that of the other, then the surface area of the larger sphere will be nine times that of the others, but its volume will be 27 times as great; as a result, it will lose heat 9 times faster than the smaller sphere, but its temperature will fall at $\frac{1}{3}$ the rate of the other.

Solar Radiation Since the color of the light emitted by a hot object depends upon its temperature, this color can be used to estimate the temperature of its surface. Measurements of light from the sun indicate a surface temperature of about 6000 degrees Kelvin. Since the size of the sun is known, the amount of radiation it emits can be calculated. Assuming that the emissivity of the sun is unity, the total energy radiated is

$$W = A \times 1 \times 5.3 \times 10^{-8} \times (6000)^4 \text{ watts.}$$

The radius of the sun is 6.9×10^8 meters (430,000 miles). The surface area (given by $4\pi r^2$) is $4 \times 3.14 \times (6.9 \times 10^8)^2$ square meters. Therefore,

$$W = 4 \times 3.14 \times (6.9 \times 10^8)^2 \times 5.3 \times 10^{-8} \times (6000)^4 \text{ watts}$$
$$= 4 \times 10^{26} \text{ watts.}$$

The part of this radiation that reaches the earth can be found as follows: the whole of the radiation from the sun spreads outward and passes through a sphere, of radius 93 million miles, surrounding the sun; every square meter of this sphere should receive equal amounts of radiation. The amount reaching any 1 square meter is, therefore, equal to the total amount divided by the area of the sphere. The area is

$$4\pi r^2 = 2.7 \times 10^{23} \text{ m}^2.$$

The amount reaching 1 square meter is

$$W = \frac{4 \times 10^{26}}{2.7 \times 10^{23}} \text{ watts} = 1.5 \times 10^3 \text{ watts/m}^2$$

which is equivalent to about 20 Calories per square meter per minute. This quantity is known as the *solar constant*, defined as the energy reaching the earth from the sun, measured in Calories per square meter per minute. It is evident that the earth intercepts only a minute fraction of the total energy radiated by the sun.

When the sun's radiation enters the earth's atmosphere, part of it is absorbed and part of it is reflected by clouds. The remainder, on the average about one-half of the radiation energy reaching the outside of the earth's atmosphere, arrives at the surface of the earth. A part of the other half is spent in raising the temperature of the atmosphere; this is the portion absorbed by air and clouds. Thus the energy reaching the surface of the earth during the day is about 10 Calories per square meter per minute; this corresponds to about 63 watts per square foot. The energy reaching the earth's surface can also be calculated, in horsepower per square mile, as follows. One square mile is (5280 feet)^2 or 2.8×10^7 square feet. Hence

$$W = 63 \times 2.8 \times 10^7 \text{ watts/sq mile}$$
$$= 1.7 \times 10^9 \text{ watts/sq mile}.$$

But 1 horsepower = 746 watts; thus

$$W = 1.7 \times 10^9/746 = 2.3 \times 10^6/\text{sq mile}$$

or about two and a half million horsepower per square mile.

The part of the sun's radiation which penetrates the atmosphere and reaches the earth is partly absorbed and partly reflected. The radiation absorbed by the earth's surface is eventually re-radiated, because the surface remains, on the average, at an almost constant temperature. The following calculation shows what the surface temperature would be if it were affected only by the radiation reaching and leaving it. Given that the radiation reaching the earth's surface is approximately one-half of that reaching the atmosphere, or, 0.75×10^3 watts per square meter and supposing, not altogether realistically, that there are 12 hours of daylight in every 24, the average rate of arrival of energy is one-half of 0.75×10^3, or 3.75×10^2 watts per square meter. The amount absorbed is $3.75 \times 10^2 \times E$, where E is the average emissivity of the earth's surface. To maintain a steady temperature the same amount of energy must be radiated. Therefore

$$3.75 \times 10^2 \times E = E \times 5.3 \times 10^{-8} \times T^4$$

whence

$$T^4 = \frac{3.75 \times 10^2}{5.3 \times 10^{-8}} = 7 \times 10^9$$

from which $T = 297$ degrees Kelvin $= 297 - 273 = 24$ degrees centigrade, or 75 degrees Fahrenheit. Thus, the average temperature at places having 12 hours of daylight out of 24 would be 75 degrees Fahrenheit.

The average temperature would be lower in regions where days are shorter; but it would also be lower for another reason. The calculations have been based on the assumption that the radiation strikes the surface at right angles (Fig. 8.9). However, the sun's rays strike most parts of the earth (and for most of the time) obliquely. As a result, the radiation arriving in a given area spreads out over a somewhat larger area of the surface (see Fig. 8.10). For example, suppose the beam of light *AB* has a cross section of one square meter; it impinges, however, on a larger surface area (represented by *AC*). The size of this area depends on the angle. In the equatorial regions of the

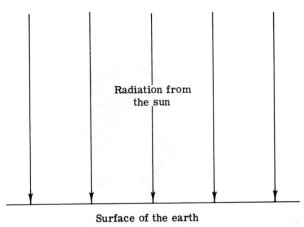

Radiation from the sun

Surface of the earth

Fig. 8.9. Radiation at right angles to the surface of the earth.

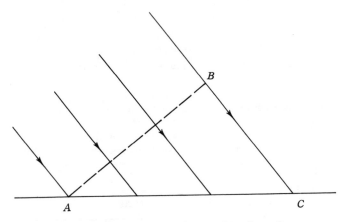

B

A   *C*

Fig. 8.10. Obliquity of the sun's rays striking the earth.

earth, the sun is nearly overhead, so that the original calculation should be nearly correct. But the angle becomes more and more oblique toward the polar regions, and the same amount of radiation is spread over larger and larger areas. This accounts for the colder climate of the polar regions. The difference between summer and winter can also be accounted for on the same basis.

During summer in the northern hemisphere (see Fig. 8.11), for example, the sun's radiation is more nearly perpendicular to the surface at *A*, which represents the latitude of Boston, than at *B*, which represents the corresponding latitude in the southern hemisphere. It will also be seen that, because of the tilt of the earth's axis, sunshine reaches the north pole in the summer, whereas it does not reach the south pole at all during the same period, which

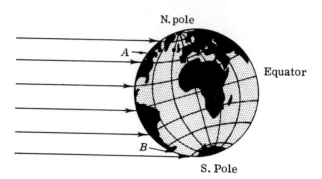

Fig. 8.11. Obliquity of the sun's rays during summer in the northern hemisphere.

is winter in the southern hemisphere. It should be pointed out that while the earth is actually a little closer to the sun during the northern hemisphere winter than it is during summer, this makes far less difference to the temperature than the changed obliquity of the sun's rays. Table 8.5 shows the variations in the amount of heat reaching the earth's surface according to the

TABLE 8.5

HEAT REACHING THE SURFACE OF THE EARTH (CALORIES PER SQUARE METER PER DAY)

	Equator	40 degrees North or 40 degrees South	North or South Pole
Midwinter	5500	1200	0
Equinox	6100	4100	0
Midsummer	5200	6600	5000

time of year and the geographical location. It is calculated on the assumption of a completely cloudless day.

It has been shown that even at the equator the average surface temperature should be somewhat lower than about 75 degrees Fahrenheit because the sun's radiation is sometimes intercepted by clouds. This figure does not depend upon any assumption concerning emissivity, which determines the proportion of radiation absorbed as well as the proportion emitted. The actual temperature of the earth is, however, higher than would be predicted on this basis. The reason is that the atmosphere acts as a sort of heat trap. Since the earth's surface has a relatively low temperature, it radiates at the relatively long wavelengths in the infrared region. Now the atmosphere absorbs a much higher proportion of infrared radiation than of the visible radiation coming from the sun, and therefore the atmosphere itself acts as a trap. It allows about 85 per cent of the sun's radiation to pass through, while at the same time absorbing about 77 per cent of the re-radiation from the surface of the earth. This effect is largely attributed to the carbon dioxide in the atmosphere and it has been suggested that the increasing amount of atmospheric carbon dioxide from automobile exhaust and other combustion products accounts for the gradual rise in the surface temperature of the earth observed over the last 50 or 60 years. The most recent reports, however, indicate that the temperature of the earth may in fact now be falling, in which case it would be unrealistic to attribute the temperature rise to the increased carbon dioxide content of the atmosphere.

Another and more familiar heat trap of this kind is the greenhouse. Visible and near infrared radiation from the sun, to which glass is transparent, pass readily into the greenhouse. The contents absorb a considerable portion of the radiation, converting it into heat. The contents of the greenhouse radiate at wavelengths (in the infrared) to which glass is not very transparent. As a result, a large proportion of this re-radiation is absorbed by the glass and remains, at least partially, within the greenhouse.

The foregoing calculations relating to solar energy would change if the radius of the sphere (i.e., 93,000,000 miles) were changed. The radiation received at distances of one-half, twice, and three times the distance of the earth from the sun can be calculated exactly as before; that is, the total amount of energy leaving the sun is divided by the area of a sphere with the appropriate radius. If the sphere has a radius one-half of that considered previously, or 46,500,000 miles it has one quarter the area of the 93,000,000 mile sphere. Therefore the same amount of energy passes through one-quarter of the area and it follows that four times as much energy will pass through each square meter. In short, if the distance is halved, the energy received is quadrupled. Similarly, if the distance is doubled, the area of the sphere is quadrupled and the energy passing through any unit area is one-fourth as great.

This leads to a simple inverse relationship (like that encountered in connection with gravitational force), known as the *inverse square law:* the energy received per unit area is inversely proportional to the square of the distance. The energy reaching each of the planets can now be calculated, given the average distances of the planets from the sun (see Table 8.6). Table 8.6 also includes the results of a calculation similar to that made previously, of the average surface temperature expected if there were no atmosphere and assuming that the sun's rays strike the surface at right angles during 12 hours of daylight in every 24.

The arrival of energy at the surface of the earth at the rate of almost 2.5×10^6 horsepower per square mile has three major effects. By far the most important is the essential part it plays in plant growth; this will be discussed in Chapter 9. Second, it causes water to evaporate. The resulting

TABLE 8.6

SOLAR ENERGY RECEIVED BY THE PLANETS

Planet	Distance from sun (miles)	Solar energy (Cal/m²/min)	Average probable temperature (°F)
Mercury	3.6×10^7	130	340
Venus	6.7×10^7	38	140
Earth	9.3×10^7	20	75
Mars	14.2×10^7	8	−60
Jupiter	48.4×10^7	0.7	−250
Saturn	88.7×10^7	0.2	−300
Uranus	178.5×10^7	0.05	−350
Neptune	279.7×10^7	0.02	−370
Pluto	$367 \quad \times 10^7$	0.01	−380

water vapor is usually carried away by air currents from the region where it evaporates. Vertical air currents, for example, carry it into upper regions of the atmosphere where the pressure of the atmosphere is lower. The air, therefore, expands and this causes its temperature to fall. The water vapor becomes supersaturated, condenses into drops and forms a cloud. (If it is cooled while still near the surface of the earth, it forms a fog.) Under suitable conditions, the cloud precipitates as rain or snow. Most of the rain either percolates into the ground, where it plays an essential part in plant life, or drains off into rivers, eventually reaching the oceans. However, some of it is stored in lakes and behind dams and is subsequently used to drive hydroelectric generators. Its potential energy constitutes an extremely small part of the total potential energy of all the water in the clouds; and hydroelectric generators produce 3 to 4 per cent of the total electrical energy generated in the United States. In mountainous countries, such as Switzerland and Norway, the proportion of energy generated in this way is much higher, currently about two-thirds. It is estimated that the world's water resources could, under ideal conditions, supply about one-third of the world's current energy requirements; only about one-tenth of the total has been harnessed.

The heating of the surface of the earth by the sun also sets up convection currents in the atmosphere. These occur when the surface of the earth is unevenly heated, sometimes because of clouds and partly because land and sea heat up and cool at different rates. The air in contact with the warmer areas is heated and rises as cooler air flows in from surrounding regions to replace it. This produces vertical air currents and horizontal air currents, or wind. Before the development of the steam engine, winds were a very important source of energy for windmills and sailing ships. It has been estimated that about 2 per cent of the energy reaching the earth's surface is used to move air.

Solar Heating In addition to these three natural types of conversion of solar energy, there are several possibilities for the artificial exploitation of the sun's energy. One is the heating of buildings. The problem here is to absorb and store sufficient heat while the sun is shining to provide for the periods when it is not.

For example, imagine a glass-roofed house with a blackened heat-absorbing surface under the roof, separated from one another by an air space. Such an arrangement, which could be used to heat water, would minimize the loss of heat and make use of the "greenhouse" effect. It is reasonable to assume that a heat-storage system based on this arrangement would serve its purpose if it could store sufficient heat to provide for 3 sunless days. It will also be assumed that the house is to be maintained at 70 degrees Fahrenheit and that the temperature of the water in the system is to be raised to 150 degrees Fahrenheit by heat from the blackened surface.

On the further assumptions that 1 million BTU's are required each day and that heat is absorbed at the rate of 10 Calories per square meter per minute when the sun is shining, the quantity of water and the roof area needed for this purpose can be estimated as follows. In 6 hours (the assumed duration of sunshine), the blackened surface will absorb 3600 Calories per square meter. One million BTU's equals about 0.25×10^6 Calories, or about 2.5×10^5 Calories per square meter. The area required is therefore $2.5 \times 10^5/3600$ square meters of collecting area. This is about 75 square meters, or approximately 800 square feet. An absorbing area of this size would collect enough heat for 24 hours of heating from 6 hours of sunshine. Since it is necessary to provide for 3 days without sunshine, the area required would be 4 times as large, which is not unreasonable for the roof of a fairly large house.

If the energy is to be stored by heating water, each pound of water will store 80 BTU (i.e., it will be heated from 70 degrees Fahrenheit to 150 degrees Fahrenheit), and this amount of heat will be available for heating the house. To heat the house for 1 day requires a total of $10^6/80$ pounds of water (about 12,000 gallons or 130 cubic feet). To allow for 3 sunless days, then 4 times as much water would be required, that is about 600 cubic feet. An alternative to the use of water for heat storage, in which the specific heat of the water determines the heat capacity, is to store the heat as the latent heat of fusion of a suitable material. Glauber salts (sodium sulfate) melts at about 90 degrees Fahrenheit, and has a latent heat of fusion of about 92 BTU/pound. The heat stored in molten Glauber salts, at 92 degrees Fahrenheit, is therefore slightly larger than that of water at 150 degrees Fahrenheit; this method has the advantage of reduced heat loss because of the lower storage temperature; the higher cost of Glauber salts must, of course, be considered. These figures assume perfect efficiency of the absorbing area and no heat loss. Although actual performance would be somewhat less satisfactory, the figures indicate that solar heating is feasible from the standpoint of receiving sufficient energy from the sun to heat a house even in the northern parts of the United States. Further south, where there is more sunshine, the problem becomes simpler. A number of houses with solar heating units have been built in various parts of the country; in the north it is necessary to supply some standby heating because the assumption of 6 hours of sunshine in every 4 days is not always realized. Various forms of auxiliary heating are possible; one of these is to use electrical heating to raise the temperature of the water storage system when it gets too low. A major disadvantage of solar heating at the present time is the very high cost of installing such a system; but apart from occasional use of the standby system no fuel would be required.

Solar Furnaces Extremely high temperatures can be achieved by focusing the sun's radiation by means of curved reflectors. In one such system (see Fig. 8.12), a curved mirror focuses the sun's reflected rays at A. A flat mirror, which reflects the sun's rays to the curved

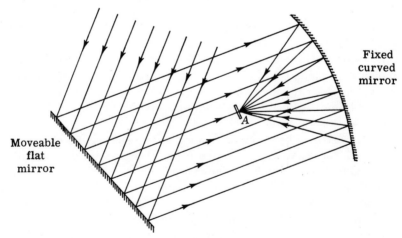

Fixed curved mirror

Moveable flat mirror

Fig. 8.12. Solar furnace.

mirror, rotates to follow the apparent motion of the sun, and thus keeps the rays focused at A. Almost all of the energy reaching the surface of the curved mirror can be brought to a focus at A. This energy is equal to 10 Calories per square meter per minute. The temperature of a small object placed at A will rise until heat loss by radiation, conduction and convection equals the heat reaching it. It cannot, under any conditions, be raised to a temperature above that of the sun by this method because it would then emit heat faster than it received it; but temperatures of 3000–4000 degrees centigrade can be reached.

Solar Cooking   The use of solar heating has been suggested as a method for cooking in countries where sunshine is plentiful but fuel is scarce. The following calculation shows the feasibility of doing this. Suppose that $\frac{1}{2}$ kilogram of water (about 1 pint) is to be heated from 20 degrees centigrade to its boiling point in 10 minutes. Since 1 Calorie will raise the temperature of 1 kilogram 1 degree, the total heat required is 40 Calories, or 4 Calories per minute for 10 minutes. The radiation falling on an area of 0.4 square meter at the rate of 10 Calories per minute for 10 minutes would be sufficient. This could be achieved by a circular reflector having a radius of 0.36 meter (about 14 inches), assuming that all the heat goes to heating the water.

Solar Energy   There are two reasons why so much attention has been given to the problem of converting the sun's radiation into usable forms of energy. First, the sun's radiation is a source of energy that costs nothing and will last, to all intents and purposes, forever, without depleting any of the mineral resources of the earth. If all the solar energy falling on an area the size of Egypt could be efficiently used, the world's energy requirements would be satisfied. Second, the sun's radiation is the only source of energy continuously available to a satellite or spaceship.

Of the several possible methods of using solar energy to produce power in large quantities, the most obvious is that of heating a boiler. The steam produced can then be used in the conventional way to generate electrical power. However, we have shown earlier, in Chapter 7, that efficient generation of power requires a high temperature and that absorption of the sun's radiation without focusing (as in the solar heating of a house) does not produce a high temperature. To achieve the necessary temperatures requires reflectors, and for large-scale power generation, these must be of a very substantial size. For example, heating a large boiler would require all the solar energy collected from an area of, say, 1 acre and concentrated on an area of a few square feet. The generation of 1000 kilowatts would involve all the solar energy reaching an area of about 16,000 square feet, assuming 100 per cent efficiency.

For several reasons the efficiency would be much less than 100 per cent. In the first place, some of the heat from the sun's radiation would be lost because of inefficient reflectors; secondly, the efficiency of power generation from a boiler does not exceed 40 per cent. If we take the over-all efficiency of collection and conversion to electrical energy to be 33 per cent, an area of about 48,000 square feet, or just over 1 acre, would provide for the generation of 1000 kilowatts. This amount would only be available during the time when the sun is high above the horizon, and therefore, 1 acre would supply 1000 kilowatts for approximately 6 hours out of 24 at most. Therefore, to generate continuously an amount of power equivalent to 1000 kilowatts would necessitate 4 acres of reflectors and a means of storing the energy for use when the sun was not shining.

Obviously the cost of installing a 4-acre reflector system would be extremely high; apart from maintenance requirements, however, this would be the only cost of generating power. It should be pointed out, further, that the actual cost of the fuel used for generating electrical energy is about one-sixth of the price paid by the consumer; capital investment and distribution costs account for the remainder. On the other hand, while conventional methods cost less for installation, there is the continuous cost of fuel: consequently, the feasibility of power generation from solar energy is an economic problem. Recent estimates suggest that the cost would be approximately 10 times that of conventional methods. It is fairly clear that the development of large amounts of power from solar energy is not likely to be economically feasible except in regions where fuel is scarce unless the price of fuels rises enormously as a result of exhaustion of supplies.

Solar Energy for Spaceships The problem of energy supply is quite different for a satellite or spaceship. Here the problem of fuel exhaustion must be considered because the limited payload of a spaceship or satellite excludes the possibility of carrying fuel in any considerable amount. Moreover, the conversion of solar energy into heat and then into electrical energy by a heat engine is not feasible with the kind of spaceship currently envisaged, because a heat engine of reasonable efficiency and its auxiliary equipment constitute a very large piece of machinery.

At the present time, however, there are three promising possibilities: thermoelectric, photoelectric, and thermionic converters. These devices, which convert the energy of radiation into electrical energy, are discussed in Chapter 10.

Temperature of a Satellite An object in space, such as a satellite, receives radiation from the sun and loses energy by radiating. It will, if permitted, reach a steady temperature at which the energy lost is equal to the energy received. This temperature depends upon the object's distance from the sun and on the emissivity of its surface. If it is assumed that the entire surface has the same emissivity, then it can be shown that the value of emissivity has no effect on the temperature. To take an example, suppose that a spherical satellite (see Fig. 8.13) with a radius of R meters is 93,000,000 miles from the sun. It will be assumed that the surface temperature of the satellite is the same all over as a result of either rapid rotation or of a high thermal conductivity. The satellite intercepts the sunlight that would pass

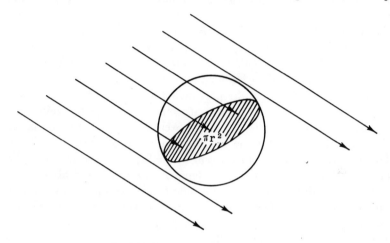

Fig. 8.13. Radiation reaching a satellite.

through a circle of radius πR^2. The energy reaching the satellite is, therefore, $\pi R^2 \times 21$ Calories per minute. This is

$$20 \, \pi R^2 \times 4200 \text{ joules/min} = 8.4 \times 10^4 \times \pi R^2 \text{ joules/min.}$$

The amount of heat absorbed is

$$E \times 8.4 \times 10^4 \times \mu R^2 \text{ joules/min}$$

or

$$\frac{E \times 8.4 \times 10^4 \times \pi R^2}{60} \text{ watts} = 4.4 \times 10^3 \times E \times R^2 \text{ watts.}$$

The heat radiated by the satellite is given by

$$W = 4\pi R^2 \times E \times 5.3 \times 10^{-8} \times T^4 \text{ watts}$$
$$= 6.6 \times 10^{-7} \times E \times R^2 \times T^4 \text{ watts.}$$

When the temperature is steady, these quantities must be equal; hence,

$$4.4 \times 10^3 \times E \times R^2 = 6.6 \times 10^{-7} \times E \times R^2 \times T^3$$

from which

$$T^4 = \frac{4.4 \times 10^3}{6.6 \times 10^{-7}} = 6.67 \times 10^9;$$

therefore

$$T = 286°K = 286 - 273 = 13 °C, \text{ or } 55 °F.$$

Thus, a temperature of 55 degrees Fahrenheit would be reached and maintained, if the whole surface had the same emissivity. Decreasing the emissivity of that part of the surface facing away from the sun raises the temperature while decreasing the emissivity of the part facing the sun lowers it. If the satellite were closer to the sun, it would receive more heat and its temperature could be controlled by reducing the emissivity of the part facing the sun, compared with that of the part facing away. Using a surface of sufficiently low emissivity facing the sun, it would be possible to avoid an excessively high temperature even if the orbit were much smaller than the earth's. However, at the other extreme the problem would become more difficult.

To calculate how far from the sun a satellite could be taken so that its temperature did not fall below the temperature calculated above, (i.e., 13 degrees centigrade), assume that the side facing the sun receives the maximum possible amount of heat, that is, has an emissivity of 1, and that no heat is radiated on the opposite side. The heat balance is as follows.

The heat radiated by this satellite is equal to one-half of that radiated by the one discussed above, since it is at the same temperature and only one-half of its surface is radiating; it must, therefore, receive heat at one-half the rate, and, by the inverse square law, it will do this at a distance that is $\sqrt{2}$ times 93 million miles, or about 130 million miles. This is roughly the radius of the orbit of Mars.

Illumination Light as a form of energy is very important in many human activities, and its measurement and quantitative description will now be discussed. The quantity of light emitted by any lamp cannot be measured as the number of watts of energy which that lamp gives out because a high proportion of the energy (over 90 per cent) is always radiated in a form in which it is not visible, that is, as infrared and ultraviolet radiation. What is needed, therefore, is a measure of the brightness of the visible light emitted, regardless of the amount of infrared radiation that might accompany it. The standard by which the brightness of a light source is measured is the standard candle. This was originally a candle of specified size, shape, and composition; but for more accurate comparison it has been replaced by the definition of the standard candle as one-sixtieth of the luminous intensity radiated by 1 square centimeter of a black surface at the melting point of platinum (1773.5 degrees centigrade).

The unit in which brightness of illumination is measured is the *lumen*, that is, the amount of illumination reaching a unit area at a unit distance from a source of 1 candle power. It follows that a standard candle emits a total of 4π lumens, because the area of a sphere at unit distance is 4π times the square of the distance. Electric lamps of the filament type depend upon the conversion of electrical energy into heat in the filament and the emission of radiation from the surface of the filament. The proportion of the energy in the form of visible light depends upon the temperature of the filament and this in turn depends upon the power of the lamp (see Table 8.7). It is always less than 3 per cent.

TABLE 8.7
CHARACTERISTICS OF FILAMENT LAMPS

Power (watts)	Brightness (lumens)	Efficiency (lumens/watt)	Candle power
25	265	10.6	27
40	465	11.6	37
100	1640	16.4	128
200	3700	18.5	290
1000	23,000	23	1810

Fluorescent lamps radiate as a result of direct electrical excitation, and not of heating; consequently, they radiate much less energy in the infrared, and the amount of light per watt is greater; however, it is still only about 10 per cent of the energy supplied (see Table 8.8). It will be seen that in this case

TABLE 8.8
CHARACTERISTICS OF FLUORESCENT LAMPS

Power (watts)	Brightness (lumens)	Efficiency (lumens/watt)	Candle power
40	2650	66	210
200	13,000	65	1000

the efficiency, as measured in lumens per watt, does not depend upon the power of the lamp. The conversion of electrical energy to light by means of the fluorescent lamp is discussed in Chapter 10.

The intensity of illumination, as distinct from the brightness of a light, is measured in foot-candles. This is, as the name implies, the illumination at a distance of 1 foot from a standard candle, and is therefore equivalent to 1 lumen per square foot. The intensity of illumination due to a light source, of brightness C candle power, at a distance of D feet, is C/D^2 foot-candles. The usually accepted standard of illumination for reading is 50 foot-candles. It will be apparent that the illumination at any point in a room is received from the walls and ceiling as well as directly from the lamps. It is therefore not easy to calculate the number and kinds of lamps required to provide a specified level of illumination in a room, but a reasonable estimate is that about half the light is received directly, and the other half indirectly in average conditions.

Sound

All the types of radiation which we have discussed so far are of the same general kind. They all travel through empty space and they all travel at the same speed. However, there are other types of wave motion which should be considered, of which the most important is sound. Sound consists of a wave motion which travels through the air or other matter but not through a vacuum. It travels much more slowly than light; its speed in air is about 1100 feet per second.

Sound is "to and fro" movement of air; the pitch depends on the frequency (number of complete "to and fro" cycles per second); middle C is about 260 vibrations per second, and higher notes correspond to higher frequencies. The human ear can detect sounds with frequencies from about 25 to 15,000. Sound can be generated by a "to and fro" movement of a diaphragm, as in a telephone earpiece or radio loudspeaker. The kinetic energy of the diaphragm is transferred to the air molecules in contact with it, which in turn transfer their kinetic energy to those further away, and so on. It follows that sound has energy associated with it and it would in principle be possible to transmit energy from one place to another by means of sound. However, it is found that the amount of energy corresponding to an actual sound is relatively small. If a loudspeaker emitted energy at the rate of 1 watt, the sound would be unbearably loud. The energy picked up by the microphone of a telephone set is also extremely small, in the neighborhood of a microwatt, i.e., 10^{-6} watt. We can estimate the energy of a sound as follows. The string of a violin is plucked, using a force of 10 grams weight or 10^{-2} kilogram weight and in doing this it is pulled aside a distance of 1 millimeter or 10^{-3} meter. The amount of work done on it is $10^{-2} \times 10 \times 10^{-3}$ joule. When it is released, it is set in vibration and the energy of this vibration is radiated as sound. If it takes 10 seconds for the sound to die away, sound would be radiated at an average rate of 10^{-5} watt.

Two indications of the level of energy in ordinary sound are the following. A speaking voice corresponds to sound energy emission at the rate of about 5×10^{-5} watt, while an exceptionally sensitive human ear can just detect sounds of which the intensity is about 10^{-12} watt per square meter. This last number is taken as the basis for the description of sound intensities. It is described as a sound of *zero decibels*. A sound 10 times as loud is 10 decibels, a sound 100 times as loud, 20 decibels and so on up to a sound intensity of 10^{12} times, which is described as 120 decibels. Some indication of the significance of these numbers is given in Table 8.9. On the basis of these numbers

TABLE 8.9

INTENSITY OF SOUND

Intensity	Decibels	Type of sound
10^{12}	120	Painful
10^{11}	110	Airplane engine
10^{10}	100	
10^9	90	Heavy traffic
10^8	80	
10^7	70	Noisy office
10^6	60	
10^5	50	Average office
10^4	40	Ordinary conversation
10^3	30	Quiet conversation
10^2	20	
10^1	10	Whisper
1	0	Lower limit of audibility

it is possible to calculate the distance at which it should be possible to hear a sound of a particular intensity. For example, ordinary conversation at 40 decibels corresponds to about 5×10^{-5} watt. A normally sensitive human ear can detect sounds having an energy of about 10^{-11} watt per square meter. If a source of sound emits energy at 5×10^{-5} watt, the distance in meters at which it can just be heard is calculated as follows:

$$\text{Total energy emitted} = 5 \times 10^5 \text{ watts}$$

Energy received per square meter $= 10^{-11}$ watt; therefore

$$5 \times 10^{-5} = 4\pi D^2 \times 10^{-11}$$

or

$$D^2 = \frac{5 \times 10^{-5}}{4\pi \times 10^{-11}} = 4 \times 10^5$$

or

$$D = 630 \text{ meters.}$$

This represents the limit of audibility on the assumption that no other sounds compete. The distance at which a conversation can be heard intelligibly would be very much less because it would be necessary for the conversation to be received at a much higher intensity than all the random noise which is always present. The upper limit of 120 decibels is imposed by the fact that sounds of greater intensity than this are no longer heard but cause pain.

Problems

8.1 A "radiator" is maintained at a temperature of 120°F in a room at a temperature of 70°F. (a) If the area of the radiator is 20 ft², how much heat does it radiate into the room? (b) How does this compare with the heat given out by one person? (c) How else does the "radiator" supply heat to the room?

8.2 A heat absorber 1 cm² in area is placed 10 cm from the center of a graphite sphere, 2 cm in diameter, of emissivity 0.5. It receives heat at the rate of 1.0 Cal/sec. (a) What is the temperature of the sphere? (b) How fast does it lose heat? (c) How much heat would the receiver collect at 5 cm, 20 cm, 30 cm, and 40 cm from the center of the sphere?

8.3 (a) Assuming that the emissivity of ice is 1, how fast does it radiate heat (temperature of ice = 0°C)?

(b) If the ice on a pond receives no heat from the air and if the water below is at 0°C, how fast does it increase in thickness?

8.4 Calculate the energy reaching the earth's atmosphere from the sun in Calories per minute, and in horsepower. (Radius of the earth = 4000 miles.)

8.5 A house of area 1200 ft² requires 10^8 BTU for heating during the winter. For how many hours must the sun shine on it to supply sufficient heat, assuming that the heat could be efficiently stored?

8.6 If the heat from the sun could be efficiently converted into work, what horsepower would be available from an area of 18 ft × 6 ft exposed to the sun?

8.7 Why is a "ground frost" much more likely to occur when the sky is clear than when it is cloudy?

8.8 A skater, weighing 150 lb, moving at 4 miles/hr, glides to rest in 100 ft. (a) What is the frictional force that slows him down? (b) How many foot-pounds of work must he do per minute in order to move at a steady 10 miles/hr? (c) How much heat (per hour) would this work be equivalent to? (d) How much ice would be melted by this amount of heat?

8.9 Which surfaces of a Thermos vacuum bottle are silvered, and why?

8.10 From the point of view of radiation, should the roof of a house be white or black? Why?

8.11 Calculate the steady temperature of a satellite, 93,000,000 miles from the sun, if its surface is (a) black (emissivity = 1), (b) shiny (emissivity = 0.1), (c) black toward the sun, shiny on the other side, (d) the reverse of (c).

Chapter 9

CHEMICAL ENERGY

The Elements
All matter consists of *atoms*, of which there are 92 kinds that are found in nature, and about 12 that have been created artificially. Each of these kinds of atom is described as an *element* and all the atoms of the same element have identical chemical properties. The elements vary enormously in their abundance on the earth. The artificially produced elements exist only for a short time and their abundance is practically zero. Table 9.1 gives the percentages of the elements

TABLE 9.1

ABUNDANCE OF ELEMENTS IN THE EARTH'S CRUST, THE OCEANS, AND THE ATMOSPHERE
(Data from "Encyclopedia Britannica")

Element		Per cent abundance	Element		Per cent abundance
Oxygen	O	50.	Carbon	C	0.19
Silicon	Si	25.7	Phosphorus	P	0.11
Aluminum	Al	7.3	Sulfur	S	0.11
Iron	Fe	4.2	Barium	Ba	0.09
Calcium	Ca	3.2	Manganese	Mn	0.08
Sodium	Na	2.4	Strontium	Sr	0.03
Potassium	K	2.3	Nitrogen	N	0.02
Magnesium	Mg	2.2	Fluorine	F	0.02
Hydrogen	H	0.95	Bromine	Br	0.01
Titanium	Ti	0.43			
Chlorine	Cl	0.21	All other elements		0.45

which are most abundant. This abundance is estimated for the part of the earth with which we are familiar, that is, the atmosphere, the oceans, and the earth's crust to a depth of about $\frac{1}{2}$ mile. It is known that the relative abundance of the elements in the interior of the earth is quite different from that at the surface.

The   Every atom consists of two parts: the *nucleus,* which is an
Atom   extremely small core and the *outer region,* in which there are
normally one or more *electrons.* All electrons are identical and have a mass of
about 9×10^{-31} kg. Electrons exert a force of repulsion upon each other
and are attracted by, and attract, the nucleus. These forces are described as
electrostatic forces. The electrons and the nuclei are said to have electrostatic
charges, negative for the electron and positive for the nucleus. The amount of
electric charge (or electricity) of the electron is the fundamental unit quantity
of electricity. In the more detailed discussion of electrostatics in Chapter 10,
it will be shown that similar electrostatic charges repel each other, dissimilar
charges attract each other, and that these forces decrease as the distance
between the charges is increased.

In its normal state an atom has as much negative charge distributed
among the electrons as positive charge in the nucleus and it is therefore
electrically neutral. Each element is characterized by its *atomic number* which
is the number of electrons in the neutral atom. It is convenient to regard the
electrons as moving around the nucleus in orbits which may be circular or
elliptical. No two electrons occupy the same orbit and consequently the more
electrons there are the more space they require. The atomic numbers of the
naturally occurring elements run from 1 for hydrogen to 92 for uranium.
Since the atomic number can be defined as the *number of electrons,* it is necessarily a whole number; electrons cannot be subdivided. Each element is also
characterized by its *atomic weight or atomic mass.* For reasons which will be
discussed in Chapter 11, the atomic weight or atomic mass is not necessarily
a whole number. Many of them are approximately integers, and they are
calculated and expressed approximately on the basis that the atomic weight
of hydrogen, the lightest of all the atoms, is equal to 1, but more precisely on
the basis that the atomic weight of oxygen is equal to 16. The atomic weights
and atomic numbers of the elements are given in Table 9.2, which also
includes the chemical symbols by which the elements are conventionally
represented. The atomic weights given in the table are relative to that of the
oxygen atom which itself has a mass of about 2.6×10^{-26} kg and is given
the atomic weight 16.

For many purposes atoms can be regarded as if they were spherical. On
this basis their radii vary between about 10^{-10} and 3×10^{-10} meters. Each
atom is held together by the force of attraction between the negative electrons
and the positive nucleus.

The electrostatic forces between nuclei and electrons have another very
important consequence. They cause atoms to be attracted to each other.
The extent of these forces of attraction depends upon the kind or kinds of
atom that are present and the result may be either to cause the atoms to

TABLE 9.2
THE ELEMENTS

Name	Symbol	Atomic number	Atomic weight
Hydrogen	H	1	1.0
Helium	He	2	4.0
Lithium	Li	3	6.9
Beryllium	Be	4	9.0
Boron	B	5	10.8
Carbon	C	6	12.0
Nitrogen	N	7	14.0
Oxygen	O	8	16.0
Fluorine	F	9	19.0
Neon	Ne	10	20.2
Sodium	Na	11	23.0
Magnesium	Mg	12	24.3
Aluminum	Al	13	27.0
Silicon	Si	14	28.1
Phosphorus	P	15	31.0
Sulfur	S	16	32.0
Chlorine	Cl	17	35.5
Argon	Ar	18	39.9
Potassium	K	19	39.1
Calcium	Ca	20	40.1
Scandium	Sc	21	45.0
Titanium	Ti	22	47.9
Vanadium	V	23	51.0
Chromium	Cr	24	52.0
Manganese	Mn	25	24.3
Iron	Fe	26	55.8
Cobalt	Co	27	59.0
Nickel	Ni	28	58.7
Copper	Cu	29	63.5
Zinc	Zn	30	65.4
Gallium	Ga	31	69.7
Germanium	Ge	32	72.6
Arsenic	As	33	74.9
Selenium	Se	34	79.0
Bromine	Br	35	79.9
Krypton	Kr	36	83.8
Rubidium	Rb	37	85.5
Strontium	Sr	38	87.6
Yttrium	Y	39	88.9
Zirconium	Zr	40	91.2
Niobium	Nb	41	92.9
Molybdenum	Mo	42	95.9
Technetium	Tc	43	99
Ruthenium	Ru	44	101.7

TABLE 9.2 (**Continued**)

Name	Symbol	Atomic number	Atomic weight
Rhodium	Rh	45	102.9
Palladium	Pd	46	106.7
Silver	Ag	47	107.9
Cadmium	Cd	48	112.4
Indium	In	49	114.8
Tin	Sn	50	118.7
Antimony	Sb	51	121.8
Tellurium	Te	52	127.6
Iodine	I	53	126.9
Xenon	Xe	54	131.3
Cesium	Cs	55	132.9
Barium	Ba	56	137.4
Lanthanum	La	57	138.9
Cerium	Ce	58	140.1
Praseodymium	Pr	59	140.9
Neodymium	Nd	60	144.3
Promethium	Pm	61	145
Samarium	Sm	62	152.4
Europium	Eu	63	156
Gadolinium	Gd	64	150.9
Terbium	Tb	65	159.2
Dysprosium	Dy	66	162.5
Holmium	Ho	67	164.9
Erbium	Er	68	167.2
Thulium	Tm	69	169.4
Ytterbium	Yb	70	173.0
Lutetium	Lu	71	175.0
Hafnium	Hf	72	178.6
Tantalum	Ta	73	180.9
Tungsten	W	74	183.9
Rhenium	Re	75	186.3
Osmium	Os	76	190.2
Iridium	Ir	77	193.1
Platinum	Pt	78	195.23
Gold	Au	79	197.2
Mercury	Hg	80	200.6
Thallium	Tl	81	204.4
Lead	Pb	82	207.2
Bismuth	Bi	83	209.0
Polonium	Po	84	210
Astatine	At	85	210
Radon	Rn	86	222
Francium	Fr	87	223
Radium	Ra	88	226
Actinium	Ac	89	227

TABLE 9.2 (Continued)

Name	Symbol	Atomic number	Atomic weight
Thorium	Th	90	231.1
Protactinium	Pa	91	231
Uranium	U	92	238
Neptunium	Np	93	239
Plutonium	Pu	94	239
Americium	Am	95	241
Curium	Cm	96	243
Berkelium	Bk	97	243
Californium	Cf	98	246
Einsteinium	Es	99	255
Fermium	Fm	100	255
Mendelevium	Md	101	256
Nobelium	No	102	258

aggregate in groups, called *molecules*, or to pack themselves together systematically to form a crystal, or less regularly, as a liquid. Oxygen exists in the atmosphere, of which it forms approximately one-fifth, in the form of molecules, each of which consists of two atoms of oxygen. The two atoms are tightly bound together because some of the electrons of each of the two atoms are shared by and attracted by both of the nuclei. There are many elements in which the atoms combine together to form molecules in this way. Another type of molecule can form between dissimilar atoms. Water consists of molecules containing two atoms of hydrogen and one of oxygen; its formula is H_2O. Here again the electrostatic forces can be better satisfied if the atoms aggregate in this form than if they all remain separated from each other. There are a few elements, of which helium is the most common example, in which the interatomic forces are very small because the electrons and the nucleus very thoroughly satisfy the electrostatic forces.

Water (H_2O) is an example of a chemical compound. There are in nature an almost infinite variety of compounds, each of which can be represented by a chemical formula of this type. The chemical formula represents the actual numbers of atoms that are joined together to form a molecule. Some molecules are extremely complicated and contain very large numbers of atoms whereas others are very simple and of the kind that has just been described.

The alternative method of aggregation, the formation of crystals, is also very common. A familiar example is that of common salt, which is a compound of sodium and chlorine. A characteristic of the sodium atom is that it can readily lose an electron, that is to say, an electron can be removed from it by the expenditure of only a small amount of work. Similarly, chlorine

readily acquires an extra electron; an electron is attracted by a chlorine atom
and is able to combine with it. Consequently, if sodium and chlorine are
mixed together, electrons from sodium atoms join the chlorine atoms and
large electrostatic forces then exist between the positively charged sodium
atoms, called sodium *ions*, and the negatively charged chlorine atoms (chlorine *ions*). These electrostatic forces are sufficient for each sodium atom not
to be content to combine with a single chlorine atom but to gather around it
as many chlorine atoms as possible, and reciprocally for each chlorine atom
to gather around it as many sodium atoms as possible. One way of achieving
this result is shown schematically in Fig. 9.1. It will be observed that each

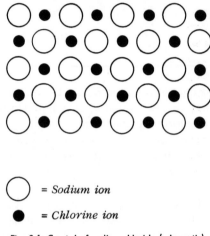

$\bigcirc$ = *Sodium ion*

$\bullet$ = *Chlorine ion*

Fig. 9.1. Crystal of sodium chloride (schematic).

sodium atom has four chlorine atoms close to it and that the sodium atoms
are further away from it; the nearest neighbors o᠆ each chlorine atom similarly, are sodium atoms. This pattern can be built up in three dimensions by
superimposing layers similar to that shown in Fig. 9.1 so that a ch!orine ion
is above each sodium ion and vice versa. This pattern, which can be extended
indefinitely, is typical of a crystal. It is not possible to identify individual
molecules of sodium chloride in a crystal of this kind, but there are equal
numbers of sodium atoms and chlorine atoms, so that this type of chemical
compound can be represented by a formula such as NaCl exactly as if it
consisted of separate molecules.

There are very many other ways in which the atoms can be arranged and
the particular arrangement which they take up depends upon the details of
the electrostatic forces between the various atoms. Another slightly different
type of crystal is that which is found in metals. The main characteristic of
the atoms of metallic substances is that they, like sodium, readily give up

electrons. Figure 9.2 shows an aggregate of copper atoms from each of which one electron has been detached; the ions are held together by the electrostatic forces between the positive charges of the copper and the electrons. In this case, the electrons do not remain bound to individual copper atoms but are free to move within the crystal. Nevertheless, the forces of attraction between the negative electrons and the positive copper ions are sufficient to hold the crystal together and to give it strength. The electrons can easily be caused to move through the metal by a suitable driving force, and this constitutes an electric current.

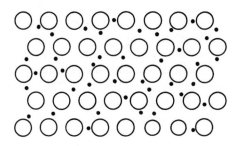

◯ = *Ion of copper*

• = *Electron*

Fig. 9.2. Crystal of copper (schematic).

Chemical compounds, therefore, exist as a result of the electrostatic forces between the atoms. If suitable atoms are brought together under appropriate conditions, they can combine to form a compound. This process is described as a *chemical reaction*. For example, if hydrogen and oxygen are brought together under suitable conditions, they combine to form water. This is represented by the chemical equation

$$2H_2 + O_2 \rightarrow 2H_2O.$$

Similarly, if ammonia (NH_3) and hydrochloric acid (HCl) are brought together, in the form of colorless vapors, they combine to form a white smoke NH_4Cl, or ammonium chloride. This reaction is represented by

$$HCl + NH_3 \rightarrow NH_4Cl.$$

No atoms are destroyed or created in a chemical reaction, and therefore the atoms on the left and those on the right must be identical. Since the atoms or ions in a molecule or crystal are held together by forces, it is necessary to do work, or supply energy, to separate the atoms or to decompose the compound. Conversely, if the separated atoms are allowed to come together, the forces acting between them cause them to accelerate as they approach each other, converting the potential energy of the electrostatic attraction into kinetic energy as they gather velocity on their way toward each other. When they come into contact the kinetic energy which they have acquired is converted into motion of the molecules which are formed, or of the individual atoms, in the form of heat. Consequently, a reaction of this kind can be expected to produce heat as a result of the conversion of the potential energy of the electrostatic forces into heat. Thus a reaction of this kind, which can occur spontaneously, results in the generation of heat, which is called the "heat of reaction." It is measured in Calories per mole where the *mole* is the number of grams of an element or a compound that is equal to its atomic weight or molecular weight. Thus 1 mole of hydrogen is 2 grams, of helium 4 grams, and of sodium chloride, $23 + 35.5 = 58.5$ grams. In order to decompose a compound it is necessary to supply an amount of energy equal to the heat of reaction.

The most familiar example of a reaction that gives out heat is *combustion*. Combustion of carbon, for example, coal, can be represented as follows.

$$C + O_2 \rightarrow CO_2 + 95 \text{ Cal.}$$

Since the atomic weight of carbon is 12, 1 mole of carbon is equal to 12 grams and it follows that if 12 grams of carbon (1 mole) are burned to form carbon dioxide, CO_2, 95 Calories of heat will be generated. Similarly,

$$2H_2 + O_2 \rightarrow 2H_2O + 116 \text{ Cal,}$$

or, expressed in words, when 2 moles of hydrogen react with 1 mole of oxygen, 2 moles of water are formed and 116 Calories are liberated. Another example is the combustion of glucose (corn sugar) of which the chemical formula is $C_6H_{12}O_6$. The reaction is represented thus:

$$C_6H_{12}O_6 + 6O_2 \rightarrow 6CO_2 + 6H_2O + 690 \text{ Cal,}$$

from which it follows that the combustion of 1 mole of glucose generates 690 Calories. One mole of glucose is equal to 180 grams, which can be readily calculated from the atomic weights of carbon, hydrogen, and oxygen.

From this discussion it might be expected that carbon would always burn when in the presence of oxygen, for example, in the atmosphere. This obviously is not the case. The reason is that a definite minimum temperature is always required to cause this kind of reaction to take place at an appreciable rate. If the temperature is too low, oxygen combines with carbon slowly and the heat generated is not sufficient to maintain the temperature at a level at which combustion would occur. However, if the combustion temperature is reached, then the reaction takes place sufficiently rapidly for the heat generated at least to maintain the temperature and usually to raise the temperature still further. Under these conditions the rate of combustion is usually limited by the rate at which oxygen can reach the burning material and the product of combustion, carbon dioxide, can leave it. As the oxygen molecules have to find their way by diffusion through the air surrounding the burning carbon, this is a relatively slow process. For more rapid combustion it is necessary to mix together the fuel and the oxygen in such a way that the delay is reduced.

The automobile engine is a heat engine in which the heat is provided by the combustion of gasoline. To permit sufficiently rapid combustion, the gasoline is vaporized and mixed with air in the carburetor. When this mixture is compressed in the cylinders and ignited by means of the spark plug, it burns very rapidly, producing the heat of combustion of the gasoline in a very short space of time. This heat causes expansion of the gases in the cylinder and this, together with the products of combustion (carbon dioxide and water vapor) exert the pressure on the piston which causes it to move in the cylinder. This provides the force which causes the crankshaft to rotate and the automobile to move. This is an example of very rapid combustion which can also be described as explosion. In any explosive, the fuel and the oxygen are already intimately mixed, either physically or chemically. In order to achieve the very rapid combustion which is necessary for driving a rocket, two techniques are possible. One is to use a mixture of fuel and oxygen. In this case the fuel is a liquid and the oxygen is in the form of liquid oxygen, in order that it can be mixed very rapidly with the fuel supply, and so that a sufficiently large amount can be carried in a relatively small space. Intimate contact between the fuel and the oxygen is achieved by very violent mixing. In the solid fuel rocket, the oxygen is one of the components of the material itself. It is there in chemically combined form and is available where it is needed to combine explosively to form a very large volume of combustion product. High explosives such as dynamite also work on the principle that the oxygen is already chemically combined in the explosive.

These conclusions can be summarized by the statement that carbon and oxygen, when not combined with each other, have potential energy which can be converted into heat energy by allowing the reaction to take place, that is, by allowing combustion to occur. Conversely, energy must be supplied to cause a reaction of this kind to go in the opposite direction. All the metals, with the exception of gold, occur in nature in the form of chemical compounds, mainly oxides, but in some cases sulfides or silicates. The reason for this is that the metals combine with oxygen with the evolution of heat, and therefore if circumstances permit, the metal and oxygen combine. A very familiar example that illustrates this is the rusting of iron. Iron, when exposed to damp air, becomes coated with rust, which is a form of iron oxide. In doing so it gives out some energy in the form of heat. This energy is given out so slowly that it is not generally noticeable. However, if iron is filed, sparks are seen; they are a result of the very rapid oxidation of the small particles of iron as they are ejected by the file. The oxidation in this case is rapid enough to raise the temperature of the filings so that they give out light. This is because a very small particle has a small thermal capacity compared with its surface area; the heat generated at the surface by oxidation therefore causes the temperature to rise rapidly, with the result that the particle becomes incandescent. It follows, therefore, that a metal such as aluminum or iron, and oxygen, separately, have potential energy which is transformed into heat when oxidation takes place. In order to reverse this reaction, that is, in order to convert iron oxide to iron or aluminum oxide into aluminum, it is necessary to supply energy. The reduction of iron oxide to iron is the first step in the manufacture of steel, which is iron containing a very small percentage of carbon. The energy required to reduce iron oxide is supplied in the blast furnace by the combustion of carbon. The basic reaction is

$$2Fe_2O_3 + 3C \rightarrow 4Fe + 3CO_2.$$

It is necessary to supply 197 Calories to reduce 1 mole of Fe_2O_3 to iron and oxygen, or 395 Calories for the 2 moles required for the reaction; the oxidation of 3 moles of carbon to carbon dioxide provides $3 \times 95 = 285$ Calories; therefore an additional 110 Calories must be supplied, or

$$2Fe_2O_3 + 3C \rightarrow 4Fe + 3CO_2 - 110 \text{ Cal.}$$

This heat is supplied by the combustion of more carbon than is required to react with the iron oxide. In practice, the carbon is in the form of coke which burns in the blast furnace and in doing so takes oxygen from the iron oxide, reducing it to iron. The combustion of additional carbon also maintains the temperature at a high enough level so that the reaction continues. This is a very much oversimplified version of what takes place in the blast furnace because there are many intermediate stages in these reactions but the essential over-all process is that the carbon deprives the iron of oxygen.

Chemical Energy and Life   A chemical reaction will procede spontaneously in one direction but not in the reverse direction. For example, a piece of coal will burn but will not "un-burn." The fact that such a reaction has a direction in which it will proceed spontaneously is closely related to the fact, already referred to, that heat will flow from a region of higher temperature to one of lower temperature, but not in a reverse direction. A chemical reaction will proceed spontaneously in such a way that the chemical energy of the materials present decreases. The energy so released does not disappear, but can be found in some other form, usually heat, but sometimes electrical energy. When it appears as heat it is called the *heat of reaction*. The energy of the whole system becomes *less available*, in the same sense that heat energy becomes less available when it is at a lower temperature. The available energy, called the *free energy*, therefore decreases in any reaction that occurs spontaneously, although the total amount of energy is unchanged.

It follows that after sufficient time all matter on the earth would be converted to its most stable form; this is, in general, the form in which substances

$$
\begin{array}{c}
\text{H} \\
| \\
\text{H—C—H} \\
| \\
\text{H}
\end{array}
\qquad
\begin{array}{c}
\text{H} \quad \text{H} \\
| \quad\; | \\
\text{H—C—C—H} \\
| \quad\; | \\
\text{H} \quad \text{H}
\end{array}
$$

Fig. 9.3. The methane molecule.   Fig. 9.4. Ethane.

$$
\begin{array}{c}
\text{H} \;\; \text{H} \;\; \text{H} \;\; \text{H} \;\; \text{H} \;\; \text{H} \\
| \;\; | \;\; | \;\; | \;\; | \;\; | \\
\text{H—C—C—C—C—C—C—H} \\
| \;\; | \;\; | \;\; | \;\; | \;\; | \\
\text{H} \;\; \text{H} \;\; \text{H} \;\; \text{H} \;\; \text{H} \;\; \text{H}
\end{array}
\qquad
\begin{array}{c}
\text{H} \quad \text{H} \\
| \quad\; | \\
\text{H—C—C—O—H} \\
| \quad\; | \\
\text{H} \quad \text{H}
\end{array}
$$

Fig. 9.5. A hydrocarbon molecule (hexane).   Fig. 9.6. Ethyl alcohol.

such as the metals and carbon are combined with oxygen or sulfur; almost all nonliving matter on the earth is in, or close to, its most stable condition. The situation with respect to living matter, however, is different. The complex structures and characteristics that a material must have in order to live demands that living matter shall be vastly more complicated than the simple compounds and crystals discussed above; the existence of such complicated molecules depends upon the particular property of carbon which permits it to form the basis of such molecules. A neutral atom of carbon has four electrons which it can readily lose and it also has the capacity to gain four electrons. Thus a carbon atom can combine with four hydrogen atoms to form a compound CH_4, illustrated in Fig. 9.3. This is the compound called methane and it owes its stability to the fact that the one electron of each of the four hydrogen atoms can be readily shared with the carbon atom. An equally satisfactory situation is illustrated in Fig. 9.4, where each of the two carbon atoms has four neighbors, thereby fulfilling its electron-sharing requirement. The essential feature of these, and all other *organic compounds*, is that the carbon atom can form four bonds with other atoms (i.e., carbon has a *valency* of four). Figure 9.5 shows that this procedure can be extended indefinitely to form a chain of any required length. Chains of this type are called hydrocarbons. Figure 9.6 illustrates an example in which one of the hydrogen atoms from a hydrocarbon has been replaced by oxygen. Oxygen has a *valency* of two, i.e., it can combine with two atoms of hydrogen, or satisfy one of the four bonds of a carbon atom and combine with one atom of hydrogen. The resulting molecule is that of ethyl alcohol. The alcohols, chemically speaking, are those molecules in which a hydrogen atom is replaced by an O–H group.

There are an infinite number of ways in which carbon atoms can be built up, not only in chains but also in rings, as in benzene (Fig. 9.7) and in many other more complicated forms. The hydrogen atoms in the basic structures

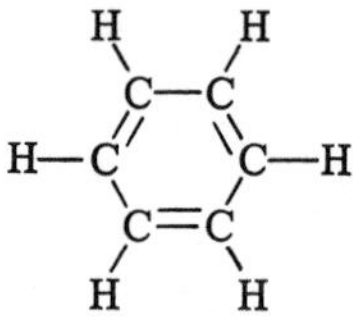

Fig. 9.7. The benzene molecule.

may be replaced by other atoms or groups. All the substances built up in this way are called organic compounds.

Photosynthesis All the molecules of living matter can be converted into carbon dioxide, water, and other simple compounds with the evolution of heat. This is equivalent to stating that all these compounds are unstable and therefore will not form spontaneously from their component materials, that is, from the carbon dioxide, water, and other compounds which would exist spontaneously in nature. It follows that energy must be supplied in order to build up organic molecules and therefore in order to build up living matter. The only source of energy continuously available for this purpose is the sun's radiation, and the most important single energy conversion process is that which takes place in living plants, that is, the conversion of solar energy into the chemical energy of the organic molecules of plant life. This takes place by the process known as *photosynthesis* which is an extremely complicated sequence of reactions in which chlorophyll, which forms the green pigment in the leaves of plants, captures energy from the sun's radiation and uses it to form organic molecules from the carbon dioxide present in the air, and water which the plant absorbs through its roots from the ground. The compounds which are formed in this way are carbohydrates, that is, molecules consisting of carbon, hydrogen, and oxygen. Sugars, starch, and cellulose are important examples of carbohydrates. The carbohydrates all have substantially more chemical energy than carbon dioxide and water. Photosynthesis is an extremely complicated process, which is not yet completely understood. So far, it has not been possible to cause photosynthesis in nonliving matter. The over-all process of photosynthesis consists of many steps, of which the first is the absorption of energy by the chlorophyl molecules. This energy is converted into chemical energy which is used to decompose water into oxygen, which is exhaled through the pores of the leaf, and hydrogen, which combines with one of the compounds that takes part in the process. Carbon dioxide that is "inhaled" by the leaf reacts with the hydrogen to form carbohydrates. The energy absorption part of the process of photosynthesis can occur only during daylight, but it appears that the utilization of the energy so stored can continue in the dark. At night plants reverse the process, absorbing oxygen and giving off carbon dioxide and water vapor. However, the extent to which this occurs is very much less than the photosynthesis that occurs in the daytime. Carbon dioxide is present in the earth's atmosphere to the extent of about 0.03 per cent. Since carbon dioxide which is not in contact with the leaves of plants cannot take part in photosynthesis, there is a limit to the extent to which the sun's radiation can be trapped and used by plants in this way. It appears that only about 2 per cent of the energy of the radiation falling upon an area of land can be utilized by the plants thereon for photosynthesis. This limit may be partly due to the fact that carbon dioxide does not reach the plants fast enough to allow more rapid photosynthesis. It has been shown that under experimental conditions the percentage utilization can be increased by artificially increasing the available carbon dioxide. It has also been shown that when the carbon dioxide supply diminishes locally as a result of very active photosynthesis the process slows down. Photosynthesis is not restricted to land plants; chlorophyll also forms the green coloring matter in algae which exist in the ocean and which trap the sun's radiation by photosynthesis in very much the same way that land plants do. The percentage utilization of the sun's radiation is probably similar.

All plant life depends on the building of molecules of carbon, hydrogen, and oxygen from carbon dioxide, water, and the energy received from the sun. Animal life depends upon the conversion of the hydrocarbons present in vegetable matter into the more complicated molecules of animal life. Whether our diet is strictly vegetarian or a mixture of vegetable and animal products, the chemical energy in it came from photosynthesis, that is, from the sun. One of the main functions of food is to supply energy, in the form of the chemical energy which becomes available when the carbohydrate or other molecules are converted back into carbon dioxide, water vapor, and energy. The discussion here will be confined to this aspect of food, although many other ingredients, such as proteins and vitamins, are equally essential. The energy available in food is expressed as the number of Calories that become available when the food is converted completely into carbon dioxide and water. It is found that an active human being requires a daily input equal to about 3000 Calories. A large proportion of this energy is used in maintaining the temperature of the human body above that of its surroundings. The amount used in this way is, very approximately, 2000 Calories per day. Assuming that the remaining 1000 Calories per day are available for conversion into useful work, the rate at which work could be done would be as follows:

$$1000 \text{ Cal/day} = 4 \times 10^6 \text{ joules/day}$$
$$= \frac{4 \times 10^6}{24 \times 60 \times 60} \text{ watts} = 46 \text{ watts or } \tfrac{1}{16} \text{ HP.}$$

The rate at which food (expressed in Calories) could be grown per square mile of the surface of the earth can be calculated as follows:

$$1 \text{ sq mile} = 2.6 \times 10^6 \text{ sq meters}$$
$$\text{Solar energy received} = 2.6 \times 10^7 \text{ Cal/min}$$
$$\text{Solar energy used for photosynthesis} = 2.6 \times 10^7 \times 0.02$$
$$= 5.2 \times 10^5 \text{ Cal/min.}$$

Assuming 12 hours of daylight per day for a growing season of 6 months, the energy stored as chemical energy is

$$5.2 \times 10^5 \times 60 \times 12 \times 30 \times 6 \text{ Cal} = 6.6 \times 10^{10} \text{ Cal.}$$

Each person requires $3000 \times 365 \simeq 10^6$ Calories per year; thus, if all the carbohydrates produced were available for food, there would be sufficient for about 66,000 people. However, there is no plant which can be used in its entirety for food, and the amount which can in fact be eaten varies from one-quarter to three-quarters. It will be assumed that it is about one-third. This brings the number of people that can be supplied with food per square mile down to about 20,000. It must also be remembered that part of the food which is grown is eaten by pests. Estimates indicate that this may be as high as 50 per cent, in which case the number of people would be decreased to 10,000. It has been assumed in this calculation that the food is eaten entirely as vegetable food. This is acceptable to some peoples, but is not regarded as adequate by Europeans or Americans, who demand a substantial proportion of their food intake in the form of meat. This is perhaps more important in relation to protein intake than to calories. However, from an energy point of view, it must be recognized that to allow an animal to eat grass is an inefficient use of chemical energy, because the amount of energy available in the form of meat is only about 10 per cent of the chemical energy in the grass eaten by the animal. This is because the animal consumes a considerable amount of chemical energy in maintaining its body temperature, walking around, and eating. It follows that the number of people who could be fed on the products of a square mile drops very sharply if the diet contains much meat. Conversely, in a very densely populated region the meat content of the diet must necessarily decrease.

It is evident that the chemical processes involved in the utilization of food are extremely complicated and there are many intermediate stages through which the food passes before its energy becomes available as heat or as work. Different animals have different capacities for storing energy in the form of fat. An animal which hibernates, for example, is able to store enough energy in the form of fat to keep it warm throughout the winter. The human being is able to store energy to a much more limited extent and finds it necessary to balance the intake of food and the output of energy in order to avoid an undesirable accumulation. He does, however, have sufficient storage capacity so that he does not need to anticipate extra exertion, and therefore the expenditure of extra energy, by previously taking in more food. The deficit can be repaired subsequently. It is instructive to calculate what this deficit might be in a simple case. A man weighing 200 pounds climbs a mountain 5000 feet high. The work done against gravity is

$$200 \times 5000 = 10^6 \text{ ft-lb.}$$

But 1 foot-pound is equal to about 3×10^{-4} Calories, so the work done is equivalent to $10^6 \times 3 \times 10^{-4}$ Cal

or about 300 Calories.

Energy Conversion by Muscles A very important chemical compound in plants and in animals is adenosine triphosphate (usually known as ATP). In plants, it is the substance in which the energy absorbed from radiation is stored before it is used to synthesize carbohydrates; in the human and other animal bodies it has the capacity to store the energy that is derived from the oxidation of carbohydrates and to make the energy available when and where it is required. It forms a very important link in the chain of reactions in which energy from food is converted into muscular work. The final stage of this conversion is when ATP, in contact with muscle, is stimulated by the proper signal from the brain and gives its energy to the muscle, which contracts and does work. In doing so, ATP becomes converted to another compound adenosine diphosphate or ADP. The ADP contains less chemical energy than ATP. It is then returned to the source of energy where it is "recharged."

Reconverting ADP to ATP requires energy which comes ultimately from the oxidation of carbohydrates into carbon dioxide and water vapor, for which oxygen is required. This oxygen is breathed in and the resulting carbon dioxide and water vapor are breathed out. The detailed mechanism for the conversion of chemical energy of ATP into the mechanical work of the muscle is not known. It is evident that this process is not a "heat engine" in the sense in which this term has been used previously, that is, it does not depend upon a heat source and a heat sink at two different temperatures; the whole process can take place at one temperature. In the case of fish or other cold blooded animals the process takes place at the temperature of the surroundings. The actual efficiency of the conversion of chemical energy of ATP to work is not known.

An active human being can maintain a rate of work of $\frac{1}{20}$ to $\frac{1}{10}$ of a horse-power for several hours; this corresponds to the average rate at which food energy is available, but this level of work output cannot be maintained continuously, and it follows that the efficiency of utilization of chemical energy is less than 100 per cent, even when allowance has been made for the large part that is used to maintain body temperature. However, it is possible to work at a much higher rate for short times. A trained athlete, for example, can exert 3 horsepower for a few seconds, but not for longer than that. This is not because the body lacks stored energy but because the products of oxidation in the muscles cannot be removed fast enough to allow the process to continue. The ADP cannot be recycled fast enough to convert it back into ATP for continuous exertion at the high rate to be maintained.

The Fossil Fuels   The sun's radiation is essential not only for maintaining the temperature of the earth and its atmosphere within the limits tolerable for human life, but also for the production of food. In this respect the human race lives from year to year; the sun's energy absorbed by plant life on the surface of the earth during the last year or two is the current food supply for the population of the world. The limit that this sets on the population that could be supported in the world is discussed in Chapter 12. In addition to the solar energy which is being received and used currently, there is a vast store of energy derived from solar radiation that was trapped in times long past. During the carboniferous era, 200 to 300 million years ago, a large amount of photosynthesis took place in the tropical forests and jungles that at that time covered much of the surface of the earth. Some of the vegetable matter formed at that time was preserved, instead of undergoing the fate of most vegetable matter, which is reconverted into carbon dioxide and water vapor by bacterial and other action. The preservation of the carboniferous forests may have been due to their being covered over by sedimentary deposits. The remains of this vegetation take three main forms, coal, oil, and natural gas. In each case the original carbohydrates have been converted into different forms, largely by bacterial

TABLE 9.3
ENERGY VALUES FOR SOME FUELS AND FOODS

Fuel	Energy	Food	Energy
Coal	5600 Cal/kg		
Gasoline	11,000 Cal/kg	Bread	2600 Cal/kg
Natural gas	500–1000 BTU/cu ft	Butter	9000 Cal/kg
Wood (dry)	4600 Cal/kg	Sugar	4000 Cal/kg
Butane	12,000 Cal/kg		

action. Part, but not the whole, of their chemical energy remains available to us. Table 9.3 gives the energy available in the fossil fuels, and for comparison, in bread, butter, and sugar. These figures lead to calculations such as the following:

1. Kerosene has a fuel value of 11,100 Cal/kg. At what rate must it be burned to supply energy, in the form of heat, at the rate of 1000 watts?

$$1000 \text{ watts} = 1000 \text{ joules/sec} = \frac{1000}{4200} \text{ Cal/sec} = 0.24 \text{ Cal/sec}$$

$$\text{or} \quad 0.24 \times 3600 \text{ Cal/hr} = 860 \text{ Cal/hr}.$$

But 1 kg of kerosene supplies 11,100 Cal, and therefore would last 11,100/860 or about 13 hours.

2. How much coal would be used to heat a house that requires 10^8 BTU per year?

The fuel value of coal is 5600 Cal/kg, or 10,000 BTU/lb. Thus 1 year's supply, 10^8 BTU, requires $10^8/10^4 = 10^4$ lb; but 1 ton is 2000 lb, so 10^4 lb is equal to 5 tons. This calculation assumes that coal is completely burned to carbon dioxide (no smoke, or carbon monoxide, etc.) and that all the heat is used in heating the house, whereas some is actually lost out of the chimney.

3. How much fuel, expressed in BTU, would grow on an acre woodlot per year? One acre is about 43,000 sq ft, that is, 4000 sq meters. Energy reaching this area is 4000×10 Cal/min. Assuming 12 hours daylight for 6 months, this is

$$1.7 \times 10^7 \text{ Cal} = 6.6 \times 10^7 \text{ BTU}$$

4. Compare the (a) food consumed per year, (b) the fuel required for heating, (c) and the gasoline required to drive an automobile 12,000 miles in terms of energy.

(a) Food: 3000 Cal/day = $3000 \times 365 = 10^6$ Cal/yr

(b) Fuel: 10^8 BTU/yr = 25×10^6 Cal/house = 5×10^6 Cal/person, assuming 5 occupants for a house that required 10^8 BTU.

(c) Gasoline: Assume 12,000 miles at 18 miles/gal, this requirement is

$$6.6 \times 10^2 \text{ gal} = 1.8 \times 10^3 \text{ kg}$$
$$11{,}000 \times 1.8 \times 10^3 = 2 \times 10^7 \text{ Cal.}$$

5. Fuel consumption for a gasoline engine, giving 250 HP, and operating at 20 per cent efficiency.

250 HP for 1 hr $= 250 \times 6.4 \times 10^2 = 1.6 \times 10^5$ Cal/hr at 20 per cent
efficiency, 8.0×10^5 Cal/hr,

but the calorific value of gasoline is 11,000 Cal/kg;

therefore, fuel required per hour $= \dfrac{8 \times 10^5}{1.1 \times 10^4} = 72$ kg/hr.

1 gal of gasoline weighs 2.7 kg;

therefore, 72 kg is $\dfrac{72}{2.7}$ gal $= 28$ gal/hr.

At 60 miles/hr, this would correspond to about 2 miles/gal. This is obviously unrealistic, because an automobile does not operate at full horsepower except on rare occasions. The above calculation shows, in fact, that if the gasoline consumption were 20 miles/gal at 60 miles/hr, the actual power that is available would only be 25 HP.

The following calculation shows how much carbon dioxide there is in the atmosphere and how much vegetation would be produced if the whole of the carbon dioxide were converted into vegetable matter. The pressure of the atmosphere at any point on the earth is about 10^4 kilograms per square meter. This is equivalent to the statement that the mass of gas in the atmosphere supported on each square meter is 10^4 kilograms. The atmosphere is 0.03 per cent carbon dioxide so

$$\frac{0.03}{100} \times 10^4 \text{ kg} = 3 \text{ kg}$$

is the amount of carbon dioxide in the atmosphere above each square meter. Carbon dioxide consists of a molecule containing 1 atom of carbon, of atomic weight 12, and 2 atoms of oxygen, each of atomic weight 16. The molecular weight of carbon dioxide is therefore $12 + 16 + 16 = 44$ and carbon therefore constitutes about one-quarter of the mass of the carbon dioxide molecule; therefore the mass of carbon in the atmosphere above each square meter is one-quarter of 3 kilograms, that is, $\frac{3}{4}$ kilogram. It follows that a very small amount of additional vegetation, enough to contain $\frac{3}{4}$ kilogram of carbon per square meter of the earth's surface, would be sufficient to use up all the carbon dioxide in the atmosphere. The return of carbon into the atmosphere as carbon dioxide takes place by the decomposition of vegetable matter and it is evident that the balance is maintained by the fact that a higher carbon dioxide content in the atmosphere would increase the rate at which photosynthesis occurs.

The following calculation provides an estimate of the length of time it would take for a 10-foot seam of coal to be produced. It will be assumed that the original vegetation had about the same calorific value as the coal. A 10-foot seam of coal would therefore be equivalent to about 3 meters of coal. The density of coal is about 4×10^3 kilograms per cubic meter; the mass of coal is therefore about 12×10^3 kilograms per square meter. Its calorific value is therefore

$$12 \times 10^3 \times 11{,}000 \text{ Cal} = 1.2 \times 10^8 \text{ Cal};$$

10 Calories were received per minute, and $2/100 \times 10 = 0.2$ Calories per minute were used for photosynthesis. It therefore required

$$\frac{1.2 \times 10^8}{0.2} = 6 \times 10^8 \text{ minutes of daylight};$$

on the basis of 10 hours per day, this is

$$\frac{6 \times 10^8}{60 \times 10} = \frac{6 \times 10^8}{600} \text{ days} = 10^6 \text{ days};$$

assuming 200 growing days per year, this is about 500 years.

The Conversion of Chemical Energy into Electrical Energy Electrons in motion have kinetic energy which can be converted into heat or work in ways that will be discussed in Chapter 10. An *electric current* is a flow of electrons in a conductor; it requires energy to make the electrons flow; this may be either kinetic energy or chemical energy. The use of kinetic energy will be discussed later; the conversion of chemical energy into the energy of an electric current depends upon the fact that an electron that forms part of an atom or a molecule has a potential energy that depends upon the particular atom or compound, and that it can do work in going from a substance where it has relatively high potential energy to another where it has lower potential energy. The potential energies are a result of the electrostatic forces of attraction between electrons and the nuclei of atoms. The ease with which an atom loses electrons depends upon the particular chemical element. The metals are the elements that lose electrons relatively easily; zinc will be taken as an example. If a piece of zinc is dipped into dilute sulfuric acid, the zinc begins to dissolve, that is to say, the zinc atoms leave the solid piece of zinc and go into solution in the acid. This is because the reaction

$$Zn + H_2^{++}SO_4^{--} \rightarrow Zn^{++}SO_4^{--} + H_2 + \text{energy}$$

is a reaction which releases energy, and therefore it can take place spontaneously in the direction shown. The zinc, before it goes into solution, is a complete atom of zinc, whereas in solution it has acquired two units of positive charges, that is, it has lost two electrons. These electrons are left behind

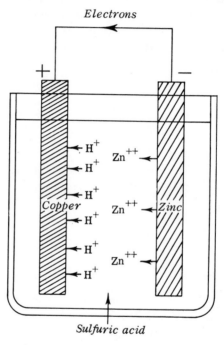

Fig. 9.8. Simple cell.

in the part of the zinc that has not yet dissolved, which therefore becomes negatively charged (the electron is the unit amount of *negative* electricity). This process goes on until the electrostatic attraction between the negatively charged zinc and the positive zinc ions is sufficient to prevent the escape of any more zinc into the solution. Thus the process suppresses itself very quickly. If a piece of copper is dipped into the same solution, the result will be much the same. The only difference arises from the fact that the amount of energy associated with the reaction will be less in the case of copper, and fewer electrons will therefore accumulate in the copper than in the zinc. If the copper and the zinc are joined together by a wire through which electricity can flow, as in Fig. 9.8, electrons will flow through the wire from the zinc to the copper. The hydrogen ions that are released from the solution as a result of the zinc entering it combine with electrons arriving at the copper electrode to form hydrogen atoms, and these pair up to form hydrogen molecules. Hydrogen gas is evolved on the copper plate, which itself remains unchanged. The over-all reaction is that zinc goes into solution, hydrogen comes out, and electrons flow through the circuit. The energy released by substituting zinc for hydrogen in the solution is available for pushing the electrons around the circuit. While a circuit is maintained, that is, while a continuous path for electrons is provided from the zinc to the copper, a current will flow and zinc will dissolve. When the circuit is interrupted, the current stops and the zinc no longer dissolves. The number of electrons that flow round the circuit is governed by the amount of zinc that dissolves, because each atom of zinc that goes into solution releases two electrons which travel around the circuit and must reach the copper electrode in order that the current can continue to flow.

The unit quantity of electricity is defined as the *coulomb*. This is the amount of electricity in 6.2×10^{18} electrons. The amount of electricity can be related to the amount of zinc that dissolves as follows. One mole of zinc contains 6×10^{23} atoms; when this amount goes into solution, it releases 12×10^{23} electrons, which is equivalent to

$$\frac{12 \times 10^{23}}{6.2 \times 10^{18}} \text{ coulombs,} \qquad \text{or} \qquad 1.93 \times 10^5 \text{ coulombs.}$$

Thus the solution of 1 mole of zinc corresponds to the release of 1.93×10^5 coulombs. A metal such as copper, in which only one electron is released for each atom would give only one-half of 1.93×10^5, that is 0.96×10^5 coulombs per mole. When this amount of current flows through the circuit it is capable of doing work or generating heat; the amount of work or heat that it can generate depends not only upon the number of electrons (or the number of coulombs) but also upon the strength of the forces that are pushing the electrons through the circuit. This is analogous to stating that the amount of work which water can be made to do when it is allowed to flow out of a reservoir depends not only upon the amount of water but also upon the height from which it comes. This second quantity, which is the driving force which pushes the electrons around the circuit, is called the *voltage*. It is defined in such a way that when 1 coulomb of electricity is made to perform 1 joule of work the voltage is said to be *1 volt;* or more generally, *the work done, in joules, is equal to the number of volts multiplied by the number of coulombs.* The coulomb is the unit quantity of electricity; the rate at which electricity flows is measured in *amperes*, the ampere is the unit of current; it is equal to 1 coulomb per second. The rate at which work is done, in watts, is equal to volts × amperes. In the case of the simple cell (copper and zinc in sulfuric acid) discussed previously, it is found that the voltage is equal to 1.1.   Therefore the work done is 1.1 joules for each coulomb of electricity that flows round the circuit. When sufficient current flows for 1 mole of zinc to dissolve, the energy in joules is equal to $1.1 \times 1.93 \times 10^5$ joules $= 2.1 \times 10^5$ joules, for 1 mole of zinc, that is, for 65.4 grams of zinc. The energy available is

$$\frac{2.1 \times 10^5}{65.4} \text{ joules/gm} = 3.2 \times 10^3 \text{ joules/gm.}$$

This is
$$\frac{3.2 \times 10^3}{4200} = 740 \text{ Cal/kg.}$$

The particular case of zinc and copper is merely an example, and almost any pair of conducting materials can be used to form a cell. All the metals can be placed in order so that the one occurring first will always be the one in which the electrons accumulate, that is, the negative pole of the cell. A voltage can be attributed to each metal so that the voltage developed by any pair of metals is the difference between the voltages of the individual metals. Table 9.4 shows the voltage (called electrochemical potentials) for a number of metals.

TABLE 9.4

ELECTROCHEMICAL POTENTIALS

Element	Volts
Potassium	−2.92
Sodium	−2.71
Magnesium	−2.34
Aluminum	−1.67
Zinc	−0.76
Iron	−0.44
Nickel	−0.25
Tin	−0.14
Lead	−0.13
Hydrogen	0.00
Copper	+0.34
Mercury	+0.80
Silver	+0.80
Platinum	+1.20
Gold	+1.68

Any metal, when paired with a metal lower in the table to form a cell, becomes the negative pole of the cell; that is, it is the one that dissolves, with the release of electrons, more easily. The metals near the bottom of the table dissolve less readily and are called the *noble metals*. Their resistance to corrosion, from which this name was derived, is another consequence of their reluctance to dissolve. When paired with metals higher on the list, the *noble metal* remains undissolved, and the *base metal* dissolves.

Polarization   As a practical method for the conversion of chemical energy to electrical energy, the cell described above has one serious disadvantage. This is the tendency, which is inherent, for hydrogen to accumulate at the positive pole, that is, on the surface of the copper. This has two effects. One is that the hydrogen has a very high electrical resistance, so that the electrons do not readily pass through it, and this decreases the amount of current that can be drawn from the cell.

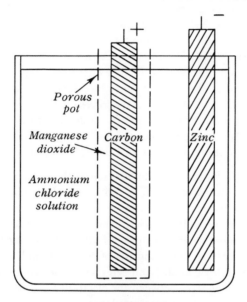

Fig. 9.9. Leclanché cell.

Secondly, the hydrogen itself has a voltage of its own, which tends to oppose that of the copper. It will be seen from Table 9.4 that the voltage difference between hydrogen and zinc is much less than between copper and zinc. The result of these two effects is that although a cell of this type will produce a current when the circuit is completed, the current drops very rapidly as the hydrogen layer develops on the copper. The cell is then said to be *polarized*. Polarization can be prevented by providing a substance in the cell which combines chemically with hydrogen; in practice a substance which readily supplies oxygen is used, as the product of the reaction between hydrogen and oxygen is H_2O, or water.

A much more practical cell, the Leclanché, is shown diagrammatically in Fig. 9.9. In this cell the poles are of zinc and carbon and the voltage developed is about 1.5. The electrolyte is a solution of ammonium chloride and the depolarizer is manganese dioxide, which is in a porous pot surrounding the carbon electrode. As the hydrogen reaches the manganese dioxide it becomes oxidized to form water.

The Dry Cell   A cell similar to this in principle, but slightly modified in practice, is the *dry cell* that is used very widely in flashlights, etc. In the dry cell the ammonium chloride and manganese dioxide are both contained in a paste which acts both as the electrolyte and the depolarizer. As is well known, this type of cell can produce energy in sufficient quantity for purposes such as lighting a flashlight or operating a transistor radio. The dry cell is able to generate a current of approximately 1 ampere. It will not do this indefinitely because the total amount of energy which the cell can supply is limited by the amount of zinc which is present. When this has been dissolved no further energy is available. The zinc is, of course, still present in the cell but it has lost the chemical energy characteristic of solid metallic zinc and it has the lower chemical energy characteristic of zinc ions in solution. From a study of Table 9.4, it will be concluded that very many pairs of metals could be used for forming a cell; there are a number of different combinations of metals and electrolytes which can in fact be used.

Storage Battery   A somewhat different type is the storage battery, the main feature of which is that it can be recharged; that is, the chemical energy can be restored, at the expense of electrical energy from a current which is passed through the battery from some other source. The commonest type of storage battery is that used in automobiles, the lead storage battery. This consists of sheets of lead and lead oxide immersed in dilute sulfuric acid. Each cell consists of many plates so as to provide a large area of contact between the electrodes and the electrolyte. When the battery is charged the negative plates consist of lead and the positive plates consist of lead oxide. The voltage developed between lead and lead oxide in sulfuric acid is about 2 volts. When a conducting circuit is provided between the electrodes, lead ions combine with the acid to form lead sulfate, not in solution but as part of the plate. Electrons are released and travel around the circuit to the positive electrode where the lead oxide combines with the sulfuric acid to form lead sulfate. In doing so, it takes up the electrons that arrive through the circuit. Thus both electrodes are gradually converted to lead sulfate as the current flows. When the cell is recharged the plates are converted back into lead and lead oxide and the electrons are forced to flow through the electrolyte in the opposite direction. It is common practice to connect three or six such cells so that the voltage is either 6 or 12, as shown in Fig. 9.10. Figure 9.10a shows the conventional symbol for a single cell. The short thick line represents the negative pole of the cell and the thin long line the positive pole. If cells are connected in series, that is, the positive of the one to the negative of the next, the voltage developed between the extremes is the sum of the voltages of all the cells individually as shown in Fig. 9.10b. The amount of electrical energy that can be stored in a storage battery is often quoted as the number of ampere-hours. A 100 ampere-hour battery would be able to deliver a current of 1 ampere for 100 hours, 2 amperes for 50 hours, and so on.

The current is 1 ampere for 100 hours = 360,000 coulombs; the voltage is 12, therefore the energy is equal to 12 × 360,000 joules = 4,320,000 or 4.3 × 10⁶ joules; but 4200 joules are equivalent to 1 Calorie, therefore the energy is equal to about 1000 Calories, or about one-third of the daily expenditure of energy of an active person.

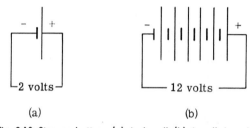

(a)   (b)

Fig. 9.10. Storage battery: (a) single cell; (b) six cells in series.

An automobile battery therefore can store the same amount of energy as about one-thirtieth of a gallon of gasoline, since one gallon of gasoline weighs 2.7 kilograms and 1 kilogram has a fuel value of 11,000 Calories. If one gallon of gasoline will drive an automobile 20 miles, at 20 per cent efficiency, it would drive it 100 miles at 100 per cent efficiency; the energy in the battery, if it could be utilized at 100 per cent efficiency, therefore, would move the automobile about 3 miles; or, more realistically, about 2 miles. The minimum amount of lead involved in this type of energy storage can also be calculated. One atom of lead releases two electrons, therefore, 1 mole or 207 grams of lead releases 2 × 96,500 coulombs, or 1.93 × 10⁵ coulombs. Thus 1 gram of lead gives (1.93 × 10⁵)/207 coulombs, which is approximately equal to 1000 coulombs. In order to produce 3.6 × 10⁵ coulombs, we therefore require (3.6 × 10⁵)/1000, that is, about 360 grams. Thus each cell must have a minimum of 360 grams of lead for the negative electrode and an equal amount for the positive electrode, that is a total of about 720 grams of lead or rather less than $1\frac{1}{2}$ pounds. The 12-volt battery would contain at least 16 pounds of lead. In practice, substantially more lead than this is used because it is not practicable for the whole of the lead to be accessible to the acid and to take part in the reaction.

Conversion of Charging a storage battery is an example of the conversion
Electrical to of electrical energy to chemical energy. There are many
Chemical Energy practical applications in which this type of energy conversion is used, of which *electroplating* is an example. If an electrode of copper and
an electrode of some other metal are immersed in a solution of copper sulfate,
and a current is passed through a solution from one electrode to the other,
copper is deposited from the solution onto the other electrode and copper
goes into solution from the copper electrode to maintain the supply. This
is the process of electroplating. The amount of any metal which is deposited

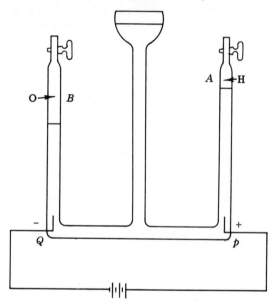

Fig. 9.11. Electrolysis of water.

in this way depends on the current in the same way as the amount dissolved
in a cell. That is, the amount of metal that is deposited is equal to 9.6×10^4
coulombs for each mole if each atom carries one electron, or twice or three
times this amount of current per mole, if the atoms give up or carry two or
three electrons. Copper and silver each give up one electron per atom, zinc
two electrons, aluminum three electrons. Electroplating is used for decorative
purposes, for the protection of readily corrodible metals and it is also used
as a method of purification of metals such as zinc and copper because many
of the impurities do not deposit when the current flows and therefore the
deposited metal is purer than the metal from which the deposit is made.

Electrical energy can also be converted into chemical energy by decomposing compounds such as water. If an electric current is passed through

water it is decomposed into oxygen and hydrogen. This can be shown in the following way. Figure 9.11 represents a system of glass tubes which is initially filled with water. Q and p are wires that pass through the glass into the water. A current is passed between them. The water between the electrodes is decomposed, and oxygen comes off at one electrode and hydrogen at the other. The tubes are arranged so that the gases are collected separately, and it is observed that the volume of hydrogen generated is twice that of oxygen. This is because there are twice as many hydrogen atoms as oxygen atoms in water. The amount of water decomposed can be calculated in the same way as before, on the basis that each mole, that is 18 grams, requires 9.6×10^4 coulombs. In this case the chemical energy could be converted into heat by burning the hydrogen.

Production of Aluminum by Electrolysis An important example of the conversion of electrical energy to chemical energy is in the production of aluminum. Aluminum is extremely abundant in the earth's surface but it always occurs in the form of oxides or other compounds which have much lower chemical energy than aluminum itself. In order to produce aluminum from the ore it is therefore essential that energy should be supplied. In the most commonly used and most efficient process for the production of aluminum ore, the oxide is dissolved in molten sodium hydroxide and a current is passed through this liquid, resulting in the formation of metallic aluminum. The amount of energy released when aluminum is oxidized to Al_2O_3 is about 400 Calories per mole. This amount of energy would also be required in order to reduce aluminum oxide to aluminum, assuming that 100 per cent efficiency could be achieved, which is never the case. This amounts to about 1.5×10^4 Calories per kilogram, or about 6.3×10^4, or about 6.3×10^{10} joules per ton. In more familiar terms this would be about 17,500 kilowatt-hours per ton of aluminum. It will be appreciated that this is a very large power requirement and the cost of the power is a major part of the cost of producing the metal from the ore. Many aluminum reduction plants have been built in places where large amounts of hydroelectric power are available.

Fuel Cells Since the conversion of chemical energy to electrical energy can take place at a fixed temperature, the efficiency is not limited, as it is in heat engines, by the available working temperatures and can approach 100 per cent; consequently it would be very advantageous to be able to convert the chemical energy of fuels directly into electrical energy at an efficiency of perhaps 90 per cent instead of indirectly by first converting the energy into heat by combustion, using the heat to raise steam and running a turbine and generator, with a maximum efficiency of 40 per cent. For this reason the concept of the *fuel cell* is an attractive one. The fuel cell may be described as a device in which an available fuel is used

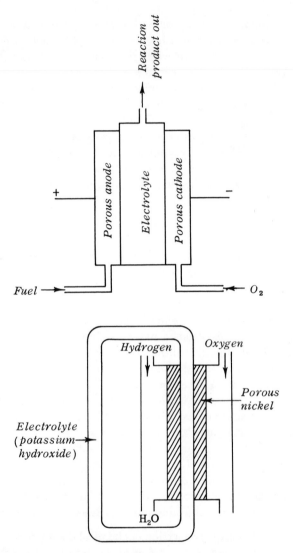

Fig. 9.13. Oxygen-hydrogen fuel cell. (Adapted from H. A. Liebhafsky and D. L. Douglas, ASME Paper No. 59-SA-22.)

for the direct production of electrical energy. In order to achieve this it is necessary that the fuel and oxygen shall be brought together in such a way that the energy which is to be released takes the form of an electron which is forced to travel around a circuit, as in the cell described above, instead of in the form of heat as in the case of combustion. There are many practical difficulties in the way of achieving this result, but substantial progress has been made and it is now possible to build a fuel cell, in which the fuel is hydrogen, which has a high operating efficiency. It is necessary in a fuel cell for the fuel and the oxygen to be brought into intimate contact with each other and with the electrode at the same time. For this purpose the oxygen may be transported through an electrolyte, arriving at the electrode into which the gas is fed. Figure 9.12 shows schematically how this might be done. One type of hydrogen cell which shows great promise is shown in Fig. 9.13.

Hydrogen as a fuel is far less economical than the natural fuels such as natural gas, oil, or coal, and the use of a hydrogen fuel cell is likely to be limited to situations in which efficiency is of greater importance than the cost of the fuel. Such a situation might arise in space ships, where carrying fuel which will be used inefficiently would probably be unacceptable. In order for a fuel cell to compete with conventional methods on a large scale it will be necessary for fuel cells to be developed in which cheap fuels can be used. The most likely device of this kind would use natural gas, which consists largely of methane, but so far no practical cell of this type has been developed.

Bacterial Fuel Cell It has recently been reported that certain bacteria are able to convert chemical energy to electrical energy. It has been demonstrated that appreciable electrical energy can be developed in a cell in which the bacteria feed on a sugar solution. The cell presumably contains two electrodes, between which voltage is developed. It is stated that almost any organic matter, including organic waste, can be used as the source of energy in this type of cell. The ultimate usefulness of this method of energy conversion will depend on the efficiency with which the chemical energy is converted, and on the costs of installation and maintenance of the plant.

Desalting of Sea Water One of the problems that becomes increasingly serious as the world's population increases is the supply of fresh water, both for drinking and for the irrigation of those parts of the land surface of the globe where rainfall is insufficient to support vegetation. The most promising source of supply is the sea. The problem is to produce fresh water from salt water at an economically feasible price. The following facts are quoted in order to put this problem in perspective. Average sea water contains about $3\frac{1}{2}$ per cent of dissolved solids and average brackish water contains one-third to one-half of 1 per cent. To be acceptable as drinking water the content of dissolved salts should not exceed one-twentieth of 1 per cent. The total rainfall over the whole surface of the earth would be more than adequate to supply a population much larger than that at present on the earth; in fact the average annual rainfall on land areas is equivalent to about 30,000 gallons per day for each inhabitant of the earth.

In the United States the amount of water used per person is roughly as follows: 750 gallons per day for irrigation, 750 gallons per day for industrial use and 150 gallons per day for household use.

The problem of supplying fresh water from sea water is essentially an economic one because there are several methods which, apart from economic considerations, are completely satisfactory. The cost of producing fresh water from sea water consists of two main parts. These are the capital cost of the plant in which the operation is conducted, and the cost of the energy which is required. This includes the energy used for the actual operation as well as energy which must be used for pumping the water from the sea to its final destination.

A substantial amount of energy is required for extracting water from a salt solution, or to put it differently, dividing a salt solution into fresh water

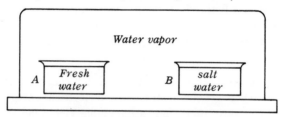

Fig. 9.14. Saturation vapor pressure.

and a more concentrated salt solution. The reason that energy is consumed in this process is as follows. Figure 9.14 represents two dishes *A* and *B*, one containing fresh water and the other containing salt water. They are in an enclosed space. Water from either dish would evaporate until the space available is saturated with water vapor. From that time on, the amount of water vapor in the space would remain constant, assuming that the temperature did not change. The vapor would then be at the *saturation vapor pressure* for that temperature. It is found that the saturation vapor pressure over the salt water is lower than the saturation vapor pressure over fresh water. Consequently equilibrium would never be established in a closed space because when the vapor is saturated with respect to the salt water it is not saturated with respect to the fresh water, which would go on evaporating. This would establish too high a vapor pressure near the salt water and some of the water would therefore condense and dilute the salt water. This process would continue until the whole of the fresh water had evaporated and had diluted the salt water. This process occurs spontaneously; it is therefore a "downhill process" and energy must be supplied in order to reverse it. In other words energy is released when a concentrated solution is diluted and must be added to concentrate a dilute solution. The energy that is released when a concentrated solution is diluted can be converted into work by the process of *osmosis*.

Figure 9.15 shows a tube T which is closed at the lower end by means of a semipermeable membrane, that is, one through which water, but not sugar can pass; the tube contains sugar solution. The lower end is dipped into a dish containing water. It is found that water passes through the semipermeable membrane and raises the level of the sugar solution in the tube, diluting it as it does so. The potential energy of the water is therefore increased because it is raised to a higher level, and work is done. It will be recognized that this process is rather similar to the transfer of water vapor previously described, except that with the semipermeable membrane there is greater

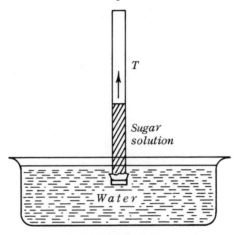

Fig. 9.15. Osmosis.

access between salt water and fresh water than when transfer must take place by evaporation. However, the air in Fig. 9.14 is semipermeable because water vapor is able to pass through it whereas salt or sugar is not. The process of osmosis illustrated in Fig. 9.15 can be reversed by applying sufficient pressure to the water in the tube T. This causes water, but not sugar (or salt) to pass through the membrane. This is the principle of one of the possible methods for desalting water. Practical difficulties arise because the pressure required is very considerable and in order to achieve rapid transfer a very strong and well-reinforced membrane would be required.

The amount of work which must be done to separate water from a salt solution depends upon how far this process is to be pushed. A small proportion of the water can be removed easily, whereas it requires a great deal more work to remove the water completely. Figure 9.16 shows how the work of separation depends upon the percentage of the water which is to be removed from the salt solution. This curve represents the smallest possible amount of energy that will perform the operation. It does not allow for any inefficiency or loss of energy in the process. It follows that the process requires the least expenditure of work if only a small proportion of the water is removed from the solution; this is feasible because there is no shortage of sea water. However, another factor must be considered; that is, that all the sea water which is to be processed must be pumped from the sea to and through the plant where the separation is to be made. The cost of performing this pumping operation increases with the amount of water that is to be pumped and therefore it increases as the percentage yield decreases. Figure 9.17 shows the energy

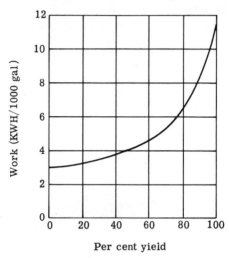

Fig. 9.16. Work required to separate water from sea water. [From B. F. Dodge, *American Scientist* Vol. 48, 479 (December 1960).]

used for pumping and the total energy used for separation for various percentage yields.

It is clear that the actual amount of energy required for pumping would depend upon the particular situation of the separation plant. The curves shown in Figs. 9.16 and 9.17 are based on the assumption that the water must be raised to a height of 50 feet and that the pump is 70 per cent efficient. On these assumptions, the total energy used is at a minimum at about 30 per cent yield. This, however, is based upon the assumption that the separation process is efficient. This can only be the case if separation is performed very slowly, because in order to speed it up an extra amount of energy must be expended. The penalty for speed is, in fact, so serious that it is not likely that the over-all efficiency of the process will exceed about 10 per cent; an energy requirement of about 30 kilowatt-hours per 1000 gallons is the minimum that is to be anticipated.

The foregoing discussion of the problem in terms of energy requirements does not depend upon the particular process which is to be used, for which there are many possible types. They fall into two main categories; first, those in which water is separated from the sea water, and secondly, those in which salt is extracted from the sea water. In the first category, the following methods are, in principle, possible; (a) evaporation or distillation, (b) freezing or crystallization, (c) solvent extraction, and (d) osmosis, using a semipermeable membrane. Each of the processes in this group is basically the reverse of that illustrated in Fig. 9.14, in which energy is supplied to make

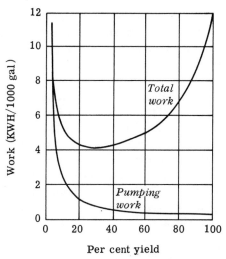

Fig. 9.17. Work required to pump sea water, and total work for separation. [From B. F. Dodge, *American Scientist* Vol. 48, 479 (December 1960).]

the reaction go in the opposite direction from that in which it will proceed spontaneously. In the case of evaporation followed by condensation, the water, but not the salt, becomes vaporized and the condensed, or distilled, water is pure. The use of freezing or crystallization depends upon the fact that ice formed from salt water contains practically no salt, the salt remaining in the water. The problem is to avoid trapping salt water in the interstices of the ice crystals. In the solvent extraction process, the water is dissolved from the salt solution in a solvent that dissolves water but not salt; it is subsequently released from the solvent by heating. The processes that involve separation of salt from brine are chemical or electrochemical in nature. At the present time it appears that the distillation process in one of its many forms shows the greatest promise and is in fact in use in various places. The cost of fresh water produced in this way is still high compared with the cost of fresh water produced in the usual way by collecting rainfall, but it can be expected that increased efficiency will result from further engineering development work. Since the cost of the energy is a substantial proportion of the total cost of a process of this type it is relevant to discuss possible energy sources. The cheapest of all forms of energy is solar energy. However, very large collecting areas would be needed in order to use solar energy for large scale desalting of sea water and the high cost of building a large installation would probably far more than overbalance the fact that no fuel costs would be required subsequently. Alternatively to solar energy, all the other methods of converting nuclear fuels or fossil fuels into usable energy are available.

Another interesting possibility is based on the fact that, as in the heat engine, energy can be extracted from any system of which different parts are at different temperatures. The water is at different temperatures at different depths in the ocean, and it has been proposed that the energy available from this vast source could be used for desalting sea water.

The importance of this problem is obvious when it is pointed out that a vast deficiency in the availability of fresh water is certain to develop over at least one-third of the area of the United States by 1980, unless the natural supply is supplemented by the development of new sources. A considerable number of experimental sea-water conversion plants are being built, and several are already in operation; for example, a plant in Texas produces a million gallons a day by distillation of sea water; one in California also produces a million gallons a day by a flash distillation process. In North Carolina, a quarter of a million gallons a day are converted by freezing, and an electrochemical method is used in South Dakota for converting a similar amount of brackish water. It should be noted that the cost of fresh water produced by these methods is currently about five times that of fresh water obtained by the traditional methods of collecting rainfall.

Problems

9.1 (a) How much heat would be generated by the combustion of 1 kg of coal?
(b) How much oxygen would be used?
(c) How much coal would be required to provide 10^8 BTU of heat?

9.2 Coal is burned in a boiler at the rate of 1 ton/hr. (a) How much heat is produced per hour? (b) If the boiler supplied steam to a steam engine, the over-all efficiency being 35 per cent, what horsepower would the engine produce?

9.3 Alcohol and dynamite have heats of combustion of 6400 Cal/kg and 1300 Cal/kg, respectively. How much dynamite is equivalent (in terms of heat of combustion) to 50 gm of water-alcohol mixture containing 30 per cent alcohol?

9.4 Kerosene has a fuel value of 11.0×10^3 Cal/kg. At what rate must it be burned to give off as much heat as a 1000-watt electric heater?

9.5 How much coal would be required to heat a house that requires 10^8 BTU per winter?

9.6 If a suitable conversion process could be devised, what size of spaceship (assumed spherical) would receive sufficient sunlight to provide the food energy for four people (a) at the same distance from the sun as the earth, (b) at 4 times that distance?

9.7 How much wood must be burned to boil 1 gal of water? (Assume that 20 per cent of the heat is used effectively.)

9.8 A ski lift is operated by a gasoline motor; if 100 people are to be lifted 1000 feet each hour, estimate (a) the horsepower required and (b) the fuel consumption of the motor.

9.9 (a) How much copper could be electroplated by using the current from a 100 amp-hr car battery?

(b) How much hydrogen could be produced by decomposing water by the same amount of current?

(c) How much heat could be generated by burning the hydrogen in (b)?

9.10 A dry cell, costing 40 cents, will give a current of 1 amp for 1 hour, at a voltage of 1.4 volts. (a) What is the cost per kilowatt-hour? (b) What is the minimum amount of zinc that could be used in the construction of the cell?

9.11 A car, weighing 3000 lb, is on a hill of 10 per cent slope. How far could its battery move it up the hill, if the starter could convert the energy of the battery into traction (via the starter) with 100 per cent efficiency? (Battery: 12 volts, 150 amp-hr.)

9.12 An automobile has two 50-watt headlights. (a) How much gasoline is consumed per hour to generate the current required for the headlamps, assuming that the engine is 20 per cent efficient and the generator is 80 per cent efficient? (Gasoline has a heat of combustion of 18,000 BTU/lb.) (b) For how long would the headlights operate if the generator did not work, assuming a 12-volt 100-amp-hr battery?

9.13 A breakfast cereal costs 31 cents for a packet containing 12 oz. The calorific value is 105 Cal/oz. What is the price of this energy, in Calories per dollar?

Chapter 10

ELECTRICAL ENERGY

Electrostatic Forces It has been pointed out in the preceding chapter that all matter is composed of atoms, each of which consist of a *nucleus*, and one or more *electrons*. The nucleus is said to be positively charged and the electron is the ultimate unit of negative charge. The atom is held together by the force of attraction between the oppositely charged nucleus and electrons, and matter, whether in solid or liquid form, is also held together by these forces, which are described as "electrostatic."

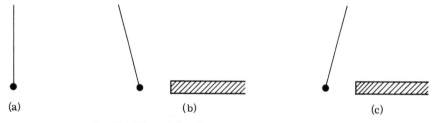

(a) (b) (c)

Fig. 10.1. Effect of electrified rod on a suspended pithball.

The many ways in which atoms can aggregate, to form metals, plastics, minerals, wood, among many others, are due to the complicated balance that is set up between the forces of attraction between positive and negative charges, on the one hand, and the forces of repulsion between positive and positive and between negative and negative, on the other hand.

Matter is usually electrically neutral; an object contains just sufficient electrons to balance the positively charged nuclei. However, it is possible in various ways to add or to subtract electrons, when the object becomes negatively or positively charged. The electrostatic charges on such objects exert forces of attraction and repulsion on each other that are exactly similar in kind to those that act in and between atoms.

These phenomena can be readily observed and studied in the following way. A light object, such as a ¼-inch ball of pith or cork, is suspended on a 3-foot-long silk thread (Fig. 10.1a). Since the ball is light, it responds observably to a rather small force. The following experiments may now be performed.

176

A rod of vulcanized rubber is rubbed with a piece of catskin or other fur. The rod is now brought near to the pithball suspended on the silk thread. The pithball is attracted to the rod, and moves toward it (Fig. 10.1b). The rod is said to be *electrified*, a conclusion which is reached because it has shown the capacity to attract the pithball in its vicinity. If the pithball is allowed to touch the rod, it then moves away from the rod (Fig. 10.1c). This shows that under some circumstances the ball may be repelled by the rod. If the two pithballs shown in Fig. 10.2 are suspended close together and each in turn is allowed to touch the electrified rod, they move apart, that is, they repel each other. This confirms the statement, made above, that similarly electrified objects repel each other. The experiment can now be repeated using a glass rod rubbed with silk instead of the vulcanized rubber rod rubbed with fur. Again the two balls repel each other when they have been similarly electrified. If, however, one is electrified by contact with the rubber

Fig. 10.2. Repulsion of two similarly electrified objects.

rod and one with the glass rod, they attract each other. The only consistent interpretation of these experiments is that there are two kinds of electricity, which for convenience are called positive and negative; that two objects charged with similar electricity, that is, both positive, or both negative, repel each other; and that objects that are oppositely charged attract each other. The terms positive and negative electricity are used because when a positive and a negative charge of electricity are added to the same object, they partially or completely cancel each other in the same way that adding plus two and minus two gives a result of zero.

A much more convenient device for showing when a charge of electricity is present, and roughly its quantity, is the *electroscope*. The electroscope consists of a metal rod A (Fig. 10.3a) to which is attached a thin piece of foil B. Gold foil is often used for this purpose because it can be made extremely thin. The rod and foil are enclosed in a box with glass sides so that it can be seen and is not disturbed by movement of the surrounding air. When a charge of electricity is placed upon the rod or the knob C at the top of the rod, it causes the leaf B to be repelled by the rod A and the leaf therefore stands out from the rod as shown in Fig. 10.3b. The angle at which it stands out increases with the amount of charge upon the electroscope. The electroscope can be charged by touching the top with a glass or vulcanized rubber rod that has been electrified. If the knob at the top is now touched with the finger, or with a piece of metal held in the hand, the charge escapes and the leaf B settles down rapidly to the position shown in Fig. 10.3c.

The rod is supported by a collar of a material that is not metallic and which is chosen for its property of not allowing the electricity to escape through it; it is convenient to classify materials according to whether they will or they will not allow electricity to pass through them. The best *conductors* of electricity are the metals but many other common substances allow electricity to pass. There are, however, a number of substances, of which glass and rubber are two, which do not permit the flow of electricity. These are called *insulators*. There are also many substances which are neither good conductors nor good insulators. Many substances such as wood come within this category. Conductors are those substances in which electrons are free to move, and insulators are those in which the electrons are firmly bound to the atoms or molecules to which they belong. The fact that atoms of metals readily

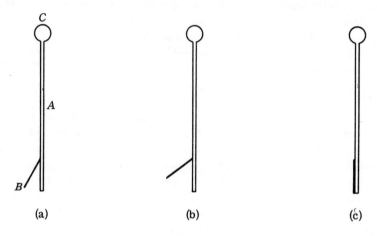

(a)   (b)   (c)

Fig. 10.3. Gold leaf electroscope.

lose electrons and become positively "ionized" is closely related to the fact that the metals in general are good conductors of electricity; in a piece of metal, some of the electrons are no longer associated with individual atoms, but are free to move.

If a charged rod (Fig. 10.4a) is brought close to the top of the electroscope, the leaf moves outward, indicating repulsion between it and the rod. This occurs even when the rod does not touch the top of the electroscope. If the rod is removed, the leaf goes back to its normal position. This is explained as follows. The charge on the rod, assumed to be positive, attracts a negative charge to the top of the electroscope and repels a positive charge to the bottom of the electroscope. On taking the glass rod away these charges recombine, with the result that there is no longer any positive charge at the bottom and therefore no longer any repulsion. This explanation implies that the electroscope, or indeed any other object which is uncharged, contains equal quantities of positive and negative electricity. These have no outside effect until they are separated from each other by the approach of the charged object. The charge of one sign can be allowed to leak away by touching the electroscope (the human body conducts electricity) while the rod is close to it. This allows the positive charge to escape, but does not allow the escape of the negative charge, which is bound by the attraction of the positive charge on the glass rod. When the electroscope is touched with the hand, therefore, the leaf collapses, but the negative charge remains at the top of the electroscope (Fig. 10.4b). If the charged rod is now removed, the negative charge is no longer bound and is able to distribute itself over the whole electroscope. It does this because of its own repulsion and it therefore distributes itself as widely as possible. Figure 10.4c shows the result. The electroscope has been charged not by contact but by *induction*. The important conclusion to be

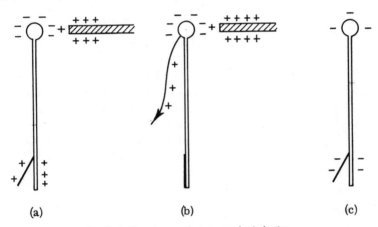

(a)   (b)   (c)

Fig. 10.4. Charging an electroscope by induction.

drawn from this experiment is that by attracting a part of the charge of an object and repelling a charge of opposite sign, the charge can be separated, the object as a whole remaining neutral. These phenomena are all compatible with the explanation that when a glass rod is rubbed with silk, some of the electrons are removed from the glass and remain on the silk. When an object is electrified by rubbing, electrons are either removed from it and are taken up by the material with which it was rubbed, or the reverse takes place. In other words, the frictional process involves the movement of electrons from one of the rubbing substances to the other. The one that acquires them becomes negatively charged and the one that loses them becomes positively charged. Therefore, although it is convenient to use the terms *positive* and *negative electricity*, it is often better to consider whether a particular object has an excess or a deficiency of electrons compared with the number it would have if it were neutral. In the experiments described above it is necessary to use light objects, such as pithballs, or gold leaf, in order that the effects may be easily seen. It may be concluded that the forces between the charges are rather small. Their magnitude can be estimated as follows: the mass of a pithball is about $\frac{1}{5}$ gram, that is, 2×10^{-4} kilogram; it is displaced a horizontal distance of 3 centimeters in the experiment represented in Fig. 10.1b in which the length of the thread is 100 cm. The horizontal force on it is represented by the line OA (Fig. 10.5) and the vertical force, that is, the weight, by OB, since the resultant force must be along the thread BA. Then

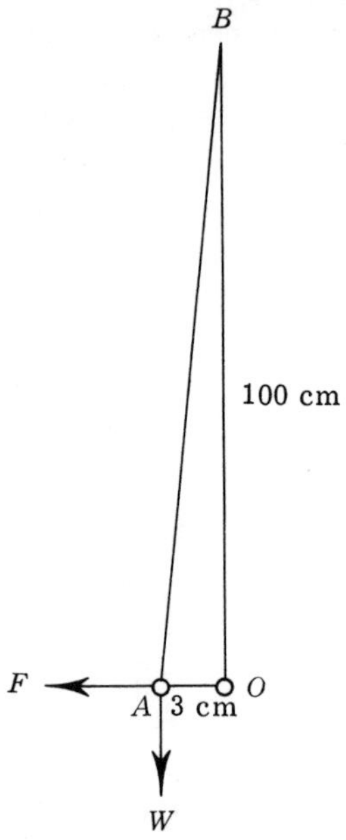

$$OA/OB = F/W,$$

where F is the required force. F is therefore equal to

$$\tfrac{3}{100} \times 2 \times 10^{-3} = 6 \times 10^{-5} \text{ newtons.}$$

This is equal to about 6 dynes.

The *coulomb* has already been defined as the unit quantity of electricity in terms of its electrochemical effects. It can also be used for the quantitative discussion of electrostatic forces of attraction and repulsion. The force exerted between two charges increases in proportion to the magnitude of the charges and decreases with the square of the distance between them. The force F, in newtons, is given by

$$F = \frac{9 \times 10^9 \times E_1 \times E_2}{D^2}$$

Fig. 10.5. Electrostatic force on a pithball.

where E_1 and E_2 are the charges, in coulombs, and D is the distance between them in meters. The amount of charge on the pithballs in the experiment discussed above can now be calculated as follows:

$$F = 6 \times 10^{-5} \text{ newtons,}$$

and

$$D = 0.06 \text{ meter;}$$

Then

$$6 \times 10^{-5} = \frac{9 \times 10^9 \times E^2}{(6 \times 10^{-2})^2}$$

or

$$E^2 = \frac{2.2 \times 10^{-9}}{9 \times 10^9} = 2.4 \times 10^{-18}$$

or

$$E = 5 \times 10^{-9} \text{ coulombs,} \qquad \text{or} \qquad 5 \times 10^{-9} \times 6 \times 10^{18},$$

that is, about 3×10^{10} electrons, since 1 coulomb is the charge of about 6×10^{18} electrons (see p. 161).

It will be noticed that the relationship between the force, the charges, and the distance is very similar to that for the gravitational attraction between any two objects. Both relationships are of the "inverse square" type; but the two effects exist for completely different reasons. One obvious difference is that gravitation is always a force of attraction, whereas electrostatic forces may be either of attraction or of repulsion.

The "driving force" that causes a current to flow in a conductor connected to the two poles of a cell has already been discussed; it is due to the accumulation of excess electrons in the negative pole of the cell. The work in joules that can be done by the electrons that are driven around the circuit is equal to the amount of the charge, in coulombs, multiplied by the driving force in volts. It follows that in order to accumulate an excess of electrons on an object, that is, to charge it, work must be done. If the object is to be charged negatively, the work is expended in bringing up extra electrons against the repulsion of those that are already there; if positively, in removing electrons against the attraction resulting from the positive charge that has already been produced. In order to charge an object, as distinct from merely moving a charge from one place to another, it is necessary to accumulate electrons that were previously remote from each other. The *voltage*, or *potential* of an object corresponds to the amount of work that must be done in bringing additional charge to it from a point so far away that there is no repulsion. The potential energy is increased by charging an object, in the same way that the potential energy of an object is increased if it is lifted upward against the force of gravity. Its potential energy is increased in the sense that all the energy is returned if it is allowed to return to its original level. In just the same way potential energy is given to a positive or negative charge which is moved toward another positive or negative charge. This energy could, in principle, be reconverted back into work if the charge is allowed to move away. In being repelled it would acquire kinetic energy or it could be made to wind up a spring, for example, thereby converting its electrostatic potential energy into elastic energy.

The *potential* of a charged body is therefore defined as the work which must be done in order to bring unit charge to it from a long distance away. For most purposes it is meaningless to speak of the potential of one object, because this implies that the charge was brought up to it from a place at which the potential is zero, and there is no way of deciding where this is. It is, therefore, more realistic to use the *difference of potential* between two objects; this corresponds to the amount of work required to move unit charge from one object to the other. The space surrounding a charged object has a particular property, by virtue of which another charge placed there experiences a force that tends to move it toward or away from the charged object. This state of affairs is represented by saying that there is an *electrostatic field* around the charged object. In the same way there is a gravitational field around the earth, the moon, the stars, and the planets, because any object in such a position has a force acting upon it. It must be emphasized that gravitational and electrostatic forces are entirely different in kind and that a gravitational force does not act upon an object because it is charged but because it has mass, and an electrostatic field does not exert any force upon a mass which is not charged. The strength of the electrostatic field at any point is the force that would act upon unit charge placed at that point. The strength of the electrostatic field depends upon the potential difference and the distance between the two objects which are at different potentials and it can be represented by the potential difference per unit distance, or volts per meter. For example, there would be a large electrostatic field between two objects whose difference of potential is a million volts and whose distance apart is 2 feet; it would be 500,000 volts per foot, whereas if the million-volt potential difference were spread over a distance of 100 feet, the electrostatic field would be only 10,000 volts per foot. The electrostatic field has a direction associated with it at any point as well as a magnitude; it is the direction of the force exerted on a positive charge at that point.

If the electrostatic field is sufficiently great, then electricity moves in the form of a spark from one object to the other. This is the movement of electrons from the object which has the excess, that is, which is negative, to the one which is deficient. The passage of a spark tends to neutralize the charge, reducing the potential difference and therefore decreasing the field strength. The actual field strength necessary to cause a spark to pass through air depends upon a number of conditions, but is around 30,000 volts per centimeter. If two spheres are placed 1 centimeter apart, it would require a potential difference of about 30,000 volts to cause a spark to pass between them. If they were 2 centimeters apart, 60,000 volts would be required. However, if one of the spheres is replaced by a point, the voltage required would be less than 30,000 volts per centimeter, because the electrostatic field is greater near a point than near a sphere. If the point is sharp enough, the charge can leak away without a spark passing. The most spectacular example of a spark is lightning and it is evident that extremely high voltages are required in order to produce lightning.

The potential of an object depends not only upon the charge on it but also upon its geometry and size. A small sphere would be raised to a higher potential than a large sphere by adding the same charge to both of them, because the charge would be more spread out on the larger sphere, and its mutual repulsion would therefore be less. The property which determines how much charge is required to raise the potential by a given amount is called the *capacity*. The measure of capacity is *capacitance*. This is illustrated by the following analogy. Two glass cylinders (Fig. 10.6) one of wide section and the other narrow are to be filled with water. A given quantity of water would raise the level (the potential energy of the water, p) less in the large than in the small cylinder; the wider one has a larger capacity than the narrower one. Similarly a large sphere requires more charge to raise its potential by a given amount than a small sphere and it has a larger capacitance. If the potential of an object is raised 1 volt by the addition of 1 coulomb, it has a capacitance of 1 *farad*. The unit defined in this way corresponds to an extremely large capacitance; a conducting sphere of about 6 million miles

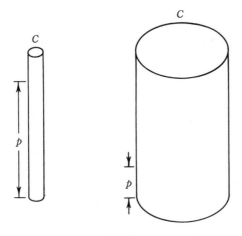

Fig. 10.6. Capacity.

radius would have a capacitance of 1 farad; that of a sphere of 1 meter radius would be about 10^{-10} farad. A much smaller unit, the microfarad (10^{-6} farad) (μF) is therefore used for most practical purposes.

It is often important to produce a large capacity in a relatively small space; parallel plates of metal that do not quite touch have a much larger capacity than the same amount of metal in the form of a sphere. The capacitance is further increased by inserting substances other than air between the plates. In addition to increasing the capacitance, an insulating substance such as mica prevents the two plates from coming into contact and thereby losing their charge. A series of metal plates or sheets of foil separated by insulating material is called a capacitor or condenser. Its capacitance C is given by

$$C = \frac{9 \times 10^{-6} \, KA}{d} \, \mu\text{F}$$

where K is the *dielectric constant* of the insulating material, A is the total area of the plates in square meters and d is the distance between them in meters. The dielectric constant K has the values given in Table 10.1.

TABLE 10.1
DIELECTRIC CONSTANTS

Air	1
Mica	7
Glass	7–10
Paraffin	2
Ice	70

The capacitance of a condenser consisting of a pair of sheets of metal foil, 100 square centimeters in area, separated by a $\frac{1}{10}$-millimeter layer of paper impregnated with paraffin is as follows:

$$K = 2, \qquad A = 10^{-2} \text{ sq meter}, \qquad d = 10^{-4} \text{ meter}$$
$$\frac{9 \times 10^{-6} \times 2 \times 10^{-2}}{10^{-4}} = 1.8 \times 10^{-3} \text{ } \mu\text{F}$$
$$\text{or} \qquad 1.8 \times 10^{-9} \text{ farad.}$$

The condenser would therefore be charged to a potential difference (between the plates) of 1 volt by 1.8×10^{-9} coulombs, or if it would hold 1 coulomb, it would be charged to a potential difference of

$$\frac{1}{1.8 \times 10^{-9}} = 5 \times 10^{8} \text{ volts.}$$

The energy stored in a condenser (W) is equal to one-half of the charge (Q) multiplied by the potential difference (V), or $W = \frac{1}{2}QV$, where W is in joules, Q in coulombs, and V in volts. This is because the energy stored is the work which is done on the charge against the potential difference. The average potential difference for the whole charging process is one-half of the final potential difference; so the work done is equal to that required to move the whole charge Q through one-half of the potential difference V, or $\frac{1}{2}QV$. The energy stored in a 1-microfarad condenser at 1000 volts is as follows: $C = Q/V$, or $Q = CV$, thus the charge Q is $10^{-6} \times 10^{3} = 10^{-3}$ coulombs. Therefore the energy, $\frac{1}{2}QV = \frac{1}{2} \times 10^{-3} \times 10^{3} = \frac{1}{2}$ joule.

The feasibility of using electrostatic energy stored in a condenser for driving a vehicle can now be considered. It is not necessary at this point to discuss the method of converting the stored electrical energy into mechanical work required to drive a vehicle; the possibility of storing sufficient energy must be settled first. As a basis for calculation, suppose that an amount of energy corresponding to 1 horsepower acting for 1 hour, that is, 1 horsepower-hour, is to be stored. This would perhaps drive a vehicle of the size of a motor scooter but would be quite inadequate for an automobile. However, if the calculation is made on the basis of 1 horsepower-hour it can very easily be used to determine what would be required in order to drive a larger vehicle. It has been shown that 1 horsepower is equivalent to 774 watts, that is, 774 joules per second. If this rate of work is maintained for 1 hour, the number of joules will be 774 times 3600, the number of seconds in 1 hour. This comes to 2.8×10^6 joules as the required amount of energy to be stored in a condenser. The characteristics of a condenser that will store this amount of energy are as follows. Assume that electricity can be stored in a condenser at a potential difference of 10^5 volts. Since the energy stored in a condenser is equal to half the charge times the voltage, and since the charge is equal to the voltage times the capacitance, the energy is equal to $\frac{1}{2}V^2C$, where C is the capacitance. If the energy W is given in joules, and V in volts, then the value of C is in farads. The energy required is about 3×10^6 joules, and that is equal to $\frac{1}{2}VC^2$, or $\frac{1}{2} \times 10^{10} \times C$, from which the capacitance C is equal to about 6×10^{-4} farads, or 600 microfarads. The condenser can be made of thin metal foil separated by an insulator with a dielectric constant of 10. It must be recognized, however, that a dielectric cannot withstand an indefinite voltage. It will break down, in the sense that a spark will pass through, if the voltage across it is too high, and it is learned from the handbooks that for paper impregnated with paraffin the maximum permissible potential is about 500,000 volts per centimeter. On this basis the layer of paraffin between the sheets of foil may not be less then 2 millimeters, if the voltage is to be 100,000. In order that a condenser will have the capacitance of 6×10^{-4} farads, with plates 2 millimeters apart, the area would be about 10^4 square meters. A condenser with this total area could be built up from a pile of sheets, each 1 square meter in area; 10^4 sheets would be required. With a space of 2 millimeters between adjacent sheets, and ignoring the thickness of the sheets themselves, this would give a pile 20 meters high. It must therefore be concluded that unless dielectric materials can be improved by a very large factor, it is entirely impractical to consider the storage of energy in capacitors for the kind of purpose under discussion.

In dry weather, it is often noticed that people and objects become electrified by friction, for example, between the shoes and a rug. The charge is often dissipated in the form of a very small spark just before a metallic object is touched. The potential is often quite high; if the spark jumps $\frac{1}{100}$ inch, which is quite common, the voltage would be about 750 volts, since the sparking potential is about 30,000 volts per centimeter, or 750,000 volts per inch. The charge which forms the spark is that which is stored on the surface of the body; the capacitance of the human body would be roughly equivalent to that of a sphere of about the same volume, i.e., a sphere of about 1-foot radius, or 30-centimeter radius. The capacitance of such a conductor would be 3×10^{-11} farads. The charge Q in coulombs is given by $V = Q/C$ or $Q = CV$, where V is the voltage and C the capacitance in farads. Thus

$$Q = 750 \times 3 \times 10^{-11} \text{ coulombs}$$
$$= 2.25 \times 10^{-8} \text{ coulombs.}$$

The energy stored by the charge is

$$\tfrac{1}{2}QV = \tfrac{1}{2} \times 2.2 \times 10^{-8} \times 75 \times 10^{2}$$
$$= 8 \times 10^{-6} \text{ joules.}$$

The reason why these "static" effects are not dangerous is that the energy involved is so small. A voltage of 750, where it drives a much larger amount of electricity, can be lethal.

An example of the way in which a condenser is used for storing energy is in the ignition system of an automobile. The purpose of the ignition system is to produce a spark at the appropriate time; this heats the air through which it passes sufficiently to ignite the gasoline vapor which is present. The combustion of the gasoline vapor produces the expansion which causes the engine to operate. The amount of heat which is generated by the spark between the points of the spark plug depends upon the amount of energy which is available and this in turn depends upon the capacitance of the circuit from which the spark comes. Unless a large capacity is included in this circuit the spark is not hot enough, that is, it will not convert enough electrical energy into heat to ignite the gasoline vapor. For this reason a condenser is always included in the spark plug circuit. If the condenser fails, which occasionally happens as a result of breakdown of the insulation between the plates of the condenser, the automobile will not run. Another illustration of the use of the condenser for storing electrical energy is in the "electronic flash" which is frequently used by photographers. In the electronic flash, electrical energy is converted into light, and the energy for this purpose comes from a small battery and is stored in a capacitor, which is frequently of about 300 microfarads capacity. The power from the battery is fed gradually into the capacitor and when sufficient energy has been stored it can be discharged in the form of the flash.

An interesting application of electrostatics is the electrostatic spray gun. Painting by means of a spray gun is usually very inefficient because a large part of the paint fails to arrive at the surface which is to be coated. However, if the surface to be coated is "grounded" and the spray gun is positively charged to 100,000 volts, then there is enough attraction between the paint drops and the object to be coated so that almost all the paint reaches the surface.

When a charge is placed on a metal sphere, the charge spreads itself over the surface as a result of its mutual repulsion. There is an electrostatic field in the space around the sphere but there is no field within the sphere because there is no tendency for the charge to move from one point to another within the space surrounded by the charge. Use is made of this fact in the Van de

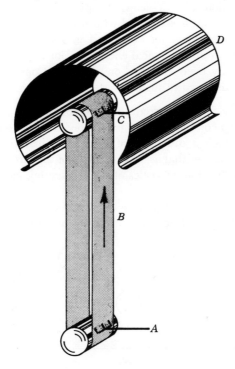

Fig. 10.7. Van de Graaff machine (schematic).

Graaff generator, which is used for producing the extremely high voltages required for certain experiments in nuclear physics. The endless belt *B* of rubber (Fig. 10.7) is charged at *A*, either by friction or by means of an external charging device, the charge is carried upward into the inside of the nearly closed dome *D*, where it is in the region of no electrostatic field. The charge which reaches the collector *C* is therefore repelled by the charge on *B* toward the dome *D*. This charge therefore adds to any charge already present on the dome and is not repelled back onto the belt *B*. Further charge can therefore be added, raising the potential of *D* to an extremely high value. Potential differences between *D* and the ground of millions of volts have been obtained.

Electric Currents   One joule of work must be expended when 1 coulomb of electricity is moved from one point to another point where potential is higher by 1 volt; this amount of energy can be recovered if the electricity is allowed to flow in the opposite direction, that is, *down* the potential gradient. The flow of electricity can be made continuous if the difference of potential is maintained, for example, by means of a battery, in which chemical energy is continuously converted into electrical energy. The continuous flow of electricity constitutes a current, measured in amperes; the energy that is associated with the current can be observed and used in various ways; it can be converted into chemical energy, heat, or work. The conversion into chemical energy, in, for example, the electrolysis of water, has already been discussed on page 166. Conversion into heat and into work will be discussed in turn.

Electric Circuits   An electric current, as distinct from a spark, can exist only if a conducting path is provided between the points between which a difference of potential is maintained. The rate at which the current flows, that is, the number of amperes, depends on the voltage and upon the characteristics of the conducting path through which it passes.

The circuit represented in Fig. 10.8 consists of a battery B, whose voltage can be varied, a *voltmeter* V for measuring the potential difference between

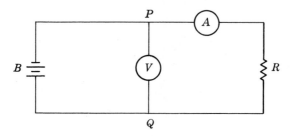

Fig. 10.8. Circuit for measuring the voltage across, and the current through, a conductor.

the points P and Q, and the *ammeter* A for measuring the current that flows through the conductor R. The various components are connected as shown by means of wires through which a current can flow. The current A that flows through R is measured for various values of the voltage V. Table 10.2 gives the results of a series of measurements which show that as the voltage is increased from 1.6 to 8.5 volts, the current increases from 1.0 to 5.7 amperes. The third column in the table shows the result of dividing V by A and it is seen that the result is almost constant. This means that for this particular conductor R, if a known voltage is applied to it, the current passing through it can be calculated. The ratio of these quantities is called the *resistance*, R, measured in *ohms*. A resistance of 1 ohm is the resistance that will permit a current of 1 ampere to flow when the potential difference across the ends of the resistance is 1 volt. Consequently, the relationship between these three quantities, voltage, current, and resistance, is $A = V/R$. Therefore in any circuit, when two out of these three quantities are known, the third can be

TABLE 10.2

VARIATION OF CURRENT WITH VOLTAGE

V	A	V/A
1.6	1.0	1.6
2.5	1.6	1.6
3.1	2.0	1.6
4.6	3.0	1.5
8.5	5.7	1.5

calculated. It should be noted that no current flows unless there is a continuous conducting path between two points which have a difference of potential between them; if there is no conducting path, R is equal to infinity and A is zero.

The current through a complete circuit depends upon the voltage and the resistance of the complete circuit, and the current through any part of the circuit depends upon the resistance of that part and the potential difference between the ends of it. Thus in Fig. 10.9, two resistances R_1 and R_2 are connected *in series*, so that the same current A passes through both of them. The

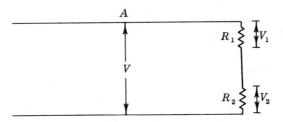

Fig. 10.9. Two resistances in series.

current A is equal to the voltage V divided by the sum of the two resistances, or $A = V/(R_1 + R_2)$. The total potential difference V is divided into two parts by the resistance R_1 and the resistance R_2. The potential drop V_1 across the resistance R_1 can be found by using the formula $A = V/R$. In this case, $A = V_1/R_1$, or $V_1 = AR_1$.

In the circuits that are used to illustrate the principles discussed here, it is assumed that the connecting wires do not have any resistance. This is never strictly true; but for many purposes it does not introduce serious error.

A second method of connecting two resistances, *parallel*, is shown in Fig. 10.10. Here the current A in the circuit is divided into portions A_1 and A_2, which pass through the resistances R_1 and R_2, respectively. The total current A is equal to $A_1 + A_2$. If the voltage of the circuit is V and the resistance R_1 and R_2, the currents through the resistance are V/R_1 and V/R_2; the total current A is equal to $V/R_1 + V/R_2$.

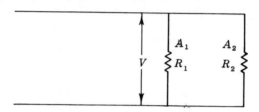

Fig. 10.10. Two resistances in parallel.

Example. Calculate the current in a circuit consisting of a 12-volt battery and resistances of 10 and 20 ohms connected (a) in series, (b) in parallel.

(a) Resistances connected in series. $A = V/R_1$, where R is the total resistance, that is, $R_1 + R_2$, or $10 + 20 = 30$ ohms. Therefore,

$$A = \tfrac{12}{30} = 0.4 \text{ ampere.}$$

(b) Resistances connected in parallel. The current through R_1 equals $12/10 = 1.2$ amperes; the current through R_2 equals $12/20 = 0.6$ ampere; therefore the total current equals $1.2 + 0.6$, or 1.8 amperes.

This method of calculation is clearly not confined to the case where there are only two resistances. Any number can be treated in the same way, that is, by adding resistances when they are in series and by adding the current when the resistances are in parallel.

The resistance R of a conductor depends upon its shape and size, and upon the *resistivity* of the material of which it is made. The *resistivity*, or *specific resistance*, of a material is the resistance, in ohms, between opposite faces of a 1-centimeter cube of the material. Values for the resistivity of some metals and alloys are given in Table 10.3, which also includes some values for nonconductors and for insulators.

The actual resistance R of a conductor in the form of a wire or strip of uniform cross section is equal to the resistivity W multiplied by the length L in centimeters and divided by the area of cross section A in square centimeters.

TABLE 10.3

RESISTIVITIES OF SOME MATERIALS

Substance	Resistivity (ohm-cm)
Silver	1.6×10^{-6}
Copper	1.7×10^{-6}
Aluminum	2.6×10^{-6}
Steel	$13–80 \times 10^{-6}$
Brass	6.2×10^{-6}
Nichrome	108×10^{-6}
Wood	$10^{10}–10^{13}$
Water	$10^4–10^8$
Glass	9×10^{13}
Rubber	1×10^{18}
Mica	1×10^{17}

For example, the resistance of a copper wire 1 meter in length and 1 millimeter in diameter is calculated as follows:

$$R = \frac{WL}{A} = \frac{1.7 \times 10^{-6} \times 100}{\pi \times (0.05)^2} = \frac{1.7 \times 10^{-4}}{7.8 \times 10^{-3}} = 0.021 \text{ ohms.}$$

The length of this wire that would have a resistance of 1 ohm can also be calculated:

$$R = \frac{WL}{A}, \text{ or } 1 = \frac{1.7 \times 10^{-6} \times L}{\pi \times (0.05)^2},$$

$$\text{or} \quad L = \pi \times \frac{(0.05)^2}{1.7 \times 10^{-6}} = \frac{7.8 \times 10^{-3}}{1.7 \times 10^{-6}} = 4600 \text{ cm or 46 meters.}$$

The resistivity of a conducting substance depends upon the temperature. The values given in Table 10.3 are for the ordinary temperature of the atmosphere. Metals increase in resistance as the temperature rises. Typically the resistivity of copper increases by about four-tenths of 1 per cent for each centigrade degree rise in temperature. The following measurements demonstrate this. A lamp is connected to a circuit in such a way that its current can be changed by changing the voltage across it. When a small current is passing through it, its temperature is approximately that of its surroundings and the resistance measured under these conditions is therefore its room temperature resistance. As the current is increased, the temperature of the filament of the lamp is increased and the measurements show that the resistivity increases.

Heating Effect of a Current It has already been pointed out that it requires 1 joule of energy to move 1 coulomb against a potential difference of 1 volt. Consequently, if 1 coulomb is moved by a potential difference of 1 volt, 1 joule of energy becomes available. The energy may be converted into various forms. The charge, in the form of electrons, may be accelerated and its energy is then in the form of kinetic energy. This can happen only when the electron is free to travel without colliding with any other atom or electron. This can happen in a good vacuum and is the basis for all the techniques used in nuclear physics for producing high energy particles. If the electron moves through a conductor, it will collide very frequently indeed with the electrons or the atoms of the conductor. It is therefore unable to accelerate continuously but instead transfers its energy to those atoms or electrons with which it collides. It increases their motion and therefore is converted into heat. Thus the energy supplied by the battery or other source of current is converted into heat. The unit of rate of production of heat is the watt, which corresponds to 1 joule per second. Consequently, if 1 ampere flows through a difference of potential of 1 volt, the rate of production of heat is 1 watt. The rate of energy conversion into heat is therefore given by $Z = V \times A$, where Z is the number of watts, V the number of volts, and A the number of amperes. Combining this formula with $A = V/R$, it follows that $Z = A^2R$ for a current of A amperes passing through a resistance of R ohms.

Example. An electric lamp converts electrical energy into heat at the rate of 60 watts. This is a 60-watt lamp. If the lamp is designed to work on a 110-volt circuit, what current does it take and what is its resistance?

$$Z = AV, \text{ or } 60 = A \times 110$$
$$\text{thus} \quad A = 60/110 = 0.55 \text{ amp};$$
$$\text{also,} \quad A = \frac{V}{R}, \text{ or } R = \frac{V}{A} = \frac{110}{0.55} = 200 \text{ ohms.}$$

If this lamp were connected to a 220-volt supply, the current would be given by $Z/R = 220/220 = 1.1$ amperes. The energy converted in this lamp would therefore by $A \times V, = 1.1 \times 220 = 240$ watts. When electrical energy is converted into heat in a conductor, the conductor rises in temperature until either it melts or it loses heat from its surface at a rate equal to the production of heat. An electric lamp is designed so that it heats up to a temperature at which the filament radiates light, i.e., is white hot, but does not melt. If the current is too large, the filament becomes too hot and reaches its melting point. This would happen in a very short time in the case of a 110-volt lamp connected to a 220-volt supply. The rate of production of heat would be four times the rate at which it is designed to operate and the filament would not radiate heat quickly enough to maintain a steady temperature before it had reached its melting point. The opposite case is that in which a lamp designed to operate at 100 watts on 220 volts is connected to a 110-volt supply. Using $Z = A \times V_1$, the current should be 0.45 ampere. The resistance therefore is $220/0.45 = 500$ ohms. If this lamp is connected to a 110-volt supply, the current A equals $V/R = 110/500$, or 0.22 ampere. The wattage therefore is $0.23 \times 110 = 25$. We find that the lamp, designed to run 100 watts, is only running at 25 watts. This amount of power would be insufficient to heat the filament to a high enough temperature to emit any appreciable amount of light.

A simple demonstration illustrates the conversion of electrical energy into heat. Figure 10.11 illustrates a circuit consisting of the 110-volt supply, a voltmeter, an ammeter, and an immersion heater, that is, a device containing a resistance wire which is insulated from the case so that a current passing through it heats the wire which in turn heats the surroundings. For this measurement the immersion heater is placed inside a thermos jar containing a known amount of water, and the rate at which the temperature of the water rises is measured. The following observations were made. Quantity of water: 2000 cubic centimeters; voltage: 110 volts; current: 2.3 amperes. It is concluded from the formula $Z = V \times A$ that the amount of electrical energy dissipated in the immersion heater is equal to $110 \times 2.3 = 250$ watts, approximately. The immersion heater is therefore a 250-watt heater. The thermos bottle contains 2000 cubic centimeters of water and observations made by means of the thermometer T show that the temperature rises 18 centigrade degrees in 10 minutes, that is, 1.8 degrees per minute. If high precision is not required, the heat capacity of the apparatus and the loss of heat of the thermos may be ignored. On this basis, the amount of heat added to the water is equal to 2×1.8 Calories per minute, that is, 3.6 Calories per minute, or 0.06 Calories per second. It follows that 250 watts (or 250 joules per second) is converted to 0.06 Calories per second, and that $250/0.060$ joules is equivalent to 1 Calorie, that is, about 4200 joules correspond to 1 Calorie. It will be remembered that this same relationship was found previously in connection with the conversion of mechanical work into heat. It follows that the whole of the electrical energy is converted into heat. This, like the conversion of work into heat by friction, is 100 per cent efficient.

The resistance of the wires of the circuit has been ignored up to this point. In many cases it is legitimate to do so, but in order to decide whether this is so or not, it is necessary to calculate the amount of energy which is dissipated in the wires as compared with the amount which is used in, for example, an electric lamp. We will consider the wiring of a house, assumed to be of copper wire of 1 millimeter diameter. The following is a calculation of the relative amounts of heat that are dissipated in a 100-watt lamp and in 100 feet of wire, which is a reasonable amount of wire to carry the current from the point where the line enters the house to the lamp and back again. The resistance of a 1-millimeter copper wire is about 0.02 ohm per meter. One hundred feet is approximately 30 meters and therefore the resistance of this wire is 0.6 ohms. A 100-watt lamp on a 110-volt circuit requires approximately 1 ampere. Using the relationship that the power $Z = A^2R$, the power

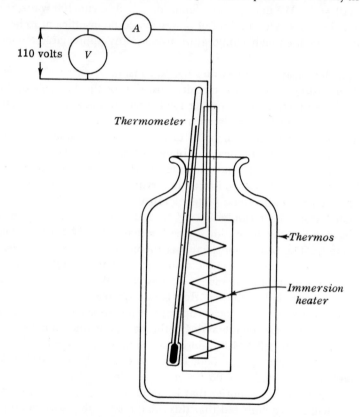

Fig. 10.11. The measurement of the heating effect of a current.

dissipated in the wire is $A^2 \times 0.6$; but $A = 1$ and this is therefore equal to 0.6 watts. Therefore 0.6 per cent of the power used in the lamp is dissipated in the wiring. If five 100-watt lamps are connected in parallel on the 110-volt supply, the current through each of them will be approximately 1 ampere, the total current in the circuit is therefore 5 amperes, and the power dissipated in the wiring is A^2R, that is, 5^2 multiplied by 0.6, which is equal to 15. In this case, therefore, 15 watts are dissipated in the wiring as against 500 watts in the lamps. It is evident that the heat produced in the wiring increases rapidly as the current increases; if the current is excessive the wiring may become dangerously hot and it must therefore be limited by means of a fuse. This is a device consisting of a piece of metal with a low melting point so designed that it will melt before the current through it reaches a level that will heat the wiring to a dangerously high temperature. It should be noted that the wiring will be heated by the current passing through it, whether the current is used for running an electric heater or lamp, or whether it is used for some other purpose such as a vacuum cleaner, where it is converted into kinetic energy instead of into heat. It is customary to use 15-ampere fuses in ordinary house circuits.

Thicker wire (which has a lower resistance) is used for special purposes where the current has to be much higher. For example, an electric range requires a special circuit wired with much thicker wire and has higher capacity fuses. The current and the power used by a variety of domestic appliances are given in Table 10.4. It will be seen that it is possible to use a 1-kilowatt

TABLE 10.4
CURRENT AND POWER FOR SOME DOMESTIC APPLIANCES

Appliance	Current (amps)	Power (watts)
Range	30 or 15[a]	3000
Refrigerator	$2\frac{1}{2}$	250
Washer	5	500
Drier	20 or 10[a]	2000
Space heater	10	1000
Vacuum cleaner	1	100
Air conditioner	$7\frac{1}{2}$	750
Radio	$\frac{1}{2}$	50
Television	1	100

[a] Range and Drier are often wired on 220-volt circuits.

electric heater on an ordinary 15-ampere circuit, but that if two of these heaters were connected in parallel, the current would be too high and the fuse should blow. If, instead, they were connected in series, the total power would be 500 watts instead of 2000.

The only substances which conduct electricity well are metals. However, other substances are able to conduct electricity to some extent, and the resistivities of some of these were noted in Table 10.3. It should be realized that the human body, though not a good conductor of electricity, is able, under some conditions, to draw a dangerously large current from the ordinary 110-volt line. This happens only when there is good electrical contact between the human body and the two sides of the circuit which it completes. One of these may be any object connected to the ground, since one side of the ordinary house circuit is grounded. Water is a reasonably good conductor and can complete a circuit.

Thermoelectric Effects   It has been pointed out above that the electrons in a metal are able to move freely through the metal, that their motion constitutes an electric current in the metal, and that they play an important part in the conduction of heat. It is to be expected, therefore, that the distribution of the electrons in a metal should be influenced by the temperature. Several phenomena, called *thermoelectric effects*, are manifestations of this interaction. If two different metals such as copper and iron are connected in the circuit shown in Fig. 10.12, no current will flow in the

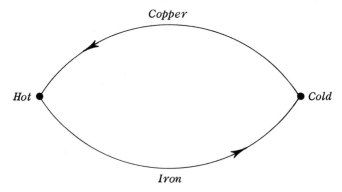

Copper

Hot   *Cold*

Iron

Fig. 10.12. Seebeck effect.

circuit, because there is no battery or other source of current. If, however, the two junctions between the copper and the iron wires are at different temperatures, a current will flow in the direction indicated in Fig. 10.12. This is the *Seebeck effect*. Alternatively, if the circuit is not complete, a potential difference will be set up between the points A and B (Fig. 10.13). The potential difference that is set up depends upon the nature of the two metals that are joined together and upon the temperature difference. In the case of iron and copper, the potential difference is quite small, about 15 microvolts per degree (centigrade) of temperature difference. By placing a number of junctions in series to form a thermopile, as shown in Fig. 10.14, the potential difference can be correspondingly increased. The potential difference for 10 junctions is 10 times that for a single junction. Whenever the circuit is completed, a current will flow.

In order to maintain the current, energy must be supplied, in the form of heat; if no energy were supplied, the junctions would come to the same temperature and the current would stop. The thermocouple, or thermopile, is therefore a device for converting heat energy directly into electrical energy without the necessity for the elaborate and complicated equipment used in the more conventional devices such as the generation of steam and its use to operate a steam turbine which turns a generator.

Junctions between pairs of metals are widely used for the measurement of temperatures in the form of thermocouples but they are of very little use for the conversion of heat to electrical energy for two reasons. One is that the

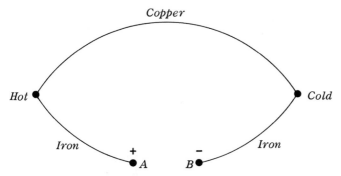

Fig. 10.13. Potential difference produced by Seebeck effect.

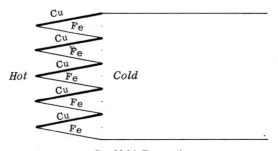

Fig. 10.14. Thermopile.

voltage developed by a single junction is extremely small and the second is that the high thermal conductivity of the metal allows considerable leakage of heat from the hot junction to the cold junction and this subtracts from the efficiency of the process. However, the recent development of semiconductors has made it possible to construct thermojunctions with much higher output than those available from metals. An example is the output of a junction made of two kinds of bismuth telluride. The thermoelectric power for this combination can be as high as 0.1 volt per degree. If a number of such junctions are connected in series a substantial voltage can be produced. Semiconductor materials such as bismuth telluride are much poorer conductors of heat than are the metals and this therefore reduces the heat leakage from the hot junctions to the cold junctions. However, low conductivity for heat is always associated with low conductivity for electricity (that is, high resistivity) and therefore when a thermoelectric device is constructed from bismuth telluride it has a relatively high electrical resistivity. When a current passes through an electrical resistance, energy is converted into heat at the rate of A^2R, where A is the current in amperes and R is the resistance. This resistance heating turns some of the electrical energy back into heat and this detracts from the efficiency of the device.

The geometry of the components is important but a compromise must be reached because while it would be desirable to use thick short conductors in order to minimize the electrical resistivity it would also be advantageous to use long, thin conductors in order to reduce the heat conduction. A thermoelectric converter of the kind under discussion is a type of heat engine in which the electrons are the working substance. They acquire energy at the hot junction and give some up at the cold junction; therefore the efficiency of a thermoelectric device suffers the same limitations as any other heat engine. That is, the maximum efficiency that could be obtained under ideal conditions would be $(T_1 - T_2)/T_1$, where T_1 is the temperature of the hot junction and T_2 that of the cold junction. In addition to its inherent limitation of efficiency, there is also the problem that some of the electrical energy is converted back into heat in the material of the device and some of the heat leaks from the hot junction to the cold junction and is therefore lost. It is reported that efficiencies of 10 per cent in the transformation of heat into electrical energy have been achieved and it is expected that these efficiencies will be higher when better materials are developed. This efficiency should be compared with the efficiencies mentioned earlier for heat engines, which run between 10 and 40 per cent, depending upon the kind and size of the installation. The highest efficiencies are obtained in conventional heat engines in the largest units, but for the thermoelectric converter it is possible to achieve as high an efficiency with a small unit as with a large one, and it is therefore likely that the utilization of this technique will be most beneficial in small conversion units, perhaps such as will be required for spaceships.

Thermoelectric Cooling The inverse of the Seebeck effect is called the *Peltier effect;* if a current is driven, by means of an external battery, around a circuit such as shown in Fig. 10.15, one junction is cooled and the other is heated. The circuit forms a heat pump, in which heat is transferred from a low temperature region to a region of higher temperature. The energy required for "pushing the heat uphill" comes from the external battery. As for the conversion of heat to electrical energy, the modern semiconductor materials have greatly increased the efficiency of thermoelectric cooling, because exactly the same kinds of materials are useful for the same reasons. It is necessary to reduce heat flow between the junctions as much as possible, and it is also necessary to reduce the electrical resistance as much as possible in order to avoid generating heat which would reduce the cooling effect at the cold junctions. Thermoelectric cooling has not yet found any wide practical application, but experimentally it is possible to lower the temperature of a junction by as much as 60 degrees below that of the surroundings. This is approaching the efficiency that will make it possible to construct appliances such as domestic refrigerators in which the cooling effect is produced by passing a current through thermojunctions. There will

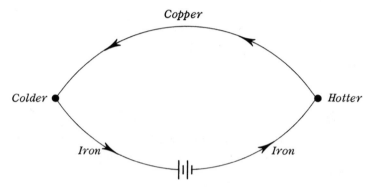

Fig. 10.15. Thermoelectric heating and cooling.

be no moving parts and, therefore, an exceptionally long life might be expected for such equipment. It is possible to increase the total cooling effect by placing thermojunctions in cascade, so that one cold junction cools the hot junction of another.

Thermionic Conversion Another method for converting heat to electrical energy is also under development. This is the *thermionic converter*, which depends upon the well-established principle that a hot metallic surface emits electrons. Some metals emit them more readily than others. The device consists essentially of two plates, A and B (Fig. 10.16). A consists of, or is coated with, a metal which easily emits electrons, and B consists of another metal plate. A is maintained at a high temperature and the electrons which it emits are collected by B. The plate A, therefore, becomes positively charged, having lost electrons, and B becomes negatively charged, having acquired them. If the circuit is completed, a current will flow and it is evident that electrical energy is thereby generated. One of the difficulties is that the electrons traveling through the space between A and B tend to repel electrons back into A. This difficulty is minimized by keeping the distance between *A* and *B* as small as possible. It must be a very small fraction of a millimeter for efficient working and this presents severe practical difficulties. In spite of these difficulties, an efficiency of 14 per cent has been demonstrated, and it is believed that 40 per cent is possible. High temperatures are, however, required in order to achieve these efficiencies. In this case, as in that of the thermoelectric converter, small units may be as efficient

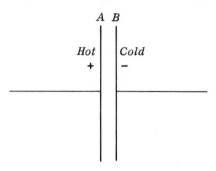

Fig. 10.16. Thermionic converter (schematic).

as large, and therefore the same kinds of applications may be contemplated. It is thought that thermionic converters may eventually be produced that weigh less than 1 pound per kilowatt of electrical energy.

Photoelectric Effect   In the thermionic converter, the electrons escape from the heated surface because of their high temperature; electrons can also acquire high energy by absorbing energy from light which falls upon a surface. The electrons that are energized in this way

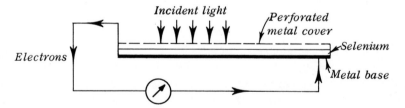

Fig. 10.17. Selenium photodiode light meter.

can, in a suitable device, set up a potential difference that causes a current to flow. The most familiar form of the conversion of light energy to electrical energy is in the light meter used by photographers.

The light meter consists of a *photodiode* and a device for measuring the current that is produced. The photodiode (Fig. 10.17) consists of a thin layer of the element selenium on a metal base, and a perforated metal cover.

The light which reaches the selenium through the perforated cover liberates electrons which travel through the meter and return to the selenium through the metal base. The efficiency of energy conversion in a selenium photodiode is only about $\frac{1}{2}$ per cent, with a maximum output of about 0.02 kilowatt-hour per day per square meter.

Solar Battery A much more efficient photodiode is that developed by Bell Telephone Laboratories for their Solar Battery, which has been used to provide energy for telephone repeater circuits and for radio transmitters in artificial satellites.

The Bell Solar Battery uses a silicon photodiode, which has an efficiency of about 14 per cent and develops a voltage of about 0.4 volt. It consists of a thin wafer of silicon, the surface layer (0.0001 inch thick) of which is "doped"

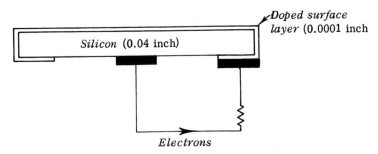

Fig. 10.18. Silicon photodiode (Bell solar battery).

with boron in such a way that its electrons are free to move, when energized, into the underlying silicon which is doped with arsenic and is about 0.04 inch thick. The construction is shown schematically in Fig. 10.18. A large number of cells would be needed to give a useful amount of energy; outputs up to 10 watts have been achieved in the form of $\frac{1}{2}$ ampere at 20 volts.

One of the problems associated with solar batteries is the variation of their output between day and night, and even during the day because of fluctuations in the amount of light reaching the receiving surface; for this reason it will often be necessary to feed the output of the photodiodes into a storage battery, from which a steady output can be taken.

"Direct" Conversion of Solar Energy The conversion of solar energy to electrical energy can, therefore, be achieved by several devices which avoid the complexity and weight of the conventional steam turbine method. These depend upon either the direct transfer of energy from the incident radiation to electrons, or on the conversion of the radiation to heat, followed by the conversion of heat to electrical energy by thermoelectric or the thermionic processes.

It is of interest to compare the efficiencies of these processes, estimates of which are given in Table 10.5.

TABLE 10.5
EFFICIENCIES OF DIRECT CONVERSION PROCESSES

	Efficiency			
	Watts/pound		Watts/square foot	
Method	Present	Anticipated	Present	Anticipated
Silicon photodiode	1.5	5	7.4	13
Thermionic	7	17	2.2	3.5
Thermoelectric	20	30	0.3	1

Fluorescent Lighting Electrons may flow through a gas if the pressure of the gas is sufficiently small and if the gas is partially ionized, which can be achieved by local heating. When electricity flows through a gas it may displace electrons in or from some of the atoms. When other electrons arrive to take the place of those which have been removed, or when displaced electrons return to their normal orbits, they lose potential energy which reappears in the form of light which is radiated. This process is highly efficient but has one serious disadvantage; the light, instead of being white, as is desirable for many purposes, has very specific wavelengths which are characteristic of the kinds of atoms that are present. Familiar examples are the neon light used for advertising signs and the sodium light (brilliant yellow to orange) sometimes used for street lighting. For domestic purposes the disadvantage of these characteristic colors is overcome by coating the inside of the tube with a compound which absorbs the characteristic light falling upon it and emits light very close to white in color.

Radio-Frequency Heating When radiation falls upon the surface of an object, part of it is absorbed and converted into heat at the surface, and part is reflected. This part is not converted into heat unless it is absorbed at some other surface. Many substances are transparent to radio or microwave radiation which are opaque to light. However, they are not completely transparent and therefore some of the radiation is absorbed in the interior of the substance. If this is sufficiently intense, it causes heating to an appreciable extent. An application of the internal heating of an object by radio frequency radiation is in so-called radio-frequency cooking, in which the temperature of the food to be cooked is raised uniformly throughout and not, as in ordinary cooking, first at the surface and then progressively inwards by conduction. The advantages of radio-frequency cooking are that it is much faster than conventional cooking as heat conduction is not relied upon to heat the interior, and secondly the interior can be raised to any desired temperature without the surface being raised to a higher temperature, which is necessary for heat to be conducted inward.

Magnetic Effects of a Current It has been shown in the preceding sections that the energy of an electric current can be converted into heat or chemical energy, and that it can be used for "pumping" heat, in thermoelectric heating and cooling. There is also another effect associated with an electric current. This is the *magnetic field* which is always present in

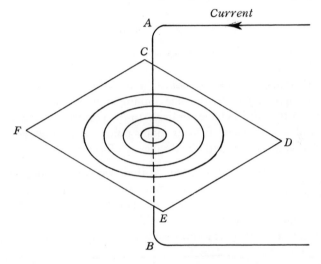

Fig. 10.19. The magnetic effect of a current.

the space surrounding a current. It is a form of potential energy; that is to say, when a current is started, energy is expended in setting up the magnetic field, and as a consequence, the current does not instantaneously reach the value that would be calculated from the voltage and the resistance; it takes an appreciable time, usually a small fraction of a second, to reach this value. The energy that is used in creating the magnetic field reappears in the form of current that continues to flow for a short time when there is no longer any voltage to drive the current.

The characteristics of the magnetic field surrounding a conductor carrying a current can best be examined by comparison with the magnetic field of the earth. The most obvious effect of the earth's magnetic field is that it causes a freely suspended magnet or compass needle to point north and south. This is because forces are exerted on the ends of the compass needle; the end described as the north-seeking, or N, pole experiences a force that moves it toward the north, and the south-seeking, or S, pole is acted upon by a force to the south. The needle sets itself along the direction of these forces, which is called the *direction of the magnetic field*.

The existence of the magnetic field near a wire carrying a current can be demonstrated as follows: The wire *AB* (Fig. 10.19) passes vertically through a horizontal card *CDEF*. If a small suspended compass needle is placed near the wire, through which a current is passed, the needle no longer points

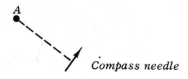

Fig. 10.20. Direction of the magnetic field.

north and south, but instead points in the direction shown in Fig. 10.20, that is, at right angles to the line joining it to the wire (*A*). Iron filings sprinkled on the card behave similarly to the compass needle, and show the direction of the magnetic field at many points; it is observed, as shown in Fig. 10.19, that the magnetic field takes the form of circles around the wire.

Forces between Magnetic Poles It can also be shown that two compass needles affect each other; there is, therefore, a magnetic field in the space surrounding each of them. If the poles of two compass needles are identified as N and S poles, it can readily be shown that dissimilar poles attract each other. It follows that each compass needle or other magnet

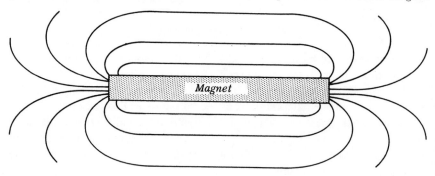

Fig. 10.21. Magnetic field of a bar magnet.

has a magnetic field associated with it. The magnetic field of a bar magnet can be studied by means of iron filings or a small compass needle; it is shown in Fig. 10.21.

An important property of any magnet is that if it is broken into two pieces, each piece is a complete magnet; it has both a north-seeking and south-seeking pole. It is impossible by breaking a magnet, or by any other means, to have only the north pole on one piece of steel, and only the south pole on another. It will be noticed that this is entirely different from the behavior of electrostatic charges; one object can be positively charged or negatively charged.

Magnetic Units   The characteristic property of a magnetic field is that it exerts a force on a magnetic pole placed in it. The force on an N pole is in the direction of the field. The direction of the force on an S pole is exactly opposite.

A magnetic field has magnitude as well as direction; its strength, in *oersteds*, is the force in dynes exerted on a *pole of unit strength*. The unit magnetic pole is a pole which repels an equal pole at a distance of 1 centimeter with a force of 1 dyne.

Magnetic "Lines of Force"   It is convenient to represent a magnetic field by means of lines which are everywhere in the direction of the field. There are the lines along which the iron filings or the compass needle point. They represent the paths along which a hypothetical "single pole" would travel; they are called "lines of force." In order to use

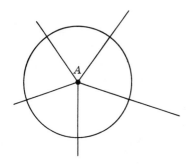

Fig. 10.22. Lines of force associated with unit pole.

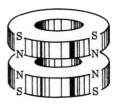

Fig. 10.23. Measurement of pole strengths of magnets.

the idea of lines of force quantitatively, it is usual to consider that each unit pole has 4π lines of force associated with it. If a unit pole were at the point A in Fig. 10.22, the lines would spread out radially, as shown, and at a distance of 1 centimeter, there would be 4π lines of force passing through a sphere of area 4π square centimeters; or 1 line per square centimeter of sphere. At the distance of 1 centimeter, however, the strength of the field is 1 oersted; it follows that *the strength of the field is equal to the number of lines of force passing through 1 square centimeter*. At a distance of 2 centimeters, the area of the sphere is $4\pi \times 4$ square centimeters, and the field strength is $\frac{1}{4}$ oersted, and at d centimeters it is $1/d^2$ oersted. If the pole at A has a strength M_1 units, there would be $4\pi M_1$ lines of force, and the field strength at a distance d would be M_1/d^2 oersteds. The force exerted on a pole of strength M_2 units at a distance d would, therefore, be M_1M_2/d^2 dynes.

It should be emphasized that the magnetic field exists in the whole of the space around a magnet, and not only where the lines of force happen to be drawn.

The force between two magnetic poles is M_1M_2/d^2; but magnetic poles never exist in isolation. The force between two magnets is the resultant of the forces between each pole of one magnet and each pole of the other; each of these four forces, two of attraction and two of repulsion, are calculated from the formula $F = M_1M_2/d^2$, and the resultant is found, by graphical or other methods. The pole strength of a magnet can be measured as follows: two ring-shaped magnets A and B (Fig. 10.23) are placed one above the other so that the force between them is one of repulsion. The upper magnet is constrained so that it can only move vertically. This can be achieved by means of a pencil which passes through the holes in the centers of the magnets. The upper magnet is supported by the force between it and the lower magnet. This force consists of the repulsion between the similar poles of the two magnets, partly offset by the attraction between the opposite poles. Because the lower pole of the upper magnet and the upper pole of the lower magnet are much closer together than any other pair of poles in these two magnets, they will have the greatest contribution to the force. A rough calculation of the strength of the poles may be made on the basis that the force between the two magnets is sufficient to support the weight of the upper magnet, which is found by weighing it on a balance. The calculation is as follows. It is found that the upper magnet comes to rest 2 centimeters from the top of the lower magnet and that it weighs 0.02 kilogram or 20 grams. The force of repulsion $F = M_1M_2/d^2 = M^2/4$ which is equal to the force required to support the upper magnet, or 0.02×9.8 newtons or 20×981 dynes. Thus, $M^2/4 = 20 \times 981$,

$$\text{or,} \quad M = 280, \text{ approximately.}$$

The magnetic pole strength is, therefore, about 280 units. The strength of the magnetic field in the space between the magnets is given by the number of lines of force, $4\pi \times 280$, divided by the cross-sectional area of the space through which they pass, which is about 12 square centimeters, for magnets of 2-centimeter radius with a hole of 0.5-centimeter radius.

$$\text{The field strength} = \frac{4\pi \times 280}{12} = 290 \text{ oersteds.}$$

It is interesting to note, for comparison, that the earth's magnetic field has a value of about 0.2 oersted.

The *Intensity of Magnetization* of a magnet is its *pole strength divided by the area of the pole;* for the magnets used in the test described above, it is

$$280/12 = 23 \text{ unit poles per square centimeter.}$$

The Origin of Magnetism Although it is convenient to describe magnetic fields as originating either from electric currents or from magnets, it is not fundamentally necessary to do so, because the magnetization of a magnet is also the result of electric currents. These electric currents are the electrons moving in their orbits in the atoms of which the magnet is composed.

Ferromagnetic Substances The atoms of most substances produce a very weak magnetic effect, because the electrons in the atom are so paired that their magnetic effects are almost neutralized; these substances are said to be *paramagnetic* or *diamagnetic*. The metals iron, nickel, and cobalt, some alloys, and some compounds (the ferrites) have very strong magnetic properties. They are called *ferromagnetic* substances.

The interaction between ferromagnetic substances and a magnetic field can be illustrated in the following way. Figure 10.24a shows the lines of force of the magnetic field between the poles of a magnet. Figure 10.24b shows the effect of introducing the iron rod *AB* into the field. The lines of force have a very strong tendency to pass through the iron rather than through the air. It can also be shown, by means of a compass needle, that the piece of iron has magnetic poles at its two ends. As would be expected, the S pole of the iron is toward the N pole of the magnet. Thus, the iron affects the magnetic field and the magnetic field affects the iron; there are far more lines of force concentrated in the iron than would be present in the same space if the iron were not there. The field within the iron is the *induction B*, measured in *gauss* and, in the case under consideration, the induction is very much higher than the magnetizing field *H*, measured in *oersteds*. The ratio of the induction to the magnetizing field is called the *permeability*, represented by μ.

The induction is the magnetic field that may be considered to exist within the iron. This could only be measured by observing it within a very small hollow space which could be imagined to exist within the iron. For iron, nickel, cobalt, and other ferromagnetic substances the permeability may be greater than 100; it depends upon the strength of the field *H*.

The effect of the magnetic field on the iron is to magnetize it. The relevant property of the iron is its *susceptibility K*, that is, the intensity of magnetization *I*, produced in the iron by unit magnetizing field. Since there are 4π lines of

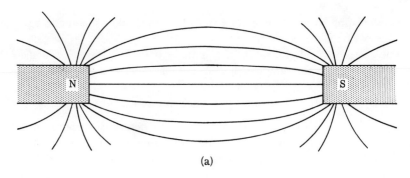

(a)

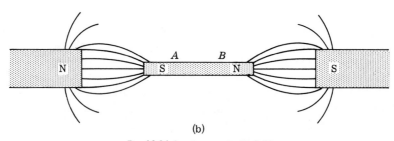

(b)

Fig. 10.24. Iron in a magnetic field.

force per unit pole, it follows that the induction B is equal to $4\pi I$ plus the original field H. Thus

$$B = H + 4\pi I \qquad \text{and} \qquad \mu = \frac{B}{H} = 1 + 4\pi K.$$

Thus, the permeability μ and the susceptibility K are different ways of expressing the same property.

Magnetically Hard and Soft Materials When the magnetizing field is removed, a substance in which induction had taken place may remain a magnet or it may become unmagnetized. The former class of substances, that is, those which retain their magnetization after the magnetizing field has been removed, are *permanent magnet materials*, sometimes called *magnetically hard* materials. The usefulness of a substance for permanent magnets depends upon the amount of magnetization which remains and upon the difficulty with which it can be demagnetized. Hardened steel is an example of a magnetically hard material and it can retain an induction of up to 8500 gauss when the magnetizing field is removed. Some other substances retain even more magnetization; a good example is the alloy Alnico which can retain 12,500 gauss. At the other extreme are the *magnetically soft materials,* that is, those in which the magnetization disappears almost completely as soon as the magnetizing field is removed.

Effect of Temperature on Magnetization The effect of temperature on magnetization is important when, for example, instruments that depend upon magnets are designed for use at high temperatures. It is always found that the magnetization disappears when the temperature reaches a specific value for any given ferromagnetic material. Figure 10.25 shows an experiment that will illustrate this. A steel knitting needle *K* is suspended so that it can move freely. A magnet *M* is held close to it and the point of the needle is attracted so that it touches and sticks to the end of the magnet. If the needle in the vicinity of the magnet is heated to a bright red heat (actually

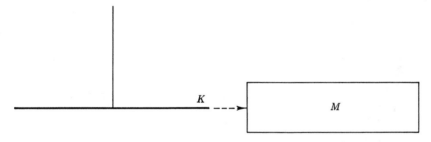

Fig. 10.25. Effect of temperature on magnetism.

about 790 degrees centigrade), it completely loses its attraction for the magnet; its induction suddenly disappears. The needle swings away from the magnet and is not attracted to it again until it has cooled down to below this temperature. The temperature at which the ferromagnetic behavior disappears, that is, at which the permeability drops to a value very close to 1, is called the Curie temperature.

All these phenomena are explained in terms of the hypothesis that in substances which behave ferromagnetically, each atom behaves as a separate magnet. There is a strong tendency for these magnets to align themselves so that the N pole of one and the S pole of the next are close together. If they all align themselves in the same way in a sample of metal, then the metal is magnetized to the maximum possible extent. How then is it possible to have iron that is sometimes magnetized and sometimes not magnetized? The answer is that the tiny atomic magnets may either all be arranged in the same direction, as in Fig. 10.26a, or they may be arranged as shown in Fig. 10.26b, so that the alignment is very good locally in each part of the magnet, but the alignments of different parts or *domains* of the magnet are not the same.

By a suitable arrangement of the domains, as shown in Fig. 10.26b, the magnet can be arranged so that at no point is there a magnetic pole at the surface and in this case there is no external magnetic field. Therefore, the material, although ferromagnetic, is not a magnet. This is the situation for a magnetically soft material such as iron when it is not in a magnetic field. On applying a magnetic field the alignments are changed so as to increase the number of atoms that are aligned parallel to the applied field and to decrease the number that are aligned in other directions. This results in induction and in the creation of magnetic poles at the surface of the piece

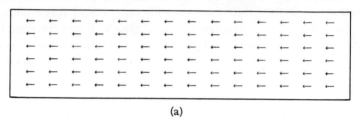

(a)

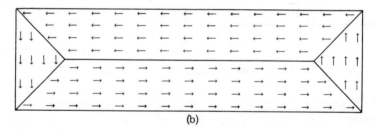

(b)

Fig. 10.26. Alignment of the atomic magnets in a ferromagnetic material.

of metal. The truth of this hypothesis has been very clearly demonstrated by observing the arrangement of very fine magnetic particles when they are placed on the surface of a piece of iron which is magnetized and on one which is not magnetized. The particles tend to take up positions on the walls between the neighboring domains, which can be seen. The effect of raising the temperature is to increase the thermal vibration of the atoms and at a high enough temperature their alignment is destroyed.

Strength of Magnetic Field Due to a Current The magnetic field due to a current is represented by lines of force that surround the conductor that carries the current. For a long straight wire carrying a current of A amperes, the field H at a distance of R centimeters from the wire is given by $H = A/5R$. If the conductor is in the form of a circular coil, as shown in Fig. 10.27, all the circular lines of force which surround the current point in the same direction within the coil and add together in the center to produce a magnetic field which is greater than that formed at any point at the same distance from a straight wire. The magnetic field due to a current of A amperes at the center of a circular coil of radius R centimeters is $H = \pi A/5R$. The magnetic field is in a direction perpendicular to the plane of the coil. If the coil consists of N turns instead of 1, then the field will be $\pi NA/5R$. An example of the use of these formulas is to calculate what current will be required in a coil and in

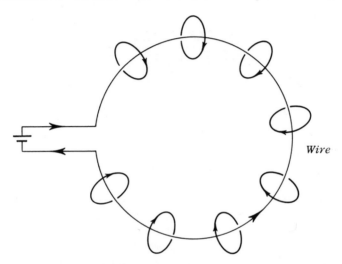

Fig. 10.27. Magnetic field due to current in a wire.

a straight wire in order to produce a magnetic field equal to that of the earth, that is, a magnetic field of 0.2 oersted. In order to produce a magnetic field of 10 oersteds at a distance of 10 centimeters from a vertical wire, the current required is given by

$$H = \frac{A}{5R} \qquad \text{or} \qquad A = 5RH$$

$$H = 0.2, \qquad R = 10$$

Hence, $\quad A = 5 \times 10 \times 0.2 = 10$ amp.

At the center of a circular coil 10 centimeters in radius, consisting of a single turn of wire, the field $H = \pi A/5R$. Thus,

$$0.2 = \frac{3.14 \times A}{5 \times 10}$$

or $\quad A \simeq 3$ amp.

About 3 amperes will produce the required field in this case. If the coil had 100 turns of wire, then only one-hundredth of the amount of current would be required, that is, 0.03 ampere. A slightly different case is that of a solenoid, that is, an elongated coil. The distinction between a coil and a solenoid is usually taken to be whether the length along the axis is

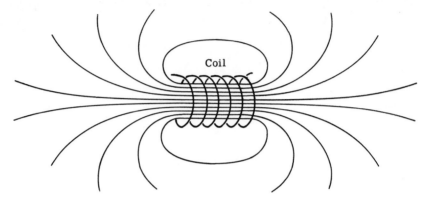

Fig. 10.28. A solenoid.

small compared with the radius (a coil) or long compared with the radius (a solenoid). Figure 10.28 represents a solenoid. The magnetic field in and around the solenoid is represented by the lines of force that are sketched in Fig. 10.28. It will be seen that these lines of force are those that would be produced by drawing circular lines of force around the various turns of the coil. Neighboring turns of the coil produce lines of force which, in the small

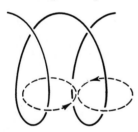

Fig. 10.29. Cancellation of field between the turns of a solenoid.

spaces between the neighboring turns, are in opposite directions and therefore cancel. This is illustrated in Fig. 10.29. However, inside the solenoid, all the lines of force are in the same direction and this is also true outside the solenoid. Hence, within the solenoid there are many lines of force all parallel to each other running the whole length of the solenoid. Outside the solenoid they resemble the lines of force of a bar magnet. The magnetic field within a long solenoid is given by the formula $2\pi NA/5$, where N is now the number of turns per centimeter of solenoid. This field is constant within the solenoid, except near the ends, where it is less. If a piece of iron is placed inside a solenoid which carries a current, the iron becomes magnetized. If the field due to the current in the solenoid is H, then the iron becomes magnetized so that its induction is B, the ratio of B to H being the permeability. It acquires magnetic poles of strength I per unit area of cross section, where I is given by the relationship

$$B = H + 4\pi I.$$

Thus, if the permeability and the current in the solenoid are known, the strength of the resulting magnet can be calculated. This is complicated by the fact that iron does not retain a constant value of the permeability and it is not possible to magnetize it beyond the point at which all the elementary magnets are turned in the same direction. It is then said to be saturated.

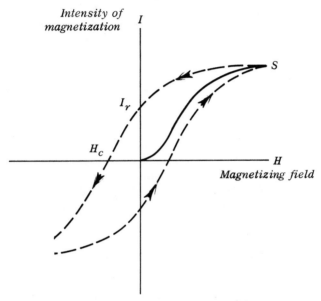

Fig. 10.30. Effect of field on magnetization of iron.

The strength of the magnetic poles produced on a bar of iron in a solenoid depends on the current. If the current is gradually increased, the intensity of magnetization increases as shown by the solid line in Fig. 10.30. Saturation has been reached at S and further increase of the magnetizing field is unable to cause any further increase of the magnetization. If the current is now reduced, the magnetization does not immediately disappear. Its decrease is represented by the broken curve in Fig. 10.30. When the magnetizing field has been reduced to zero, there is some magnetization remaining. This is the *remanent magnetization* represented by I_r in Fig. 10.30. The magnetizing field must be reversed in direction and reach a value of H_c called the *coercive force*, before the magnetization disappears altogether. If the magnetizing field is increased in the direction opposite to the original direction, then saturation is eventually reached in the reverse direction and the whole cycle can be completed by reducing the magnetizing field to zero and increasing it in the original direction again.

The Hysteresis Loop   It can be shown that when a piece of iron is taken round this cycle, magnetizing it first in one direction and then in the other, and then in the first direction again, some energy of the magnetic field is converted into heat. This is a relatively small amount but it becomes important, as shown later, when the cycle is repeated a very large number of times. The loop shown by the broken line in Fig. 10.30 is called the *hysteresis loop*. Its area shows how much energy is dissipated as heat each time the material is taken through the complete cycle. The width of the loop and its area vary from one material to another. It is very large for a permanent magnet material where the remanent magnetization is very high, and where demagnetization is difficult, which makes it a good permanent magnet. If I_r and H_c are both large, the hysteresis loop has a large area; if they are both small, then the hysteresis loop is correspondingly small.

The Electromagnet   An iron core in a solenoid carrying a current is a strong magnet when the current is flowing and a very weak magnet when the current is not flowing. This is the basis for the *electromagnet*, which finds many applications. A very simple application is that of the electric bell, the circuit for which is as shown in Fig. 10.31. When the switch is closed, the current flows through the whole circuit and this energizes the electromagnet. The electromagnet pulls the armature A, also made of iron, toward it. This causes the striker to hit the bell and it breaks the

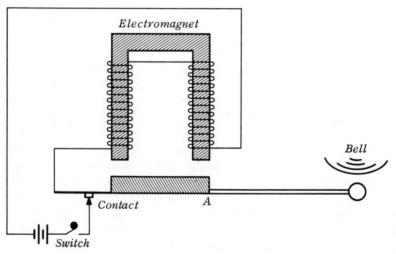

Fig. 10.31. The electric bell.

circuit by pulling the spring away from the contact. As soon as the contact is broken, the electromagnet ceases to be energized, the spring pulls the armature and striker back to its original position, where contact is again made. So long as the switch is closed, the current alternately flows and stops; each time it flows the bell is struck.

Another type of electromagnet is the solenoid valve. The solenoid valve consists of a solenoid through which a current passes when a circuit is closed. A rod of iron is partly inside and partly outside the solenoid as shown in Fig. 10.32. When the current flows in the solenoid, the bar of iron is pulled

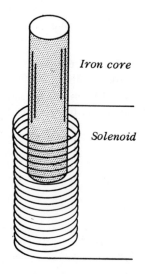

Iron core

Solenoid

Fig. 10.32. Solenoid valve.

into it. This operates the valve or other mechanism which is to be moved whenever the current flows.

"Degaussing" of Ships   Another application of these principles is in the "degaussing" of ships. During World War II, a type of mine was used which was fired whenever a compass needle within the mine was deflected by a ship passing over it. The compass needle was set to rotate about a horizontal axis. In the earth's field, such a compass needle would normally set nearly vertically with its N pole pointing down. For the purpose of the magnetic mine, the compass needle was so counter-balanced that it would set with the S pole pointing down and the N pole pointing upward. When a ship passed over it, the vertical magnetization of the ship resulting from the induction from the vertical component of the earth's magnetic field repelled the N pole of the compass needle in the mine and attracted the S pole. If this attraction and repulsion were sufficiently strong, it caused the compass needle to invert, making the electrical contact which caused the mine to explode. The defense against this type of mine was to reverse the magnetization of the ship. This was done by passing a current through a large coil surrounding the ship in a horizontal plane. The ship was *degaussed* by either reversing the field or reducing it to a very small value. The compass needle in the mine was not acted upon sufficiently strongly by a ship in which the degaussing coil was carrying the proper current. Another technique that was used was to set off the mine by producing a magnetic field in a coil carried by an aircraft which was flown over the surface; any mine that came within range of the magnetic field was exploded without damage to ships.

Motors, Generators, and Transformers   The two magnets represented in Fig. 10.33a repel each other, because similar poles are in close proximity, and those in Fig. 10.33b attract because dissimilar poles are close together. These forces can also be explained in terms of lines of force,

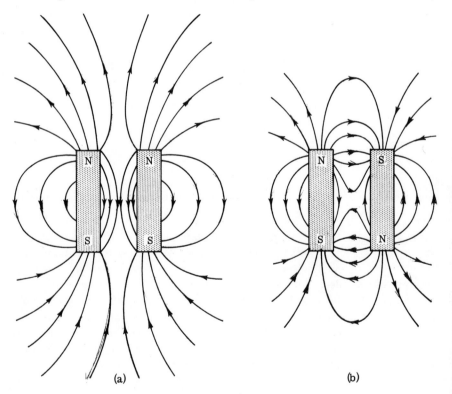

Fig. 10.33. Forces between two magnets.

on the basis that the energy of a magnetic field is decreased as the lines of force become shorter and, if in the same direction, further apart. The repulsion in Fig. 10.33a is due to the tendency of the lines of force between the magnets to move further apart; the attraction in Fig. 10.33b is due to the tendency of the lines to get shorter, partly by the cancellation of adjacent lines in opposite directions.

The interaction between the magnetic field due to a current in a wire and an external magnetic field can now be understood. In Fig. 10.34, a magnetic field is represented by straight lines of force NS. A wire, perpendicular to the plane of the paper, passes through it at *A*. The magnetic field due to a

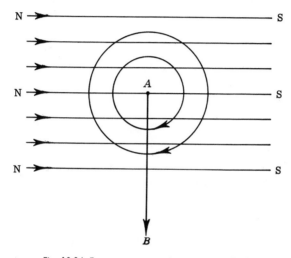

Fig. 10.34. Force on a current in a magnetic field.

current in the wire is represented by a series of circular lines of force, of which two are shown in the diagram. It will be seen that the lines of force due to the current are in the same direction as those of the magnetic field in the upper part of the diagram, while in the lower part they are opposite in direction. It follows that the wire carrying the current experiences a force in the direction *AB* because above the point *A* the lines of force are repelled and below the point *A* the lines of force are attracted. It can therefore be concluded that there is an interaction, which takes the form of a force, between a magnetic field and a current flowing in a conductor. The direction of this force is at right angles both to the magnetic field and to the direction of the current. The magnitude of this force, in dynes, is equal to $HAL/10$, where H is the strength of the field in oersteds, A is the current in amperes, and L the length of the conductor within the magnetic field. This formula can be applied for finding the field strength of a permanent magnet in the following way. The permanent magnet NS in Fig. 10.35 is placed so that its magnetic field is horizontal, that is, so that the line joining the centers of the poles is horizontal. A vertical wire is suspended in the center of the magnetic field so that it is free to move. A thread attached to the wire at the center of the magnetic field passes over a pulley and has a weight attached to it. A current is passed through the wire and the strength of the current is measured by means of an ammeter. In a measurement of this type the weight attached to the thread was 10 grams which just balanced the force on the wire when

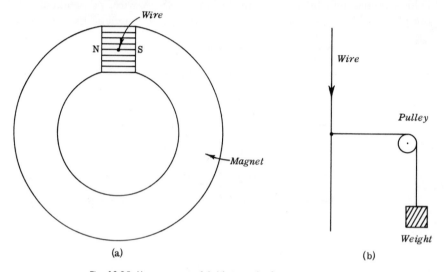

Fig. 10.35. Measurement of field strength of a permanent magnet.

the current was 3.6 amperes. The length of wire in the magnetic field was 4 centimeters. The strength of the field is calculated as follows:

$$F = \frac{HAL}{10}$$

or, $$10 \times 981 = \frac{H \times 3.6 \times 4}{10},$$

since the force corresponding to the weight of 10 grams is 10×981 dynes. Hence

$$H = 6800 \text{ oersteds.}$$

One of the simplest applications of the force between a current and a magnetic field is in the moving coil loud speaker, the construction of which is represented in Fig. 10.36. A permanent magnet is constructed so that one pole, the N pole, is in the center of an annular space which is surrounded by the S pole. There is, therefore, a radial magnetic field in the annular space. A circular coil is held in this space. Its position is indicated in Fig. 10.36. When a current is passed in one direction round this coil, it moves to the right, and when a current is passed in the opposite direction a force is exerted on it to the left. Thus, a fluctuating electric current, which is the signal provided by an amplifier for conversion into sound, causes the coil to move alternately to the right and to the left. The coil is attached to the cone of the loudspeaker which in turn is forced to move alternately to the right and to the left. This movement generates the sound which is heard.

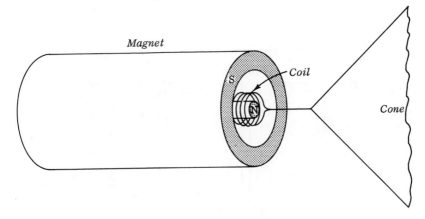

Fig. 10.36. Moving coil loudspeaker.

The Electric Motor   The most important application of this principle is in the electric motor, in which electrical energy is converted into work. To understand the electric motor, consider the behavior of a coil of wire placed in a magnetic field. The coil of wire A in Fig. 10.37 may consist of one or more turns. When a current is passed through it, in the direction indicated in the diagram, the wire or wires at the right-hand side of the coil move outward and those on the left move inward. In other words, the coil experiences a force tending to make it rotate in the magnetic field. Figure 10.38 illustrates this further. In the position shown in Fig. 10.38a, the two sides of the coil experience forces in opposite directions; this tends to cause the coil to rotate. If rotation is permitted, the coil will turn to the position shown in Fig. 10.38b and eventually to that shown in Fig. 10.38c. It will be observed that when the position in Fig. 10.38c is reached, forces are still exerted on the coil but there is no tendency for it to rotate. If the rotation of the coil is opposed by means of a spring, then the amount of the rotation is an indication of the strength of the current flowing in the coil. This principle is used in many instruments designed for measuring electric currents, such as ammeters.

An electric motor is a device designed for converting electrical energy into kinetic energy of rotation and it is therefore necessary to arrange for it to rotate continuously. This is achieved as follows: The coil is attached to a spindle so that it can rotate freely. If a current is passed through it when it is in the position shown in Fig. 10.38a, it will rotate and acquire some angular momentum. This will carry it past the position shown in Fig. 10.38c into the position shown in Fig. 10.38d. If the current still flows in the same direction, the force will now tend to restore the coil to the position of Fig. 10.38c. If, however, the direction of the current is reversed, the directions of the forces

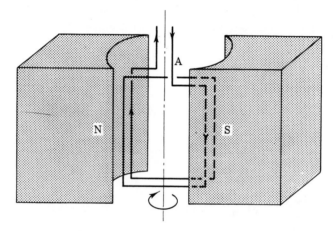

Fig. 10.37. Principle of the electric motor.

will also be reversed and the force will tend to continue the rotation of the coil in the original clockwise direction. The reversal of the direction of the current is achieved by means of a simple switching device called the *commutator*. This is illustrated in Fig. 10.39. The two ends of the coil are attached to two metal sectors represented by A and B. These two sectors are separate pieces of copper which extend part of the way around the shaft, but are insulated from each other. The current is led into the coil by means of the two brushes labeled P and Q, the brush P always makes contact with whichever sector of the commutator is uppermost. As the coil rotates, this will be alternately sector A and sector B. The brush P is supplied with a positive voltage and Q is negative. Consequently, the current flows from P into the coil, through the coil and out at Q. As the coil rotates, the direction of the current in the coil itself will be reversed every half-revolution and this will maintain the direction of rotation of the coil in the magnetic field. A small electric

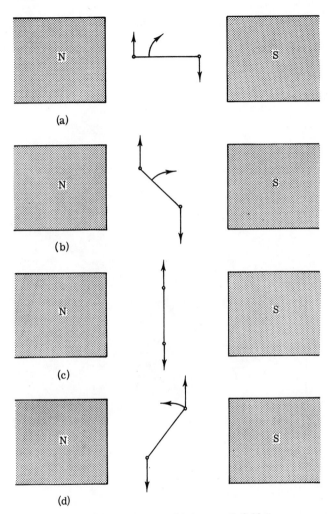

Fig. 10.38. Force on a coil in a magnetic field.

motor may be constructed using a permanent magnet, whereas a larger motor usually requires an electromagnet which is energized by the same current that is supplied to the motor. The field coil, that is, the coil carrying the current that energizes the electromagnet, may be either in series or in parallel with the armature, that is, the rotating coil.

It is evident from the foregoing that an electric motor is able to do work, the energy corresponding to which must come from the electric current that passes through the coils. In this case, therefore, some of the electrical energy is converted into the energy of motion of the motor. It follows that more

work must be done in forcing the current through the coil if it forms part
of an electric motor which is working, than would be required if the coil
were simply an equal length of copper wire not forming part of the motor.
This means that a higher voltage is required to pass the same current through

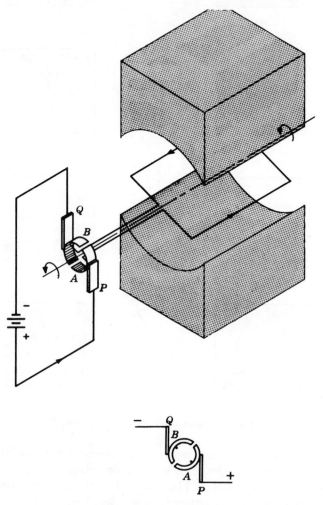

Fig. 10.39. The commutator.

the coil of the working motor. This is because the motor itself generates a
voltage which opposes the passage of the current in the coil. It is this opposing
voltage multiplied by the current that gives the amount of electrical energy
converted into kinetic energy, whereas the current multiplied by the total

applied voltage gives the total energy converted; the difference between these is the energy converted into heat in the wire of the coils. The conclusion from this is that when a conductor, such as the coil of the motor, moves in the magnetic field, a voltage is set up in the wire; in this case this voltage tends to oppose the current passing through the wire, but the effect is much more general than the case just considered.

This can be demonstrated with a permanent magnet, in the field of which a wire is placed (Fig. 10.40). This wire is connected to a *galvanometer*, which is a sensitive instrument for measuring electric currents. If the wire is moved across the magnetic lines of force (that is, in the direction *AB*, Fig. 10.40), a current will be detected flowing in the galvanometer. This means that

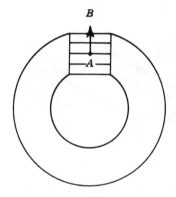

Fig. 10.40. Voltage produced by the motion of a conductor in a magnetic field.

when a conductor is moved across the lines of force of a magnetic field, a voltage is set up in the wire. If a complete circuit is provided, a current will flow. The magnitude of the voltage generated in this way is equal to the number of lines of force cut per second, multiplied by 10^{-8}; (a field of 1 oersted corresponds, as shown above, to one line of force per square centimeter). If the wire in Fig. 10.35 is moved at a speed of 1 centimeter per second, the voltage generated would be as follows: The strength of the magnetic field was found to be 6.8×10^3 oersteds. There are, therefore, 6.8×10^3 lines of force per square centimeter. A wire of length 4 centimeters in the magnetic field, therefore, cuts $4 \times 6.8 \times 10^3$ lines of force while it moves through 1 centimeter. The voltage generated is equal to $2.8 \times 10^4 \times 10^{-8}$ volts if it moves 1 centimeter in 1 second. This is equal to 2.8×10^{-4} volts. Although this is a very small voltage, it illustrates the principle which is used for the generation of electricity, that is, that work can be converted into an electrical potential difference, which can be used to drive a current.

The voltage generated by moving a conductor in a magnetic **The Generator** field can be increased in three ways. The length of wire moving in the magnetic field can be increased, usually by making a coil instead of a single wire; secondly, the strength of the magnetic field can be increased, and thirdly, the speed of motion of the wire in the field can be increased. All three of these methods are used when this principle is applied for the generation of useful quantities of electricity. The basic method is represented in Fig. 10.41 in which the coil C, attached to a shaft, is rotated in the field of the magnet NS. The turns on the two sides of the coil A and B produce current in the same direction in the coil when it rotates in the field, because the side A moves upward and the side B moves downward

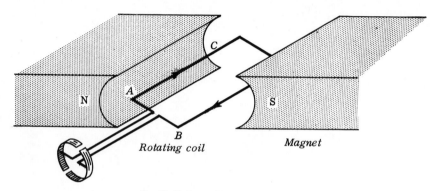

Fig. 10.41. Principle of the generator.

and this causes a current to the right in the side A and to the left in the side B. The two ends of the coil are attached to a commutator, with which brushes make contact as in the case of the electric motor. The commutator of the type described in Fig. 10.39 causes a current which is always in the same direction although it is intermittent since there is no current produced while the coil is exactly perpendicular to the magnetic field. This corresponds to the position in which the coil of the motor experiences no force, illustrated in Fig. 10.38c. This difficulty is overcome in practice by the use of a considerable number of coils instead of just one, so that some are always in the most favorable position, that is, the plane of the coil along the lines of force of the magnet.

Alternating Current For many purposes a different type of contact is used. In this case, as shown in Fig. 10.42, one end of the coil is attached permanently to one ring and the other end to a second ring so that the two brushes which make contact with the two rings are fed alternately with positive and negative charge; that is, the direction of the voltage supplied to the brushes is reversed twice for each rotation of the coil. This produces *alternating current.*

Practically all of the current supplied for domestic and industrial use in this country is alternating current with a frequency of 60 cycles. This means that the generator rotates 60 times per second, that the current flows 60 times per second in each direction, or changes direction 120 times per second.

The torque required to turn a generator depends upon whether there is a circuit through which the current can flow; if so, electrical energy is generated, which in turn is converted into heat or some other form. The energy input is the work done in turning the generator. If there is no circuit, the only force opposing the rotation of the generator is its friction; if a current is allowed to flow, the force is increased because the current in the coils themselves is in such a direction that its interaction with the field opposes the

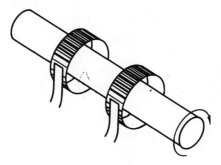

Fig. 10.42. "Slip rings" for alternating current.

motion of the coil. The work used to overcome this opposing force is the work which is converted into electrical energy.

Both electric motors and electric generators are highly efficient. The efficiency is usually considerably in excess of 90 per cent. This should be contrasted with the very low efficiencies of many other devices which have been considered. It should be clearly recognized that in both the motor and the generator the output, that is, either kinetic energy of rotation or current, is obtained at the expense of energy input, that is, electrical energy in the case of the motor and kinetic energy or work in the case of the generator. More energy can never be extracted from a machine than is put into it.

Transformers A voltage can, as shown previously, be generated by motion of a conductor in a magnetic field, that is, by moving a conductor so that it cuts the line of force of a field; a voltage can also be generated by causing the lines of force to move so that they cut a conductor. A conductor in which no current is flowing has no magnetic field associated with it, and no lines of force. If a current is caused to flow in it and is gradually increased, the magnetic field around the wire increases and this corresponds to the production of an increasing number of lines of force surrounding the wire. As the current is increased, these lines move outward. A second conductor placed close to the first one will therefore be cut by the moving lines of force and it will therefore have a voltage *induced* in it. This phenomenon is described as *electromagnetic induction*. The number of lines of force set up by a given current increases if the wire carrying the current is in the form of a solenoid surrounding an iron core, because the magnetization of the iron core corresponds to the induction of a large number of lines of force. If the current in the coil of an electromagnet is increased or decreased, then any conductor in the vicinity of the electromagnet is cut by lines of force and a voltage is generated. In order to maximize this effect, a second coil may be wound around the same core, as shown in either Fig. 10.43a or 10.43b. This is a *transformer*. Whenever the current in one coil, called the *primary*, increases or decreases, a voltage is induced in the *secondary* coil. A convenient way of increasing and decreasing the current in the primary is to use alternating current. If the number of turns in the secondary coil is equal to the number in the primary coil, then the voltage induced in the secondary will be approximately equal to the voltage supplied to the primary. If, however, the number of turns in the secondary is much greater than the number in the primary, then the voltage in the secondary would also be much greater. This is because the number of lines of force cutting the secondary will be the same in both cases, and the voltage induced is proportional to the number of lines of force times the number of turns of the coil. Therefore, if the secondary coil contains 100 times as many turns as the primary coil then the voltage induced in it will be 100 times that of the primary coil. This does not mean that energy is created in a transformer; the current which can be taken from the secondary coil would be less by at least a factor of 100 than current flowing in the primary coil, because a current taken from the secondary coil flows through the coil itself and this sets up an opposing voltage. Transformers can be designed with very high efficiency, but this is never 100 per cent because of the conversion of some electrical energy into heat each time the magnetization of the core goes around the hysteresis loop. Transformers are used for very many purposes, one of the most important of which is to change the voltage of an electrical supply, both in the upward and in the downward directions; that is, by using step-up and step-down transformers. The reason for doing this is that it is economically advantageous to generate electricity on a large scale at relatively few locations. This is largely because the steam turbine plant frequently used for this purpose only reaches a reasonable efficiency if it is of very large size. Central generation of electrical power necessitates its distribution over great distances. The distribution of electrical energy requires that the current shall flow through cables, which may be either overhead or underground. These cables necessarily have some resistance, and therefore, some of the electrical energy is converted into heat, while the current is passing from one place to another. It is desirable to minimize the conversion of electrical energy into heat and this is achieved by keeping the current as small as

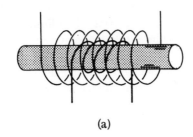

(a)

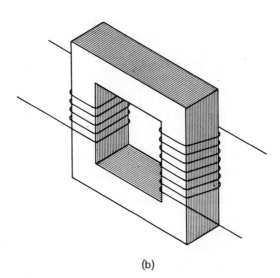

(b)

Fig. 10.43. Two types of transformers.

possible, since the heating effect of the current is A^2V. In order to keep the current small and to transmit a required amount of energy, it is necessary that the voltage should be high. Power can be distributed across country at 200,000 volts and transformed to 110 volts for local distribution. To transmit 1 kilowatt at 200,000 volts requires only 1/200 ampere, but it would require 9 amperes at 110 volts. Assuming that a conductor carrying the current has a resistance of 1 ohm, the energy dissipated in the form of heat in the conductor is given by

$$A^2R = \frac{1}{200^2} = 2.5 \times 10^{-5} \text{ watts}$$

for a current of 1/200 ampere, and 81 watts for a current of 9 amperes. It is evident that the higher the voltage and therefore the smaller the current, the less is the loss of energy due to heating. The limitation to the voltage that can be used in practice is the insulation required to prevent sparking. The transformer requires alternating current since the current in the secondary is only produced as a result of changes in the current in the primary. Direct current cannot be transformed to higher or lower voltages except by the elaborate procedure of using the current to drive a motor which in turn drives a generator.

Ignition System for Automobiles A second application of the principles discussed above is in the ignition system of an automobile. The 6-volt or 12-volt battery of the automobile feeds current to the primary of the ignition coil. When the current from the battery is interrupted, by means of the contact breaker, a high voltage, 20,000 volts, is produced in

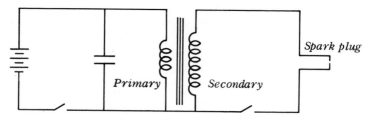

Fig. 10.44. Ignition system of an automobile.

the secondary circuit of the coil. The circuit is illustrated in Fig. 10.44. The voltage generated in the secondary circuit is sufficient to cause a spark to pass between the points of the spark plug and this ignites the gasoline vapor-air mixture in the cylinder. A spark is required each time a cylinder fires. The distribution of the sparks between the various cylinders is provided by the *distributor* which connects the secondary of the ignition coil to the various spark plugs in turn. The circuit breaker is operated at the appropriate time by a mechanical device connected to the cam shaft, which is rotated by the motor itself.

Eddy Currents Attention has been directed to the induction of voltage in a wire in a moving or changing magnetic field. Any conductor, however, experiences a voltage when it is cut by moving lines of force; if the conductor is sufficiently massive, then the current induced by motion of or through a magnetic field may be entirely within the conductor. This is illustrated by the following demonstration. The pendulum illustrated in Fig. 10.45a consists of a rod *A* and a disk *B* which may consist of copper or aluminum. The pendulum is suspended so that it can swing freely. If it is allowed to swing between the poles of a powerful magnet, its swing stops very abruptly as soon as it is within the magnetic field. This is because the currents induced in the copper disk interact with the lines of force of the magnetic field to produce a force opposing the motion of the disk. The energy of motion of the disk is transformed first into electric current and then into

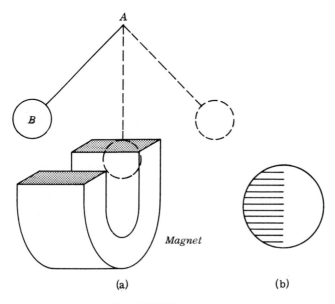

Fig. 10.45. Eddy currents.

heat as a result of the flow of current within the material of the disk. If the disk has a number of parallel cuts as shown in Fig. 10.45b, the effect is greatly reduced. This is because it is no longer possible for the current to flow within the disk as freely as before. These currents, which are produced locally, as a result of motion of a conductor in a field, are called *eddy currents*. Eddy currents would, if allowed, occur within the iron core of a transformer or induction coil, and thereby reduce efficiency by converting some of the electrical energy into heat. To avoid this, the core is nearly always made of thin sheets of iron instead of one massive bar. Electromagnetic damping of the kind just described is used in electric light meters in order to prevent moving parts from continuing to turn after the current has stopped flowing.

An interesting and sometimes alarming example of electromagnetic induction can be caused by lightning. A lightning strike close to a house may induce current in the electrical circuits in the house itself. This sometimes causes damage to lamps or to the wiring itself. This is not caused by the lightning itself actually passing through the wires, but by the magnetic field set up by the lightning interacting with the conductors constituting the wiring in the house and inducing currents which are large enough to be damaging. The duration of these currents is extremely short and the total heating in the circuits is usually very small.

Magneto-hydrodynamics Conductors in the form of solid wires of metal have been discussed so far. However, very hot gases conduct electricity to an appreciable extent, because some of the atoms are ionized, that is, the atoms have lost some of their electrons and are therefore positively charged, and the electrons are either free or are attached to other atoms which are then negatively charged. A very hot gas stream is therefore capable of acting as a conductor of electricity. It is called *"plasma,"* and when it is moving it constitutes an electric current. The behavior of liquids or gases carrying electric currents in magnetic fields constitutes the study of *magnetohydrodynamics*, often abbreviated as MHD, a topic which has received much attention recently, largely because of its potential importance in connection with nuclear energy, discussed in Chapter 11. There are two possible applications of magnetohydrodynamics which are relevant at this point. These are the *magnetohydrodynamic generator* and the *magnetohydrodynamic motor*.

The MHD Generator Figure 10.46 illustrates the principle of the magnetohydrodynamic generator. The purpose of the generator is to convert the kinetic energy of motion of a very hot gas into electrical energy. The hot ionized gas is passed between the poles of the magnet NS in Fig. 10.46. The force acting upon the current going from left to right in the magnetic field (which is vertical on the page) is at right angles to both, that is, at right angles to the page. The ions which are so affected are moved either out of or into the page according to whether they are positive or negative ions. They are collected on the collecting electrodes placed in front of and behind the region of the magnetic field. These are the plates *A* and *B*. The arrival of positively charged ions at *A* and negatively charged ions at *B* causes the potential difference which drives a current in a circuit. This is therefore a generator. The energy which is received is electrical energy; this is taken out of the gas as a result of the slowing down of the gas molecules resulting from their interaction with the magnetic field. The molecules that are not ionized are slowed down to some extent as a result of the collisions that they have with the ions whose motion is affected by the field. The first effect of the field is to move them transversely, that is, toward the collectors, but their motion toward the collectors produces an interaction which exerts a force on them opposite in direction to their original motion. Thus, the average kinetic energy of the gas is reduced, and this energy is converted into electrical energy.

The original source of the energy that is converted into the electrical form is the heat as a result of which the gas is ionized and moves into the generator with high energy. Some of the kinetic energy of the moving gas is converted into electrical energy. This type of converter is subject to the efficiency limitation inherent in heat engines, but it can be used with an extremely high

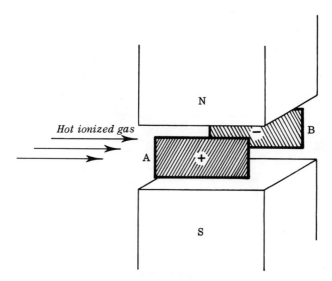

Fig. 10.46. Magnetohydrodynamic generator.

upper temperature and its efficiency can accordingly be high compared with that of a steam turbine or gas turbine system.

The MHD Motor The magnetohydrodynamic motor is related to the electric motor in the same way that the magnetohydrodynamic generator is related to the ordinary electromagnetic generator. The purpose of the magnetohydrodynamic motor is as follows. One of the major problems that will be encountered in space flight is that of changing either direction or velocity of motion. The momentum of a space ship is unchangeable, except by ejecting some material. In order to conserve the material that must be carried on the spaceship for this purpose, it is necessary to give it the highest possible momentum when it is ejected, and this means that it must have the highest possible velocity. The magnetohydrodynamic motor is a device for increasing the velocity with which material can be ejected for purposes such as this. A stream of hot gas is passed between the poles of a magnet and between the electrodes of an electric field placed at right angles. In this case the effect of these two actions is to increase the speed of the particles. Consider a positive ion traveling from left to right close to the positive electrode, Fig. 10.47. It is repelled by the positive electrode and moves toward the negative one. This gives it a velocity across the magnetic field and this causes a force on it to the right in the diagram. Similarly, an electron or a negatively charged ion traveling close to the negative electrode will be repelled by it toward the positive electrode. This gives

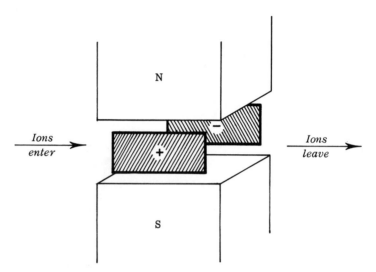

Fig. 10.47. Magnetohydrodynamic motor.

it a transverse velocity which, interacting with the magnetic field, increases its longitudinal velocity. Some of the ions only will be affected in this way. Those which are negative and are close to the positive electrode will be attracted to it and will decrease the voltage of the plate and vice versa. It therefore follows that the plates must be maintained continuously at their high voltage, which would otherwise disappear as positive ions reach the negative plate and negative ions reach the positive plate. There will therefore be a current flowing in the circuit connected to the two plates, and the energy which is put into this circuit is that which is supplied to the ions which are accelerated out of the magnetic field. The result is that those ions which get through the electrostatic and electromagnetic field have increased velocity and therefore increased momentum. Another device which is under consideration for the same purpose is the electrostatic motor in which the ions are accelerated by means of an electrostatic field without the use of a magnetic field. This is illustrated in Fig. 10.48. Hot ionized gas is supplied at *A*. The positive ions are accelerated by a potential difference between *A* and *B*, which is a plate with holes in it through which the ions may pass. The ions which pass through the holes have a high velocity and therefore a large momentum relative to their mass. In order that the spaceship should not become negatively charged, electrons are added to the ion beam at the point *C*, where a filament emits electrons as a result of its high temperature.

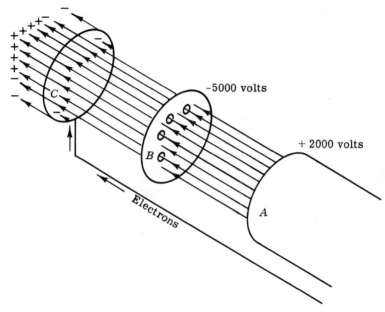

Fig. 10.48. Ion propulsion motor.

Problems

10.1 A circuit takes a current of 1 amp when it is connected to a 110-volt supply. (a) What is its resistance? (b) What power (in watts) does it use?

10.2 What is the resistance of a copper wire 2 mm thick and 1 km long?

10.3 Which is heavier, an aluminum wire or a copper wire of the same length and the same resistance? (Density of copper = 9.0 gm/cm³; density of aluminum = 2.7 gm/cm³.)

10.4 How much heat (in Calories per minute) is generated if a 6-volt battery is connected to a lamp designed to run at 40 watts on a 110-volt supply?

10.5 (a) Two 60-watt lamps intended for a 110-volt line are to be used on a 220-volt line; should they be connected in series or in parallel?

(b) What will happen if they are connected wrongly?

10.6 A 1 HP electric motor is to run on the 110-volt line; how much current will it take?

10.7   A 740-watt generator and an electric motor of 1 HP are connected to the same shaft, so that the motor drives the generator; the output of the generator is used to drive the motor. Can this device be used to drive a lathe that requires $\frac{1}{2}$ HP?

10.8   A house wiring circuit which has a resistance of 2 ohms is connected to the 110-volt supply. A 100-watt lamp and a 1000-watt electric toaster are connected as

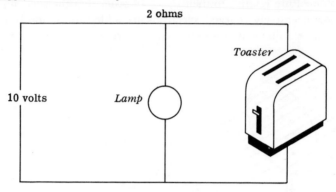

2 ohms

10 volts   *Lamp*   **Toaster**

shown in the diagram. Calculate how the power of the lamp changes when the toaster is switched on.

10.9   The primary and secondary windings of a transformer consist of 100 and 1000 turns, respectively. If the current in the primary is 1 amp of direct current and the voltage 110 volts, what is the voltage in the secondary?

10.10   (a) How many 6-volt 20-watt lamps should be connected so that they can be used on a 110-volt line?

(b) How should they be connected?

(c) What will be the current (amperes) and the power (watts)?

10.11   A wire of resistance 1 ohm/meter is to be used for making a solenoid, which is to be wound on a tube of 20-cm circumference. (a) What magnetic field can be produced in the solenoid if the source of current is a 12-volt battery? (b) How many turns of wire would you use?

10.12   An electric kettle has a 1-kw heating element. (a) What is its resistance? (b) What fuse does the circuit require (5, 10, or 15 amp)?

10.13   A room is lit by five 100-watt lamps. How many Calories are generated per hour?

10.14   An electric kettle holds 1 liter of water, and is designed to work on the 110-volt line. The water is to be heated from 20°C to the boiling point in 3 minutes. (a) Neglecting heat loss, and the heat absorbed by the kettle itself, what should be the resistance of the heater? (b) Can it be used on a line with a 15-amp fuse?

10.15   (a) A current is passed from A to D along the wire shown in the diagram. Will there be any force between the parts AB and CD? If so, in what direction?

(b) Is this changed by using alternating current instead of direct current?

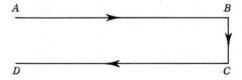

A B

D C

Chapter 11

NUCLEAR ENERGY

The chapter on chemical energy was concerned with the type of chemical conversion in which atoms change their state of association with each other, changing, for example, from separate atoms to molecules or crystals or vice versa. It must be emphasized that in such conversions each atom retains its identity and does not change its chemical nature or behavior. An atom of oxygen, having taken part in a series of reactions, is still an atom of oxygen. It may, at various stages, have been an oxygen ion, but its nucleus remains unchanged throughout. In this chapter various energy conversion processes will be considered in which the nucleus does not remain unchanged.

Radioactivity It has been known for about 70 years that the atoms of a few elements spontaneously undergo changes in which the chemical nature of the atoms is modified. This process is known as *radioactivity*. It occurs spontaneously, and, as far as individual atoms are concerned, unpredictably, and no method has been discovered for changing the rate at which it occurs. The process is the disintegration of the nucleus of an atom, in the course of which particles and energy are emitted. The particles are of two types, called *α-particles* and *β-particles*. The α-particles are identical with the nucleus of the helium atom and may be regarded as consisting of two protons and two neutrons. The β-particles are electrons. In addition to α-particles and β-particles, *gamma-rays* are also given off. These are electromagnetic waves of the same character as radio waves, light waves, and x-rays but of much shorter wavelength even than x-rays. The emission of energy that accompanies each disintegration takes the form of the kinetic energy of the emitted particle and of the atom itself, and the radiation energy of the gamma-rays. Radium is an example of a radioactive substance. The disintegration of a radium atom occurs when an α-particle leaves it. This results in the conversion of the nucleus of the atom from radium to radon. Radon itself is radioactive and transforms by the emission of α-particles to radium A, which in turn transforms to radium B. The final product of this chain of transformation is lead.

Half-Life The exact moment when a particular atom undergoes the disintegration process is apparently determined by chance. Statistically it is possible to predict with great accuracy that half of the atoms in a given sample of a radioactive material will disintegrate in a known period of time called the *half-life* for that substance. In the next equal period of time half of those remaining will disintegrate, and so on for an indefinite time. The number remaining at the end of one half-life is always equal to one-half of the number present at the beginning of it, unless more are formed during the intervening period as a result of

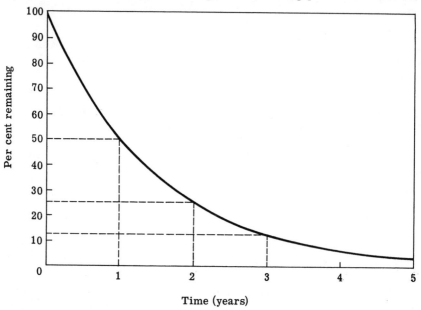

Fig. 11.1. Radioactive decay, half-life of 1 year.

disintegration of another radioactive element. Consequently, the number remaining at the end of any time is given by a curve of the type shown in Fig. 11.1 which is drawn for a substance of which the half-life is 1 year. The actual half-lives of radioactive substances vary enormously. That of radium is 1600 years, and of thorium, about 1.6 times 10^{10} years, whereas some of the products of these elements have half-lives as short as 10^{-3} second. As an indication of the amount of energy associated with these disintegrations it may be stated that a gram of radium gives out about 0.14 Calories per hour, in spite of the fact that its half-life is 1600 years. The enormous amount of energy that this corresponds to over the life of the radium sample is evidence that the α-particles are emitted with extremely high kinetic energy. Their velocity is in fact equal to about 1.5×10^7 meters per second. In order to give an electron a kinetic energy equal to that of the α-particle, it would be necessary to accelerate it by means of a voltage of 4.7 times 10^6 volts. Its energy would then be expressed as 4.7×10^6 electron volts. One *electron volt* is equal to about 1.6 times 10^{-12} ergs or 1.6×10^{-19} joules. The extremely high energies of the α and β particles and of the gamma-rays are sometimes transferred to atoms with which they collide as they pass through matter. They may also ionize atoms close to which they pass. Their energy is therefore reduced, either gradually or abruptly, and this limits the distance that they can travel through any substance. The range of α-particles is quite short, amounting to a few centimeters in air and much shorter distances through denser substances. In aluminum, for example, the range is about 4×10^{-3} centimeters and in lead about 2.4×10^{-3} centimeters. The range of β-particles is much greater, amounting to a few meters in air and a few millimeters in aluminum. The penetration of gamma-rays is very much greater.

The emission of energy by nuclear disintegration of this kind is uncontrollable; the fact that it occurs spontaneously to the heaviest naturally occurring atoms indicates that the nuclei of these atoms are unstable. That is, that some of the energy which binds the component parts of the nucleus together can be released when disintegration takes place.

Radiation Damage   As particles are slowed down and radiation is absorbed, their energy is transferred to the atoms or molecules of the material in which they are traveling. The energy that is transferred can cause various kinds of damage, as a result of atoms being knocked out of their proper positions, or of ionization, which is the displacement of electrons. Intense radiation can cause so much damage to the cells of living organisms as to be lethal. This can be used beneficially for the sterilization of surgical dressings, but it also represents a serious health hazard, especially when the radioactive substance is ingested into the human body. Less obvious, but no less serious, is the possibility of genetic damage, which can result in mutations which, in human beings, are almost always undesirable. Radiation induced mutations in plants, however, may occasionally produce highly desirable mutants. These would probably take much longer to occur by "spontaneous mutation" which may itself be induced by *cosmic radiation*, a type of nuclear radiation that reaches the earth from sources outside the solar system.

Increase of Mass with Velocity   It has been shown experimentally that when an object such as an electron travels at an extremely high speed it behaves as if its mass were increased above the value which it has when at rest. It is found, as predicted by Einstein, that the more closely the velocity approaches that of light, the greater the apparent mass becomes. Another way of stating this is that it becomes increasingly difficult, or requires an increasingly greater force, to give a specified acceleration to an object which is traveling at a speed approaching that of light. It is predicted that it would require an infinite force to accelerate a mass to a velocity equal to

TABLE 11.1
INCREASE OF MASS WITH VELOCITY

Per cent of speed of light	Per cent of increase of mass
1	0
10	$\frac{1}{2}$
50	15
75	50
80	67
90	129
99	2100
100	Infinite

that of light. The measurements that have been made on the apparent masses of particles traveling at very high speed are consistent with this conclusion. Table 11.1 shows how the speed would be expected to increase as the velocity of light is approached. The basis on which these measurements are made is as follows. Electrons traveling along a path AB in Fig. 11.2 enter a region C where there is a large electrostatic field transversely to the direction of

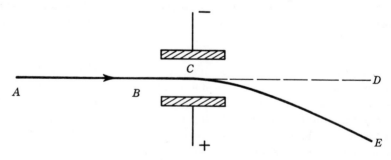

Fig. 11.2. Measurement of mass of electrons.

motion of the electrons. The electrons are attracted by the positive side of this field and repelled by the negative side and a force is therefore exerted upon them in the direction transverse to that of their motion. This causes their path to change and the lateral acceleration which they develop can be calculated from the displacement of their path resulting from the electrostatic field. It is displaced from D to E at the region where the electrons are detected. It is found, as predicted by the theory, that as the velocity approaches 3×10^8 meters per second (the velocity of light) the deflection is less than would be calculated from the electrostatic force exerted upon the moving electron. Therefore more work is done on it to deflect its path by a given amount. It has more kinetic energy than would be calculated from one-half its original or rest mass times the square of its velocity; this can be simply stated in the form that its mass has increased since it is known that its velocity has not changed. Thus, in all respects the particle behaves as if it has a greater mass as a result of its very high speed. If in slowing down it does work upon some other object, the amount of work it can do is a measure of the apparent mass rather than of its actual rest mass. Therefore we can say that the additional mass due to velocity can be transformed into work and therefore can be identified as energy.

Relationship between Mass and Energy   An extension of this concept, also a result of the theory of relativity, is that not only the additional mass due to velocity can be identified as energy but also the mass which an object has when at rest. The amount of energy associated with a given mass is given by the relationship $E = MC^2$, where E is the energy corresponding to a mass M, C is the velocity of light, where E is in joules, M is in kilograms, and C in meters per second. If a mass of 1 kilogram of matter could be converted completely into energy, the amount of energy would be given by $E = 1 \times C^2 = 9 \times 10^{16}$ joules. This is about 2×10^{13} Calories or 8.5×10^{13} BTU. This may be compared with a chemical reaction such as combustion in which the amount of heat generated is typically of the order of 5×10^3 Calories per kilogram. Thus it is seen that the amount of heat that would become available if 1 kilogram of matter could be converted into energy would be greater by a factor of more than 10^{10} than the amount that could be obtained by combustion of the same amount of fuel. No way is known at present for converting the whole of any substance into energy but part of the mass of some substances can be converted into energy by *fission* or by *fusion*.

Isotopes   The masses of atoms must now be considered in more detail; most chemical elements consist of atoms which, while identical in chemical properties, may have any one of several different masses. The atoms of an element which have the same mass constitute an *isotope* of that element. Most elements are found in nature as a mixture of various isotopes. All the isotopes of a given element have identical chemical properties but different masses; these masses are all close to whole numbers (based on 1 for hydrogen or 16 for oxygen). The whole number is the *mass number* of the isotope. For example, hydrogen occurs as H^1 and H^2, carbon as C^{12} and C^{13}. Chlorine consists of about 75 per cent of Cl^{35} and 25 per cent of Cl^{37}. The chemical atomic weight of chlorine, consequently, is 35.5.

Packing Fraction   When very precise measurements are made of the masses of the individual isotopes, it is found that they depart slightly from whole numbers. It is usual for these purposes to take the mass of oxygen as 16 as the basis for other measurements. The difference of the actual isotopic mass from the mass number is expressed as the *packing fraction*. This is the difference of mass divided by the mass

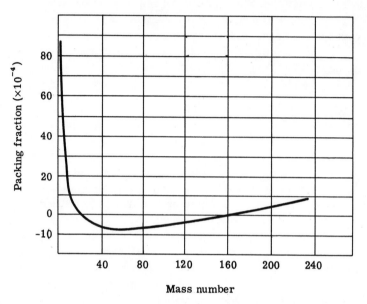

Fig. 11.3. Variation of packing friction with mass number.

number. It varies from plus 81×10^{-4} for hydrogen to minus 8×10^{-4} for copper. The variation of the packing fraction with the mass number is shown in Fig. 11.3. It will be seen that the elements at both ends have high packing fractions and those with mass numbers between 8 and 74 have negative packing fractions. It is now evident that the elements at the high end of the scale are likely to be unstable because their mass is relatively high and therefore they have a relatively large energy content.

It will be assumed for the purpose of this discussion that the nuclei of all atoms consist of protons and neutrons. The number of protons is equal to the atomic number and the number of protons plus neutrons is equal to the mass number. If the mass of the nucleus were exactly equal to the sum of the masses of all the protons and neutrons in it, the packing fraction would always be zero, because the total would always be a whole number. For example, oxygen has six protons and six neutrons, and hydrogen has one proton. The fact that the atomic masses are not all whole numbers indicates that the packing of the component parts to form the nucleus involves a change of mass and therefore a change of energy.

Fission It is evident from the packing fractions that an atom of one of the heaviest elements is likely to be unstable in the sense that its energy can be reduced by splitting it into two lighter atoms. This does not occur spontaneously, but it was discovered in the 1930's that it can be induced to happen. Specifically, it was discovered that an atom of uranium-235, when struck by a neutron, may disintegrate into two atoms, for example, barium and krypton, and emit three neutrons. This is an example of the process of *fission*. Another example of the same process is the fission of uranium-236 into molybdenum and lanthanum and two neutrons. The energy that is released in this nuclear reaction can be calculated from the difference between the initial mass of the atom of uranium-236 and the sum of the masses of the fission products, that is, molybdenum and lanthanum and the neutrons. The mass of the atom of uranium-236 is 236.133, the masses of the isotopes of molybdenum and lanthanum that are formed are 138.995 and 94.946. The mass of the neutrons is equal to 2.018. It follows that

$$
\begin{array}{ll}
\text{Initial mass} & = 236.133 \text{ kg} \\
\text{Final mass} & = 235.959 \text{ kg} \\
\hline
\text{Decrease in mass} & = 0.174 \text{ kg}
\end{array}
$$

Hence the decrease in mass per kilogram is $0.174/236.133$. This is the amount of mass that is converted into energy in accordance with the relationship $E = MC^2$. The energy released, is, therefore

$$
\frac{0.174}{236} \times 9 \times 10^{16} \text{ joules/kg.}
$$

$$
\text{or} \quad 6.6 \times 10^{13} \text{ joules/kg}
$$

$$
\text{or} \quad 1.4 \times 10^{11} \text{ BTU/lb}
$$

For comparison, the amount of coal that will provide the same quantity of energy is as follows. The energy liberated by the combustion of coal is 5.6×10^3 Calories per kilogram. 5.6×10^3 Calories is equivalent to $5.6 \times 4.2 \times 10^6$ joules, or 2.3×10^7 joules are produced by the combustion of 1 kilogram of coal. To produce 6.6×10^{13} joules, therefore, would require $(6.6 \times 10^{13})/(2.3 \times 10^7) = 2.9 \times 10^6$ kg; thus about 3000 tons of coal would be required to generate the amount of heat that could be produced by the fission of 1 kilogram of uranium. This does *not* assume the total conversion of the mass of the uranium into energy, but only that part which corresponds to the packing fractions.

There are very many different ways in which an atom of uranium-235 can split up into two fission product atoms. These are almost always atoms with atomic masses between 70 and 160; the sum of their mass numbers plus the number of neutrons equals the mass number of the uranium atom. The fission product atoms that are formed are not the same as the corresponding atoms found in nature. They are radioactive and therefore they give out radioactive particles and radiation. Each of them decays with a characteristic decay time as with other radioactive processes.

The Fission   If an atom of uranium-235 that undergoes fission is sur-
Chain   rounded by other similar atoms, the neutrons from the first
Reaction   atom to disintegrate may strike other atoms and cause them
to disintegrate in turn. Alternatively the neutrons may escape from the mass

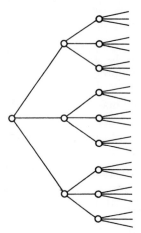

Fig. 11.4. Divergent chain reaction.

of fissionable material since they are able to travel considerable distances before striking the nucleus of another atom. Consequently, if the mass of uranium-235 is very large, almost all the neutrons that are produced would cause fission in other atoms and since there are three neutrons produced for each atom that undergoes fission, the number of atoms undergoing fission would increase extremely rapidly. This is illustrated diagrammatically in Fig. 11.4. This is an example of a *chain reaction* of the type which is described as divergent. This can occur only if each neutron produces on the average more than one neutron as a result of its own collision with other atoms.

**Critical
Mass**
It is evident that the chain reaction can still occur even if some of the neutrons do not cause fission. If, however, the loss of neutrons is too great, the reaction does not become divergent. This is shown in Fig. 11.5 in which the nuclei of the uranium atoms are shown as circles, and the paths of neutrons by arrows; the fission products are not shown. A neutron entering from the left causes fission at *A*; one of the neutrons from the fission of *A* strikes the atom *B* and causes fission; similarly, *C* undergoes fission, but all the neutrons from *C* leave the

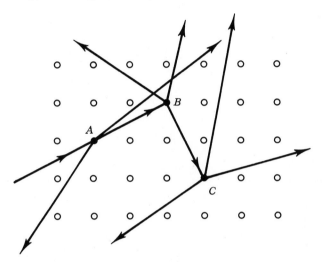

Fig. 11.5. Chain reaction is not sustained.

mass of uranium without causing further fission. Whether the reaction is of the sustained, divergent type or not depends upon the amount of uranium and upon the presence of other substances than uranium which can capture neutrons undergoing fission. The former of these two conditions is the more important and leads to the idea of the *critical mass*. The critical mass is the mass of the piece of uranium which is just large enough for sufficient neutrons to be captured and to cause fission for the reaction to be divergent. If the mass is below this value, the reaction dies away, if it is above, the reaction is rapidly divergent. The reaction, whenever it occurs, is extremely fast because the neutrons emitted by the atoms undergoing fission move with extremely high velocity.

**The
Atomic
Bomb**
The divergent chain reaction described above is that which occurs in an atomic bomb. The bomb is detonated by supplying neutrons and bringing together masses of uranium which are individually below the critical mass, but which jointly exceed it.

The size of an atomic bomb is discussed in terms of the amount of TNT that would give an equivalent explosion, that is, that would release an equivalent amount of energy. The unit for expressing the size is the "kiloton," that is, 1000 tons or 10^6 kilograms. The heat of combustion of TNT is 3.6 Calories per kilogram. Thus the heat of combustion of 1 kiloton of TNT is 3.6×10^9 Calories, or $3.6 \times 4.2 \times 10^{12}$ joules, that is about 1.5×10^{13} joules. This amount of energy is created in the atom bomb by destroying an amount of mass M given by $E = MC^2$ or $M = E/C^2$, where $E = 1.5 \times 10^{13}$ joules and $C^2 = 9 \times 10^{16}$ (meter/second^2). Thus $M = (1.5 \times 10^{13})/(9 \times 10^{16})$ kg $= 1.7 \times 10^{-4}$ kg, or 0.17 gram. This is the amount of mass that is converted into energy; the amount of uranium-235 that must undergo fission for this to occur is calculated as follows. The packing fraction for uranium-235 is about 5×10^{-4} and that for the fission products is about -7×10^{-4}. The total mass converted into energy is therefore about 12×10^{-4} or 1.2×10^{-3} of the total mass M of uranium that undergoes fission. Therefore, $1.7 \times 10^{-4} = 1.2 \times 10^{-3} \times M$, or $M = 0.14$ kg or 140 grams. This is an estimate of the amount of uranium-235 that would be required per kiloton of explosion if it were completely converted into fission products, neutrons, and energy. The first atomic bombs were of about 10 kiloton size. This calculation does not, however, give any indication of the critical mass, which cannot be estimated without much more detailed information.

Natural Uranium as a Nuclear Fuel Natural uranium consists of about 99.3 per cent of uranium-238 and 0.7 per cent of uranium-235. The uranium-235 that is present is sufficient to cause a self-sustaining divergent chain reaction and to allow sufficient neutrons to be extracted from this process to cause changes in the uranium-238 which is also present. The

Fig. 11.6. Conversion of uranium-238 to plutonium.

uranium-238 can capture neutrons which are traveling slowly with the following sequence of results. The uranium-238, on capturing a neutron, becomes uranium-239. This undergoes radioactive decay by the emission of β-particles with a half-life of 243 minutes with the formation of *neptunium* which in turn decays with a half-life of 23 days to form *plutonium*-239. This sequence of changes is shown in Fig. 11.6. In order to arrange that natural uranium should perform the tasks of sustaining a chain reaction, by means of uranium-235, and producing plutonium from uranium-238, it is necessary to slow the neutrons down without absorbing them. This is shown schematically in Fig. 11.7 in which the *moderator*, which slows down the neutrons, is represented by the material M. In addition to sustaining the chain reaction and converting uranium-238 to plutonium, this device converts a substantial amount of mass into energy. It is therefore a possible basis for the production of useful energy from a nuclear reaction. In order to use it in this way it is necessary to extract the heat from the uranium, where it is generated, and to control the chain reaction so that it does not become too rapid.

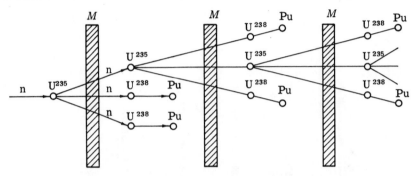

Fig. 11.7. Production of plutonium from natural uranium.

Nuclear Reactor   A *Nuclear Reactor* is a device in which heat is extracted from a controlled chain reaction; the main purpose may be to generate energy, or it may be to produce plutonium, which is itself able to undergo fission and is used for atom bombs and as the fuel for some types of reactors.

The type of nuclear reactor shown schematically in Fig. 11.8 consists of the following components; its *fuel rods F* consist of natural uranium encased in aluminum to protect them from corrosion by the coolant C, which may be air, carbon dioxide, or water. The coolant is pumped through the tubes which surround the fuel elements; it enters at a relatively low temperature at A and emerges at B at a higher temperature. The moderator M is usually either graphite or heavy water, both of which substances are effective in slowing down neutrons without excessive absorption. The moderator occupies the space between the coolant tubes. The control rods R contain a substance that has a high capacity for absorbing neutrons, such as cadmium or boron; they can be rapidly inserted into the moderator if the reaction begins to accelerate and can be withdrawn in a controlled fashion to allow the reaction to proceed as required.

Because only 0.7 per cent of natural uranium is uranium-235, the critical size for this kind of reactor is quite large. The reactor is built in the form of a 10 to 20 foot cube consisting mainly of moderator and containing a very large number of fuel elements.

When the coolant leaves the reactor it goes to a heat exchanger where it transfers the heat it has received from the nuclear reactor to water which is thereby converted into steam. From there on the generation of electrical power follows conventional lines. For efficient production of electrical energy from heat energy it is necessary to operate with a high temperature. This

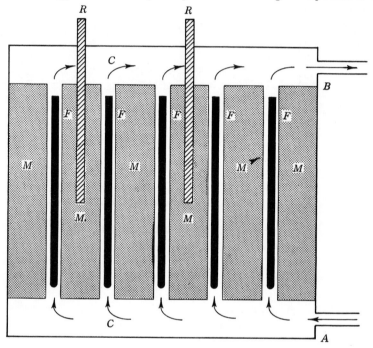

Fig. 11.8. Schematic diagram of a slow neutron reactor. F, fuel; M, moderator; C, coolant; R, control rod.

imposes very severe problems for the design of the reactor. For an air or gas-cooled reactor, it is necessary to avoid using materials that either react with the gas or become too weak at the working temperature. In the case of a water-cooled reactor, it is necessary to apply considerable pressure in order that the water will not turn into steam within the reactor itself. Steam is a much less efficient heat transfer material than water, and therefore it would be undesirable to allow steam to be generated in the reactor. Therefore high pressures are required and this in turn involves pipes or other containers which are designed to withstand high temperatures and pressures.

The type of reactor described so far was designed primarily for the purpose of producing plutonium, which shares with uranium-235 the property of undergoing fission. For a nuclear reactor which is designed purely for the production of energy, it is not necessary to use natural uranium and it is often preferable to use uranium that has been enriched by the addition of more uranium-235 or plutonium. This has the advantages of substantially reducing the critical size of the reactor and at the same time allowing the introduction into it of many materials for construction and for carrying coolant which would otherwise be unacceptable because of the neutron absorption which they would introduce. A reactor will gradually use up the uranium-235 or plutonium that is in it and the fuel elements must be replaced from time to time. This is not only because of the "burn-up" of the fissile material but also because some of the fission products themselves have a high capacity for absorbing neutrons. The problems associated with processing and disposal of the fission products, which have an extremely high level of radioactivity, are very serious and difficult.

The most practical type of reactor at the present time is that which uses enriched uranium, that is, uranium containing a substantially higher content of uranium-235 than is present in natural uranium, cooled by pressurized water at 2000 pounds per square inch and operating at a temperature of 500 degrees Fahrenheit. Steam produced in a heat exchanger outside the reactor is used to operate a conventional steam turbine and generator. The output of such a reactor would be about 60,000 kilowatts.

Shielding Within a reactor itself and in its vicinity there are very large numbers of neutrons and a very high intensity of gamma-rays as a result of the fission process and of the radioactive decay of fission products. These particles and radiations can cause structural damage to materials in which their energy is absorbed. Biological damage has already been referred to; deterioration of plastics, ceramics, and metals can also occur in or very close to nuclear reactors, where the neutron energy and intensity is extremely high. The possible damage to the materials of the reactor itself, and of the structure which supports them, must be taken into account in designing a reactor. Both gamma-rays and neutrons are able to penetrate large amounts of solid matter and therefore the problem of shielding a reactor so that the radiation does not endanger anyone in its vicinity must be considered. The type of shielding which is used for this purpose is a very thick layer of a special concrete which contains a high proportion of heavy elements. This concrete shield must be many feet thick in order to completely absorb the neutrons and the gamma-rays.

One of the major problems associated with the design of nuclear reactors for relatively small power production, such as for an automobile, is that of shielding. It is estimated that the shielding necessary for a 100-horsepower nuclear reactor would weigh at least 50 tons.

"Breeder" Reactors   The supply of uranium-235 is obviously limited, especially since the total world resources of uranium appears to be relatively small. It is therefore necessary to produce more fissionable material in the form either of plutonium or of uranium-233, which is produced from thorium in much the same way that plutonium is produced from uranium-238. It is possible to design reactors in which the total amount of fissionable material increases while the reactor is operating. This is called a *breeder reactor*. It is an enriched reactor surrounded by a layer of uranium-238 or thorium so that neutrons which escape from the reactor itself are trapped in the surrounding layer, causing the transition from uranium-235 to plutonium or thorium to uranium-233.

Fusion   The second type of nuclear reaction is *fusion*, in which a heavier atom is built up from lighter ones. This can occur only among the atoms of very low atomic mass because it is only at this end of the series that the packing fraction decreases as the atomic number increases. A possible example is the formation of one atom of helium from two atoms of heavy hydrogen, that is, atoms of the isotope of mass number 2. The energy that should be generated by this process is calculated, as before, from the decrease of mass;

Mass of one atom of heavy hydrogen $= 2.0162$
Mass of one atom of helium $= 4.0038$

Therefore decrease in mass $= 4.0324 - 4.0038 = 0.0286$ kilogram. Therefore 4 kg of heavy hydrogen give energy equivalent to 0.0286 kg, that is, $0.0286 \times 9 \times 10^{16}$ joules $= 2.574 \times 10^{15}$ joules; or, 1 kg of heavy hydrogen gives $(2.574 \times 10^{15})/4 = 6.43 \times 10^{14}$ joules.

It is evident from the packing fraction curve that energy would be released by this type of reaction. However, the conditions under which it can occur are entirely different from those for fission. The problem consists in bringing two heavy hydrogen nuclei together with sufficient violence for them to combine together instead of merely repelling each other away. The repulsive force must be very large when the nuclei are very close together and it is therefore necessary that they should approach each other at extremely high velocities. This can be achieved only by providing conditions of very high temperature, of the order of tens of millions of degrees centigrade. Such temperatures exist in the interior of the sun and other stars, and in these places the fusion reaction is sufficient to maintain the temperature at the level at which the reaction will continue. The fusion reaction is, in fact, the source of the sun's energy. The critical mass for such a reaction is obviously very large as the loss of energy by radiation at such temperatures must be tremendous. As is well known, it has been found possible to produce the conditions for the fusion reaction artificially in the *hydrogen bomb*, in which a nuclear reaction of the fission type is used to generate the high temperature required to cause the fusion reaction to occur. This is a chain reaction which occurs with extreme violence and rapidity.

The problem of power generation from the fusion reaction is very much more difficult than that of the fission reaction because of the difficulty of containing material at the extremely high temperature required for sustaining fusion. For a controlled reaction it would be necessary to supply fuel continuously and to maintain a region of high enough temperature for the reaction to proceed continuously. The most promising approach to this problem is to use magnetohydrodynamic methods for producing and containing the required high temperature, but at the present time there is no immediate hope of achieving a controlled sustained fusion reaction. The best result so far is that recorded by the Livermore Laboratory at the University of California where a temperature of 3×10^6 degrees has been sustained for a thousandth of a second.

To summarize the present position on nuclear energy therefore, it is clear that fission reactors are already beginning to play a significant part in the generation of power for marine propulsion, particularly in submarines; their use for the generation of electricity is not yet economic except where the high cost of coal or oil, due to remoteness or other special causes, makes the conventional methods exceptionally expensive. As natural fuels become more scarce, and therefore more costly, nuclear reactors will play a progressively increasing part in the provision of the country's electrical energy. It is expected that by the end of this decade the cost of generating electricity by fission will no longer be greater than by combustion; it will, however, be much longer before fission replaces coal, because increasing demand will require the construction of both nuclear and coal-burning generating plants. The use of nuclear fission energy for aircraft and rocket propulsion is under serious consideration and appears to be technically feasible, although the problem of shielding for manned flight is still a very serious one.

Problems

11.1 If the mass of hydrogen is 1.0081, and that of helium is 4.0038, each in grams per mole, how much energy would be produced if 1 kg of hydrogen were "fused" to form helium?

11.2 Uranium-236 can split up into molybdenum-95 and lanthanum-139 and two neutrons; the masses of these products are 138.995, 94.946, and 2.018 for the two neutrons. The mass of uranium-236 is 236.133. Calculate the energy that should be released in this fission process, per gram of uranium-236.

11.3 How much coal would be required to give an amount of energy equal to that of a pound of uranium-236?

11.4 How much water, stored in a dam at an elevation of 3000 ft above sea level, would provide an equal amount of energy?

11.5 When the reaction $C + O_2 = CO_2 + 67$ Cal takes place, should there be any change in the mass of the materials that are present? If so, how much?

11.6 If 1 lb of uranium-235 produced 11×10^6 KWH of energy by fission, how much does its mass decrease?

11.7 How fast would uranium-235 be consumed to generate 60,000 kw of power?

11.8 If the sun's energy is supplied by the fusion of hydrogen, at what rate is the sun's mass decreasing? (Assume that its output of energy is sufficient to give 20 Cal per square meter per minute at a distance of 93×10^6 miles.)

11.9 Is there any possibility of producing either fission or fusion of copper (atomic mass 63.5)? (Give reasons.)

Chapter 12

THE SOURCES AND USES
OF ENERGY

The abundant availability of energy combined with the technology which allows us to make use of it has had two major effects. In the first place, it allows us to do many things with very much less effort than was previously required; moving from one place to another by any of the mechanized means of transportation, digging the ground, heating the home, and cooking the food can all now be accomplished very much more easily and more quickly than was the case 100 years ago. In addition, the technological applications of energy make it possible to do things now which were not possible at all a century ago. Examples of this kind are flight and refrigeration. All these and many other of the benefits of civilization depend upon devices of which the sole purpose is the conversion of energy from one form to another. Figure 12.1 summarizes, in a very condensed form, the existing processes and methods of energy conversion.

Many of these processes have been discussed in principle and some have been discussed in detail in the preceding chapters, but it will be realized that we are not yet able to exploit all possible types of energy conversions; for example, there is, as yet, no artificial device which imitates the action of the muscle in directly converting chemical energy to work, and some of the other possible energy conversion techniques have not been developed to the point where they are useful. The fuel cell is an example and so also is thermoelectric conversion. It is evident that as new energy conversion techniques are developed we may expect that new methods will be adopted for making life more productive, more pleasant, or more dangerous; that is, for making available the fruits of technological progress.

As an example, it is of interest to consider the automobile and how it could conceivably develop in the future. In the early days of automobiles, the competition was between automobiles operated by steam, by electricity, and by the internal combustion engine. Of these the internal combustion engine rapidly gained supremacy over the steam engine, largely by virtue

ENERGY CONVERSION PROCESSES

From \ To	NUCLEAR	RADIATION	HEAT	CHEMICAL	ELECTRICAL	KINETIC	GRAVITATIONAL	ELASTIC
NUCLEAR		Nuclear explosion The sun's radiation	Nuclear reactor Fission Fusion					
RADIATION		Fluorescence	Absorption at a surface Radio-frequency heating Infrared heating	Photosynthesis Photographic process	Photocell Ion emission Solar battery			
HEAT		Radiation from a hot surface Electric light		Endothermic reactions (Reduction of ores)	Thermoelectric generator Thermionic convertor	Heat engines Wind Ocean currents Rocket	Convection	Thermal stress
CHEMICAL		Cold emission of light (Fish and insects)	Combustion Heat of solution Metabolism		Storage battery Cell Fuel cell Bacteria cell	Muscle [Rocket] [Explosion]	[Flight]	
ELECTRICAL		Electronic flash Radio Radar X-Rays, Spark Fluorescent light	Electric heater Thermoelectric heater and cooler Spark	Electrolysis Electroplating Storage battery	Transformer	Electric motor Loudspeaker Particle accelerator Electrostatic tweeter		
KINETIC			Friction Impact Mechanical refrigerator		Electric generator Microphone	[Collision] Wind mill	Trajectory Pendulum	Recoil spring Tire pump Watch spring
GRAVITATIONAL					Hyroelectric generator	Falling object Grandfather clock Pendulum Tides		"Pogo stick"
ELASTIC			Cooling by expansion Compression ignition		Piezoelectric crystal	Clock (spring) Air rifle	"Pogo stick"	

Fig. 12.1 Energy Conversion Processes

of convenience, because steam engines take a long while to start, and over the electric motor because of the bulk and weight of the storage batteries required for storing the energy in the automobile. The following calculation shows why the most economically available storage battery, that is, the ordinary automobile storage battery consisting of lead plates and sulfuric acid, would not be feasible for automobile propulsion at the present time except in rather special circumstances. It will be assumed that the automobile is required to travel 150 miles between refueling stops, and that it uses 1 gallon of gasoline for 15 miles of travel, at an over-all efficiency of five per cent. The amount of energy that must be available after refuelling is 5 per cent of the energy of 10 gallons of gasoline, i.e., $\frac{5}{100} \times 10 \times 12.6 \times 10^7$ joules, which is 6.3×10^7 joules. An automobile battery (12 volt, 50 ampere-hours) stores 2.1×10^6 joules; therefore 30 batteries would be required. Each battery weighs approximately 40 pounds, and the total weight is, therefore, 1200 pounds. Since the only feasible method of refueling would be to exchange charged batteries for exhausted ones, this would be a very inconvenient procedure. The weight and bulk of the batteries would also be excessive. If, in the future, a storage battery were developed that had 10 times the capacity for storage, for a given weight or bulk, then the problem would be entirely reversed and the propulsion of automobiles by batteries could become a very attractive proposition.

The foregoing discussion of electrical propulsion for automobiles disregards two very important considerations. One is the fact, discussed below, that a time may come when gasoline will no longer be available, and an alternative method will be needed for providing "portable energy" for personal and commercial transportation. This will be preceded by an accelerating increase in the price of gasoline; this introduces the other essential consideration, the relative cost of energy in its various forms. Table 12.1 gives typical figures for the number of Calories corresponding to a dollar's worth of various types of energy source; there is, however, considerable variation from one location to another, even within the United States. It will be noticed that the natural fuels, that is, wood, coal, oil, natural gas, and gasoline supply the greatest number of Calories per dollar, followed by electricity, then foods, and finally the flashlight battery, which illustrates the fact that energy in a very conveniently packaged form is worth a much higher price than energy in a form which is, for some purposes, much less convenient. It should also be noticed that whereas the natural fuels are the most economical methods for providing heat as such, electricity may be at least competitive if the energy is to be used in the form of work rather than heat, because of the inherent limitations of efficiency in the conversion of heat to work, which does not apply to the conversion of electrical energy to work. The development of fuel cells which directly convert the chemical energy of natural fuels to electrical energy, without encountering the efficiency limitation of the heat engine, may at least double the amount of work that can be produced from a given amount of fuel.

TABLE 12.1

Cost of Energy in Various Forms

(Cal/dollar)

Source of energy	Price (Cal/dollar)
Wood	1.6×10^5
Coal	1.5×10^5
Fuel oil	2.2×10^5
Natural gas	1.7×10^5
Gasoline	1.3×10^5
Electricity	3.4×10^4
Sugar	9×10^3
Butter	5.5×10^3
Bread	8×10^3
Flashlight battery	6

Domestic Heating   It is also of some interest to discuss the various possible methods that could be used for supplying the energy required in the form of heat for heating a house. The possible methods are (1) the combustion of a fuel, (2) the conversion of electrical energy into heat, (3) heat pumps, and (4) solar energy. If only the cost of the energy itself were to be considered, then, clearly, solar heating would be the choice in those parts of the country where there is sufficient sunshine for solar heating to be adequate. In places where solar heating is not adequate, some auxiliary heating would be required. This would somewhat change the picture. However, a disadvantage of solar heating is the high cost of the installation; the question then becomes the economic one of whether the high cost of installation is preferable to the higher cost of some other form of heat. Next most economical from the point of view of the cost of the fuel itself is a heat pump. This is capable of supplying up to three times as much heat as would be produced by combustion of the fuel consumed. Here again the cost of installation of the necessary equipment is very substantial and that is why this method of heating has thus far found little application. It does, however, have the advantage, as pointed out earlier, that the same installation can be used for cooling by reversing the direction of heat pumping. In the comparison between the various fuels and electrical heating we are on more familiar ground although the figures given for the costs per Calorie of the various kinds of fuel and of electricity vary substantially from one part of the country to another and according to the amount of the fuel that is used. Therefore a realistic calculation of the relative costs of various forms of heating would necessitate a study of the detailed costs of the fuels in the locality under consideration.

All of the methods of heating that have been discussed are technically feasible; but the criterion that determines whether a particular method is more desirable than another depends not only upon technical feasibility but also upon the economics of the situation. This cannot be discussed in terms of energy alone as it depends upon the relationship between cost of fuel and the interest and amortization on the capital investment of a more expensive but more economical heating system.

Energy for Spaceships Many of the problems associated with the exploration of the solar system are related to the conversion of energy from one form to another; in order to emphasize the basic nature of this point of view, it is of interest to consider the energy requirements of a spaceship, and how they might be met. Attention will be directed to the energy supply once the spaceship is away from the earth; that is, when it is dependent on the energy supply it carries, and on the sun's radiation. The total energy requirement can be divided as follows:

(1) To sustain life; food, 3000 Calories per day per person. Oxygen; this is included in the 3000 Calories, since the energy needed would be the amount required to reconvert water and carbon dioxide back into carbohydrates and oxygen. The total requirement is about 10^6 Calories per year per person.

(2) To maintain the temperature in the space ship. This would depend upon the distance from the sun; in the vicinity of the earth's orbit, the sun's radiation would suffice; at much greater distances, a continuous supply of energy would be needed. The requirement would be reduced by maintaining a low-emissivity surface on the vehicle. The energy required to maintain the temperature of a sphere of radius 10 feet, with an emissivity of 0.1, would be about 3×10^7 Calories per year. To produce this amount of heat by combustion would require about 3 tons of oil per year, and about $2\frac{1}{2}$ times as much oxygen. This requirement could be reduced only by decreasing the emissivity of the surface of the vehicle; if it could be reduced to 0.01, for example, the heat requirement would only be one-tenth of the amount given above.

(3) Communication. The energy requirement for intermittent communication with the earth would be quite small, in the general range of a few watts.

(4) Navigation. Any change in momentum (i.e., change in direction or speed) inherently requires the ejection of mass, since the momentum of the ship itself, including all its contents, cannot be changed. The amount of mass required to produce a given change in momentum is decreased as the

velocity with which it is ejected increases. But this increases the kinetic energy which it must be given, and it increases, therefore, the energy requirement for this purpose. The use of energy and mass for navigation would, however, be intermittent. The problem of landing on, and take-off from, the moon or one of the planets also has severe energy requirements. When a space vehicle approaches the moon, for example, the potential energy due to the moon's gravity is converted into kinetic energy; to achieve a "soft landing," this kinetic energy must be converted into some other form. When there is no atmosphere, the energy cannot be converted into heat, as it is during re-entry into the earth's atmosphere. The only possible way is to slow the vehicle down by the use of retro-rockets, which depend upon the emission of mass with high velocity in the *forward* direction. This reduces the momentum of the vehicle, but requires the expenditure of mass and energy. The problem of take-off is similar; mass and energy must be expended in order to achieve the escape velocity, which ranges from 2.4 miles per second for Mercury to 37 miles per second for Jupiter, compared to 7.0 miles per second for the earth and 1.7 miles per second for the moon.

The development of nuclear motors, in which the energy of fission is converted into the kinetic energy of the ejected gas, is likely to be an important step in the direction of sustained, controlled space flight, because nuclear energy is by far the most efficient form on the basis of available energy per unit mass of fuel.

Energy Consumption   The preceding paragraphs illustrate some of the ways in which energy is used; the *amount* of energy which is used, however, is one of the most revealing indications of the level of industrial development that a country has reached. Figure 12.2 shows how the consumption of energy in the United States has increased between the years 1850 and 1955. This increase is accounted for partly by the great increase in population of the United States in that time but also to an important extent by an increase in the *per capita* consumption of energy, which has gone up by a factor of about 20 during the time under consideration. This energy is used in many ways; in the form of heat, it is used for domestic heating and cooking, and for industrial processing of metals, ceramics, and many other materials; as mechanical work, it is required for propulsion, transportation, fabrication, agriculture, refrigeration, and many other purposes; electrical energy in the form of electric current is converted by means of electric motors into mechanical work and is also used more directly for heating, lighting and various industrial processes such as electroplating. All of the energy is actually used in one or other of these three forms. The relationship between the three usable forms of energy and their applications is shown in Fig. 12.3.

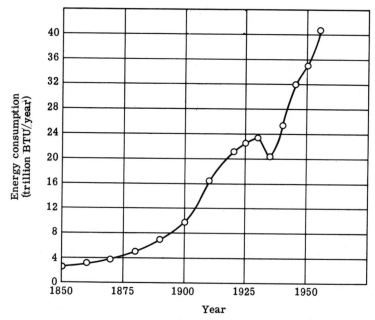

Fig. 12.2. Energy consumption in the United States, 1850–1955. (Data from S. H. Schurr and B. Netschert, "Energy in the American Economy," Johns Hopkins Press, Baltimore, Maryland, 1960.)

Energy is delivered to the consumer mainly in the form of electrical energy or fuel, and the fuel may be either that which is used for internal combustion engines (mainly gasoline), or fuel which is used for direct combustion such as coal, kerosene, or wood. There have been very striking changes in the way in which energy is supplied to the consumer since 1920. Table 12.2 shows the amounts used in the United States in the form of electrical energy, internal, combustion fuels, and all the other forms, mainly coal. From this

TABLE 12.2*

	Electrical ($\times 10^{15}$)	Internal combustion fuels ($\times 10^{15}$)	All other ($\times 10^{15}$)	Total ($\times 10^{15}$ BTU)
1920	2.2×10^{15}	0.5×10^{15}	17×10^{15}	19
1930	2.4×10^{15}	$2 \ \ \times 10^{15}$	18×10^{15}	22
1940	3.1×10^{15}	3.2×10^{15}	18×10^{15}	24
1950	5.6×10^{15}	5.7×10^{15}	22×10^{15}	34
1960	7.6×10^{15}	8.0×10^{15}	24×10^{15}	40

* Tables 12.2, 12.3, and 12.4 are based on data from S. H. Schurr and B. Netschert, "Energy in the American Economy," Johns Hopkins Press, Baltimore, Maryland, 1960, with the permission of the publisher.

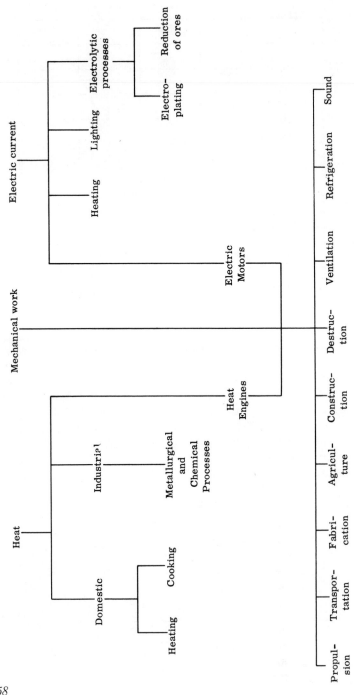

Fig. 12.3. The uses of energy.

table we see that the total has doubled during this period of 35 years, and that this increase has been shared almost equally by the three categories shown in the table.

The distribution of energy consumption is also of interest. In 1955 the energy used in the United States was divided as shown in Table 12.3 while the household use was divided up as shown in Table 12.4.

TABLE 12.3

ENERGY CONSUMPTION (U.S. 1955) ACCORDING TO USER*

Industry	15.7 × 10¹⁵ BTU
Commercial	3.4 × 10¹⁵
Household (excluding transportation)	7.5 × 10¹⁵
Transportation (including private cars)	8 × 10¹⁵
Government	1.8 × 10¹⁵
Agriculture	0.7 × 10¹⁵
Total	37.1 × 10¹⁵ BTU

TABLE 12.4

HOUSEHOLD USE OF ENERGY (U.S. 1955)*

Direct fuel consumption:	
Space heating	4.3 × 10¹⁵ BTU
Other (cooking, water heating, etc.)	1.4 × 10¹⁵
Electrical	1.4 × 10¹⁵
Transportation	3.7 × 10¹⁵

* Tables 12.2, 12.3, and 12.4 are based on data from S. H. Schurr and B. Netschert, "Energy in the American Economy," Johns Hopkins Press, Baltimore, Maryland, 1960, with the permission of the publisher.

It has, however, been estimated that in the industrialized parts of the world, about 30 per cent of the energy is used in the home, mostly for space heating; 30 per cent is used by industry (also largely for heating) and 20 per cent is used for transport. The discrepancy between these estimates indicates that the United States differs from other industrialized countries in its greater use of energy in industry; the power per worker is three times as high in the United States as in the United Kingdom. It is significant that the productivity per head is in about the same proportion.

The consumption of 7.5 × 10¹⁵ BTU per year for household purposes is equivalent to about 5 × 10⁷ BTU per person per year, or in more familiar terms, the amount of energy used is on the average equivalent to 40 kilowatt-hours of electrical energy per person per day.

Returning now to the over-all energy consumption picture, it is significant that the United States consumed a little over one-third of the total of the world's energy in the years 1950–1955, whereas the population of the United States was only about 6 per cent of that of the world as a whole; that is to say, the energy consumed per capita in the United States is about 6 times as high as that of the world as a whole.

It is significant that there is a good correlation between the per capita energy consumption and the per capita national income, if these are compared for all countries for which data are available. Figure 12.4 shows that the per capita national income increases in almost direct proportion to the national income.

The World's Food Supply The various types and sequences of energy conversion that have been discussed are useful and desirable. The only one which is *essential* to human life is that in which radiation from the sun is converted by photosynthesis into chemical energy which, in the form of vegetation, is necessary to support life. In view of the fact that the population of the earth is increasing very rapidly it is of interest to consider the actual and potential supply of food. The essential step in photosynthesis is the conversion of carbon, present as carbon dioxide in the atmosphere, into the form of carbohydrates. The conversion of carbohydrates to carbon dioxide and water supplies the energy which sustains life. The amount of food which is required by a human being can therefore be considered in terms of the amount of carbon contained in it. It corresponds to about 260 pounds of carbon per year per person. For this purpose, as in earlier discussion of this topic, attention will be directed to the energy content of the food, and all the other essential food components, such as proteins and vitamins, will be ignored. The reason for doing this is that the ultimate limitation to the food supply of the world must be considered in terms of Calories, rather than of any of the other nutritional requirements.

Over the whole surface of the world, including oceans as well as land, a total of about 150×10^9 tons of carbon are converted to carbohydrates by photosynthesis each year. Of this total, about 16×10^9 is on land, and about 4×10^9 on cultivated land. If this total amount of 4×10^9 tons could be completely used as food, it would adequately support about 30×10^9 people. The present population of the earth is about 3×10^9, that is, three billion people. Thus the total plant growth on presently cultivated land could adequately support about 10 times the earth's human population if the following assumptions are justified: (1) that the vegetation is consumed by humans and not converted into meat by animals, in which process only 3 per cent of it is eventually usable as food; (2) that we are able to eat the whole of the plant and not just selected portions; and (3) that there is no competition in the form of fungi, insects, rabbits, etc. None of these assumptions is justified. At the present time about one-half of the total food from cultivated land is fed to animals and 3 per cent of this is available as meat

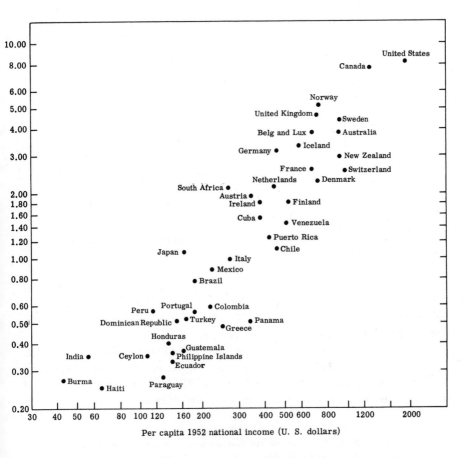

Fig. 12.4. Correlation between per capita energy consumption and per capita national income. (From "The World's Requirement for Energy," Vol. 1 of *The Peaceful Uses of Atomic Energy*.)

or other animal products. This provides about 0.06×10^9 tons of available carbon per year. Of the other half of the plant life grown on cultivated land, only about 20 per cent is usable as food because the human digestive mechanism cannot accept parts of plants such as stalks, husks, and most roots. The 20 per cent that is acceptable provides about 0.4×10^9 tons of carbon per year. This would support about 3.5 billion people, but if a 35 per cent loss due to pests of various kinds is assumed, the total becomes 2.3 billion, which is substantially less than the present world population. It is therefore evident that many people must be living on a diet which is substantially less than the amount which is regarded as adequate. The above calculations assume a diet of 3000 Calories per day and even if the total food production were uniformly distributed there would not be sufficient for this level of nutrition. In 1954 the result of this over-all shortage of food was as shown in Fig. 12.5,

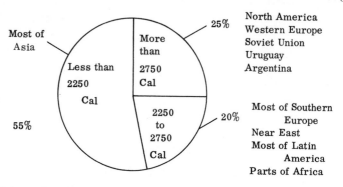

Fig. 12.5. Level of nutrition in different parts of the world, 1954. (From H. Brown, J. Bonner, and J. Weir, "The Next Hundred Years," Viking, New York, 1957.)

from which it will be seen that about one-quarter of the people received an adequate diet (that is, in excess of 2700 Calories) 20 per cent received a diet of marginal value, that is, 2250–2750, while 55 per cent received an inadequate diet of less than 2250 Calories per day.

The total food supply is, however, not distributed uniformly and the adequacy of diet depends to a very large extent on the local relationship between food production and population. Table 12.5 gives estimates of the food production per cultivated acre, the number of cultivated acres

TABLE 12.5

EFFICIENCY OF FOOD PRODUCTION (IN CALORIES OF FOOD PER CULTIVATED ACRE PER DAY) AND DENSITY OF POPULATION (CULTIVATED ACRE PER PERSON)*

	U.S.	Western Europe	Latin America	U.S.S.R.	Japan	India	Asia
Cal/acre	4500	7500	4700	2300	13,200	2500	4000
Cultivated acres/ capita	2.4	0.9	1.0	2.8	0.17	0.9	0.6
Cal/capita	11,000	6700	4700	6400	2200	2000	2400

* Data taken from H. Brown, J. Bonner, and J. Weir, "The Next Hundred Years," Viking, New York, 1957.

per member of the population and the food production per person for various parts of the world. In those countries in which the number of Calories produced per person is high a relatively large proportion of the food is eaten as animal products. In the case of the United States, this proportion is about one-third. In Asia, where the food production is much lower, less than 5 per cent of the food is in the form of animal products. The figure for Western Europe is about 20 per cent. The very great difference in food production per acre from 2300 for U.S.S.R. to 13,200 for Japan is a result largely of the way in which the land is cultivated rather than the nature of the soil itself or the adequacy of the rainfall. Adequate and efficient use of fertilizers and irrigation seems to be the main cause of high productivity. If this is indeed the case, it would seem that the productivity of the cultivated land throughout the world could be raised to a substantially higher level than it has so far reached, and the total food production of the world could be increased so that there would be adequate food for the whole population. However, these are questions related to organization and education and not to energy, since it seems that there must certainly be enough solar energy if it were properly used to permit food production of at least 13,200 Calories per acre, which is actually achieved in Japan, and this would support a much larger population than the world now has.

The Sources of Energy Finally, the world's energy sources and resources must be considered. The only known sources are the sun's radiation, nuclear energy (that is, fission and fusion), the energy associated with the rotation of the earth and the moon in their orbits, and the heat stored and generated in the earth (geothermal energy). The possibility of harnessing really significant amounts of energy from the tides seems to be very remote. The utilization of the earth's heat is also of very limited promise in relation to the world's energy requirements as a whole. There are, however, a few localities, such as parts of New Zealand, where geothermal energy is readily available. It is possible to raise substantial quantities of steam by means of buried pipes, and the amount of energy that can be obtained may have an important influence on the local power supply. An installation that is being built in New Zealand, for example, will generate about 70,000 kilowatts of electrical power. The development of energy from controlled *fission* is very much more promising. At the present time, nuclear power stations are just beginning to make a contribution to the supply of power in a few countries in the world and it is reasonably certain that this will become a very important source of energy in the next few decades. The rate at which this will happen will be determined largely by economics and this will depend upon the development of more economical and more efficient reactor systems and upon the rate at which other sources of energy become

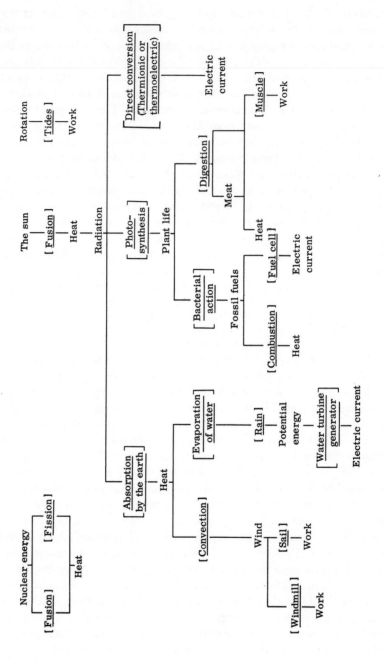

Fig. 12.6. Sources of energy.

depleted. The development of methods of controlling the *fusion* process has not proceeded yet to the stage where any forecast can be made. Undoubtedly there is an almost unlimited supply of power that could be made available from the fusion process, but the technology will have to be developed and this cannot begin until the principles of the methods to be used have been firmly established. It follows that at least at the present time and in the near future we will be dependent upon the energy that comes from the sun in the form of radiation. This is available in two forms; that in which it arrives at the present time, and that in which it is stored in the form of the fossil fuels, that is, energy that was trapped by photosynthesis during the carboniferous era and has been preserved by the geological accident which covered it up and prevented it from reverting to the lower energy form of carbon dioxide and water. Figure 12.6 shows the conversion processes and the intermediate stages by which the energy from these primary sources is converted into the useful forms of heat, work, and electric current.

Almost all of the energy which is used in the various ways which have been discussed above comes from coal, oil, natural gas, hydroelectric power generation and wood. Table 12.6 shows how the relative quantities of these forms

TABLE 12.6
SOURCES OF ENERGY IN PERCENTAGES OF THE TOTAL (U.S.A.)*

	Coal	Oil	Natural gas	Hydro-electric	Wood
1850	9.3	—	—	—	90.7
1900	71.4	2.4	2.6	2.6	21.0
1930	57.5	23.8	9.1	3.3	6.1
1955	28.7	40.0	25.0	3.7	2.6

* The data in Tables 12.6, 12.7, 12.8, and 12.9 are taken from S. H. Schurr and B. Netschert, "Energy in the American Economy," Johns Hopkins Press, Baltimore, Maryland, 1960, by permission of the publisher.

of energy have changed since 1850. It is worthy of note that hydroelectric power generation has remained a very small proportion of the total while oil and natural gas together now amount to two-thirds; in 1850 almost the whole of the energy used was derived from the burning of wood. It must be remembered in interpreting this table that the numbers given are the percentages of the total energy consumption at that time and that the total was actually increasing rapidly. In Table 12.7 this increase is shown for each of the five, 1900 being equal to 100 parts. It will be seen that although wood has dropped from supplying 90.7 per cent of the total energy in 1850 to only 2.6 per cent in 1955, nevertheless, the actual amount consumed has gone up by a factor of nearly 20. Only in the case of coal has there actually been a decrease in consumption. The per capita consumption of wood and of coal in tons per year of coal and the coal equivalent of wood in tons per year are given in Table 12.8. It is evident that oil and natural gas have to a

TABLE 12.7

INCREASE IN FUEL CONSUMPTION RELATIVE TO 1900 (U.S.A.)*

	Coal	Oil	Natural gas	Hydro-electric	Wood
1850	3.2	0	0	0	24
1900	100	(100)	100	100	100
1930	199	2575	760	314	247
1955	177	7652	3570	598	425

TABLE 12.8

PER CAPITA CONSUMPTION OF WOOD AND COAL (U.S.A.)*
(tons/year coal equivalent)

	Wood	Coal
1850	3.5	0.36
1900	1.01	3.45
1930	0.45	4.24
1955	0.24	2.70

TABLE 12.9

ESTIMATED WORK OUTPUT OF ANIMALS AND MACHINERY (U.S.A.)*
(billion HP-hr)

	Animals	Machinery	Average conversion efficiency (%)
1850	5.4	3.6	1.1
1880	11.1	16.0	1.8
1900	16.9	57.6	3.0
1920	15.2	268.1	7.0

* The data in Tables 12.6, 12.7, 12.8, and 12.9 are taken from S. H. Schurr and B. Netschert, "Energy in the American Economy," Johns Hopkins Press, Baltimore, Maryland, 1960, by permission of the publisher.

large extent supplanted the use of wood and to some extent of coal for the production of energy. An estimate of the work output of animals compared with that of machinery is also of interest. Table 12.9 shows how the relative amounts changed in the years 1850 to 1920. The numbers refer to billions of horsepower hours. The average conversion efficiency of the machinery also increased rapidly during that period. In calculating the per capita consumption of energy in the United States it is necessary to recognize that wood was in a special category because of its very great availability, especially up to about 1900.

World Fuel Reserves It is estimated that the current world consumption of the fossil fuels is as follows: coal, 2×10^9 tons per year; oil, equivalent to 1.2×10^9 tons of coal per year; gas, equivalent to 0.5×10^9 tons of coal per year, giving a total of 3.7×10^9 equivalent tons of coal per year. Coal reserves are estimated at about 2500×10^9 tons of coal that could be mined. This would last 1200 years, at the present rate of consumption. Oil reserves are estimated at 280×10^9 tons of coal equivalent which at the present rate of consumption would last about 1000 years. However, if the rate of increase of consumption of these fuels characteristic of the last 50 years were to continue, it is possible that the future world consumption would eventually rise to 100×10^9 tons of coal per year, in which case the reserves would only last about another 37 years. It seems probable that the reserves of coal will last far longer than those of oil or of natural gas. Estimates such as those given above cannot be regarded as accurate because it is impossible to determine with any precision how much coal and oil there is that has not yet been discovered, but the best available estimates indicate without ambiguity that if the whole world were to become strongly industrialized, it would only be a matter of decades, not centuries, before sources of energy other than coal and oil would become essential. These reserves are literally and absolutely unreplaceable because the photosynthesis which is taking place at the present time is not being stored in the form of coal or oil. The only possible solution would be either to develop nuclear energy on a very large scale or find better means than those at present available to exploit the fact that photosynthesis does actually produce the equivalent of about 150 billion, (150×10^9) tons of coal a year, including the photosynthesis that takes place within the oceans. Even if the oceans are excluded, the total is about 16 billion tons per year; if that which is formed on cultivated land is subtracted for food, we are still left with the equivalent of 12 million tons of carbon per year largely in the form of wood; this is four times the present world consumption of energy. It is, however, difficult to imagine an industrialized world in which the main source of energy is the combustion of wood or of algae from the oceans; it is much more likely that the demand will be met by the widespread use of nuclear fission or fusion.

BIBLIOGRAPHY

This book is, at best, an introduction to "Energy." Some readers may wish to go further into this all-pervading subject. This may be achieved by learning more of the basic physics and chemistry upon which the concept of energy is based; or the reader may wish for more information about some of the new energy conversion processes that are achieving headline status by virtue of their actual or possible applications. The third direction in which further reading can be suggested is in the very limited list of books that deal with the subject of energy as such. These three categories of books are listed below:

1. Basic Science

There are very many Physics books at all levels from introductory to very advanced; the following are good examples:

a. "Physical Science for Liberal Arts Students" (H. N. Swenson and J. E. Woods: Wiley, New York, 1957)

b. "Physics for the Enquiring Mind" (E. M. Rogers: Princeton Univ. Press, Princeton, New Jersey, 1960)

c. "Matter, Energy and Radiation" (J. R. Dunning and H. C. Paxton: McGraw-Hill, New York, 1941)

d. "Fundamental Physics" (J. Orear: Wiley, New York, 1961)

e. "Physics for Students of Science and Engineering" (D. Halliday and R. Resnick: Wiley, New York, 1960)

f. "Foundations of Modern Physical Science" (G. Holton and D. H. D. Roller: Addison-Wesley, Reading, Massachusetts, 1958)

g. "Physics for Science and Engineering Students" (W. H. Furry, E. M. Purcell, and J. C. Street: McGraw-Hill, New York, 1952)

"General Chemistry," by P. W. Selwood (Holt, New York, 3rd ed., 1959), includes and goes far beyond the aspects of chemistry that are directly relevant.

2. Specialized Topics

The following references are to more specialized topics:

Solar Energy

"Progress in Solar Power" (H. Tabor: *Sci. American*, July, 1956)
"Solar Energy Research" (F. Daniels and J. A. Duffie, editors: Univ. of Wisconsin Press, Madison, Wisconsin, 1955)

Photosynthesis

"Photosynthesis and Related Problems" (E. Rabinowitch: Interscience, New York, 1945–6)

(D. I. Aaron: *Sci. American*, November, 1960)

"Plants and the Atmosphere" (L. Nash: Harvard Univ. Press, Cambridge, Massachusetts, 1952)

Thermoelectric Effect

"Applications of Thermoelectricity" (H. J. Goldsmit: Methuen, London, 1960)

"Revival of Thermoelectricity" (A. F. Jaffe: *Sci. American*, November, 1958)

Nuclear Energy

"Nuclear Energy and the U. S. Economy 1955–80" (National Planning Assoc., Washington, D. C., 1958)

"Atomic Energy" (L. J. Crammer and J. C. Peierls: Penguin, Baltimore, Maryland, 1950)

"On Nuclear Energy" (D. J. Hughes: Harvard Univ. Press, Cambridge, Massachusetts, 1957)

Fuel Cells

"Fuel Cells" (G. J. Young: Reinhold, New York, 1960)

Desalting of Sea Water

"Fresh Water from Saline Waters" (B. F. Dodge: *Am. Scientist*, Vol. 48, December, 1960)

Space Flight

"Satellites and Space Flight" (Macmillan, New York, 1958)

"Re-entry from Space" (J. V. Becker: *Sci. American*, January, 1961)

"Realities of Space Travel" (L. J. Carter, editor: McGraw-Hill, New York, 1957)

3. Energy, Its Sources and Uses

The following references deal with broader aspects of energy resources and uses:

"Energy in the American Economy" (S. H. Schurr and B. Netschert: Johns Hopkins, Baltimore, Maryland, 1960)

"The Next Hundred Years" (H. Brown, J. Bonner, and J. Weir: Viking, New York, 1957)

"The Atom and the Energy Revolution" (N. Lamsdell: Penguin, Baltimore, Maryland, 1958)

"Energy in the Future" (P. C. Putnam: Van Nostrand, Princeton, New Jersey, 1953)

"The World's Requirements for Energy," Vol. 1 of *The Peaceful Uses of Atomic Energy* (United Nations, New York, 1956)

"Energy in the Service of Man" (UNESCO Publications, No. 1 (A. C. Egerton: N.S. 74); No. 6 (P. E. Simon: N.S. 79)

This is by no means an exhaustive bibliography, but will show the way towards further reading.

Appendix B

CONVERSIONS

The following table of approximate conversions will be helpful in solving some of the problems and for other purposes. To convert, multiply by the number given.

From \ To	BTU	Cal	Ft-lb	Joules	Hp-hr	KWH
BTU	1	0.25	778	1055	3.9×10^{-4}	2.9×10^{-4}
Cal	4.0	1	3090	4200	1.56×10^{-3}	1.2×10^{-3}
Ft-lb	1.3×10^{-3}	3.2×10^{-4}	1	1.4	5.0×10^{-7}	3.8×10^{-7}
Joules	9.5×10^{-4}	2.4×10^{-4}	0.74	1	3.7×10^{-7}	2.8×10^{-7}
Hp-hr	2500	6.4×10^2	2.0×10^6	2.7×10^6	1	0.75
KWH	3400	8.6×10^2	2.7×10^6	3.6×10^6	1.3	1

1 ft = 30 cm   1 mile = 1600 meters
1 kg = 2.2 lb   1 mile/hr = 1.5 ft/sec
1 ton = 900 kg   1 mile/hr = 1.6 km/hr

ANSWERS TO PROBLEMS

Chapter 1

1.1 (a) 0.45 kg; (b) 39.4 in.; (c) 2.11 pints; (d) 88 ft/sec; (e) 62 miles/hr. **1.2** 0.26 radian/hr. **1.3** (a) 450 ft; (b) 30 ft/sec. **1.4** (a) 180 meters; (b) 6 meters/sec. **1.5** (a) 2640 ft; (b) 1.46 ft/sec/sec.

Chapter 2

2.1 (a) 2 sec; (b) 2 sec. **2.2** (a) 4 ft; (b) 2 sec. **2.3** 30,800 ft. **2.5** (a) 64 ft/sec/sec; (b) 11.2 ft/sec or about 1 rev/sec. **2.6** 2700-ft radius. **2.7** $6\frac{1}{2}$ degrees. **2.8** 68-ft radius. **2.9** 600 ft. **2.10** 43 ft. **2.11** 17,000 miles/hr.

Chapter 3

3.2 10 ft/sec. **3.4** (a) 129 sec; (b) 2040 poundals or 64 lb-wt; (c) 0.69 ft/sec/sec. **3.8** (a) About $2\frac{1}{2}$ tons; (b) 8800 ft.

Chapter 4

4.1 (a) 1.55×10^4 ft-poundals; (b) 6.2×10^4 poundals or 1900 lb-wt; (c) 1200 ft. **4.3** Height at end of swing = 0.045 ft; speed = 1.7 ft/sec. **4.4** (a) 4×10^6 ft-poundals; (b) 2×10^3 ft-poundals. **4.5** (a) 1.3×10^{15} ft-lb; (b) 3×10^5 ft^3/hr; (c) about 12 in. **4.6** 4800 ft-lb. **4.7** Velocity = 250 ft/sec; range = 200 ft, if it is shot at 45°. **4.8** Acceleration = 0.5 ft/sec/sec; 0.12 HP. **4.9** (a) 2933 poundals or 91 lb-wt; (b) 0, 8, and 16 HP.

Chapter 5

5.1 (a) −18°C; (b) −37°C; (c) −40°. **5.2** 54 Cal. **5.3** 0.5 BTU; 0.126 Cal. **5.4** (a) 33 min; (b) 4 hr. **5.5** 270 Cal. **5.6** −459°F. **5.7** 30.4 psi. **5.9** 4.4 km/sec. **5.11** 14.4 psi; 1,008,000 dynes/cm². **5.12** 34 ft. **5.13** 750 ft-lb/BTU. **5.14** 250 Cal/min. **5.15** $6\frac{2}{3}$ F degrees. **5.16** 0.13 F degrees/mile.

Chapter 6

6.2 108 Cal/min; 15 kg of ice/min. **6.3** 3000 ft-lb. **6.4** No; heat transmission would be 13,000 BTU/hr. **6.6** 60 C degrees/hr. **6.7** (a) 322 joules/kg; (b) 24 joules/kg. **6.8** 1.5×10^5 Cal. **6.9** 60 KW. **6.10** 300 BTU/hr.

Chapter 7

7.1 (a) 27 per cent; (b) 0.37 HP. **7.2** (a) 70,000 BTU/hr; (b) 56,000 BTU/hr.

Chapter 8

8.1 (a) 200 watts; (b) about double.   **8.2** (a) 1700°K; (b) 1.0 Cal/sec; (c) 4.0, $\frac{1}{4}$, $\frac{1}{9}$, and $\frac{1}{16}$ Cal/sec.   **8.3** (a) 700 watts/square meter; (b) 2.4 mm/hr.   **8.4** 2.4 × 10^{15} Cal/min; 2.2 × 10^{14} HP.   **8.5** 400 hr.   **8.6** 9.1 HP.   **8.8** (a) 27 poundals; (b) 710 ft-lb/min: (c) 14.5 Cal/hr; (d) 180 gm of ice/hr.   **8.11** (a) 5°C; (b) 5°C; (c) 57°C; (d) −67°C.

Chapter 9

9.1 (a) 8000 Cal/kg; (b) 2.6 kg; (c) 3 tons.   **9.2** (a) 8 × 10^6 Cal/hr; (b) 5000 HP.   **9.3** 77 gm.   **9.4** 70 gm/hr.   **9.5** 5 tons.   **9.6** (a) 17-meter diameter for 100 per cent conversion; (b) 4 times the diameter.   **9.7** About 1 lb.   **9.8** (a) 10 HP (7.5 if no friction is assumed); (b) about 1 gal/hr.   **9.9** (a) 228 gm; (b) 3.6 gm; (c) 210 Cal.   **9.10** (a) $280/KWH; (b) 1.25 gm.   **9.11** 3 miles.   **9.12** (a) $\frac{1}{50}$ gal/hr; (b) 12 hr.   **9.13** 4000 Cal/dollar.

Chapter 10

10.1 (a) 110 ohms; (b) 110 watts.   **10.2** 5 ohms.   **10.3** The copper wire is about twice as heavy.   **10.4** 0.12 watt or 1.8 × 10^{-4} Cal/min.   **10.5** (a) In series.   **10.6** 6.7 amp.   **10.8** It drops from 97 watts to 77 watts.   **10.10** (a) 18 lamps; (c) 3$\frac{1}{3}$ amp; 366 watts.   **10.11** (a) 9 oersteds.   **10.12** (a) 12 ohms; (b) 10 amp.   **10.13** 400 Cal/hr.   **10.14** (a) 6 ohms; (b) no; 18.6 amp.

Chapter 11

11.1 6.4 × 10^{12} joules or 1.8 × 10^6 KWH.   **11.2** 6.5 × 10^{10} joules or 1.9 × 10^4 KWH.   **11.3** 1000 tons.   **11.4** 2.6 × 10^6 tons.   **11.6** 0.44 gm.   **11.7** 16 gm/hr.   **11.8** 4 × 10^8 tons/min.

INDEX

Ablation, 101
Absolute temperature, 71, 76
Absolute zero, 107
  of temperature, 71
Absorption, 118
Abundance of elements, 141
Acceleration, 3, 5, 6, 7, 8, 9, 10, 11, 12, 19, 21, 25, 33, 36, 40
  angular, 13, 14
  of gravity, 7, 21, 22, 27
Acid, 160
Adenosine diphosphate (ADP), 155, 156
Adenosine triphosphate (ATP), 155, 156
Aerodynamic heating, 100, 101
Agriculture, 256
  energy consumption in, 259
Air, as a thermal insulator, 99
  friction of, 100
  resistance of, 8, 27, 42
Air conditioning, 85, 86, 87, 88, 89
Air pressure, 67
Air-cooled reactor, 246
Aircraft, 100
  high-speed, 27
  propeller-driven, 35
Aircraft engine, 112
Alcohol, 152
Alcohol thermometer, 61
Algae, 153, 267
Alnico, 209
Alpha particle, 235, 236, 237
Alternating current, 224, 225, 226, 228
Aluminum, production of, 167
Ammeter, 188, 220
Amortization, 255
Ampere, 161
Ampere-hour, 165
Angular acceleration, 13, 14
Angular momentum, 33, 34
Angular velocity, 3, 21
Animal life, 153
Animals, cold blooded, 156
  work done by, 266

Apparent weight, 11
Armature, 221
Artificial satellite, 25, 201
Athlete, 156
Atmosphere, 118, 130, 145, 158
  as heat trap, 129
  carbon dioxide in, 158
  earth's, 27, 78, 256
  planets', 79
  pressure of, 50, 52, 60, 65, 67, 78, 81
  weight of, 78
Atom, 141, 147, 148, 159, 176
Atomic bomb, 243, 244
Atomic mass, 142
Atomic number, 142, 143, 144, 240
Atomic weight, 142, 143, 144, 240
Atoms, vibrations of, 80
Attraction, electrostatic, 148
  forces of, 80
  gravitational, 8, 26, 30, 33, 79
Audibility, limit of, 139
Automobile, 29, 158, 185, 251
  battery, 165
    propulsion by, 253
Automobile engine, 112, 149
Automobile exhaust, carbon dioxide from, 129
Automobile ignition system, 228
"Available energy," 151
Availability of energy, 107
Avogadro's number, 75
Axis of rotation, 34

Bacterial action, 156
Bacterial fuel cell, 169
Ball, medicine, 32
Bar magnet, 204
Barometer, 65, 66
Base metal, 163
Battery, automobile, 165
    propulsion by, 253
  flashlight, 253
  solar, 201

storage, 164, 165, 166, 201, 253
Bell, electric, 214
Bell solar battery, 201, 202
Bell telephone laboratories, 201
Beta particle, 235, 237
Bicycle, 22, 23, 29
Bi-metal strip, 61
Biological damage, 247
"Black out," 22
Blast furnace, 150
Blast velocity, 35
Boiling, 64, 81, 82
Boiling point, 64
  of water, 60, 81
Bomb, atomic, 243, 244
  hydrogen, 249
Braking distance, minimum, 24
"Breeder" reactor, 248
Brightness of light, 136
British Thermal Unit, (BTU), 62
"Burn-up," 247

Calorie, 61, 62, 63, 64, 148
Candle, standard, 136
Candlepower, 137
Capacitance, 183, 184, 185, 186
  of human body, 185
Capacitor, 183, 185
Capacity, 183
  heat, 102
Capital investment, 255
Carbohydrate, 152, 153, 154, 155, 156, 260
Carbon dioxide, 129, 159
  in atmosphere, 158
  from automobile exhaust, 129
Carbon dioxide fire extinguisher, 36
Carboniferous era, 156, 265
Carboniferous forest, 156
Cell, 161, 162
  dry, 164
  fuel, 167, 168, 169, 251, 254
  Leclanche, 163
  simple, 160
Cellular material as a thermal insulator, 99
Celsius, 60
Center of rotation, 13
Centigrade, 60
  centrifugal force, 21, 22, 23, 25, 57
Centripetal force, 21, 23, 24, 26
Chain reaction, 242, 244

Charge, electrostatic, 142, 176, 205
Chemical compound, 145, 147
Chemical energy, 141, 151, 152, 154, 155, 156, 157, 159, 166, 169, 188, 254, 260
  and life, 150
  of fuel, 167
Chemical formula, 145, 148
Chemical reaction, 147, 150, 151
Chemical symbol, 142
Chlorophyll, 152, 153
Circuit, 161
  electric, 188
  telephone repeater, 201
Circular orbit, 25
Cloud, 126, 130
Coal, 156, 157, 159, 169, 249, 253, 257, 265, 266, 267
Coefficient of friction, 23, 24
Coercive force, 213
Coil, induction, 229
  magnetic field in, 211
  primary, 226
  secondary, 226
Coldblooded animals, 156
Collisions between molecules, 76
Color, 115
Color temperature, 123
Combustion, 34, 35, 148, 149, 150, 168, 186, 239, 241, 254
  of fuel, 103, 107
  heat of, 149
Combustion chamber, 35, 108
Combustion engine, external, 108
  internal, 108
Commercial, energy consumption, 259
Communication (in space), 255
Commutator, 220, 224
Compass needle, 203, 207
Component of force, 45
Compound, 148, 151
  chemical, 145, 147
  organic, 151, 152
Compressed gas, 50
Compressibility of liquids, 52
  of water, 52
Compressor, 35
Condenser, 183, 184, 185
Conduction, 91, 93, 99
  of electricity, 92
  heat, 92, 95, 198

Conductivity, thermal, 95, 99, 197
Conductor, 159, 178, 188, 192
Connection in parallel, 190
  in series, 165, 189
Conservation of energy, 43, 44, 107, 255
Conservation of momentum, 30, 32, 33
Constant, dielectric, 183, 184, 185
Construction, graphical, 23
Consumer, 257
Contact breaker, 228
Control rod, 245
Controlled space flight, 256
Convection, 91, 92, 93, 99, 130
Convection current, 93, 100
Conversion of energy, 159, 193, 251, 252
  heat into work, 103
  of solar energy, 201, 202
  thermionic, 199, 200, 201, 202
  thermoelectric, 134, 201, 202, 251
  of work into heat, 82, 83
Conversion plant, sea water, 174
Conversions, 1
Converter, photoelectric, 134
  thermoelectric, 198
  thermionic, 134
  thermoelectric, 200
Cooking, 256
  radio frequency, 202
  solar, 133
Coolant, liquid, 101
Cooling, by evaporation, 80, 81
  Newton's law of, 94
  by radiation, rate of, 123
  thermoelectric, 198, 199
Corrosion, 162
Cosmic radiation, 237
Cost of energy, 170, 253, 254
Coulomb, 161, 162, 180, 181, 183, 184
Critical mass, 243, 244, 249
Critical size, 245
  of reactor, 247
Crowbar, 14
Crystal, 146, 147, 148, 151
Crystalline solid, 79
Crystallization, 173
Curie temperature, 209
Current, 161
  alternating, 224, 225, 226
  convection, 93, 100
  eddy, 228, 229

  electric, 166, 188, 265
  energy of, 203
  force between magnetic field and, 217
  heating effect of, 192
  magnetic effect of, 203
  magnetic field due to, 210, 211
Cyclist, 22, 23

Dam, 46
Damage, genetic, 237
  radiation, 237
Damping, electromagnetic, 229
Decay, radioactive, 236
Decay time, 242
Deceleration, 7, 11, 25
Decibel, 139, 140
Deformation, elastic, 50
  potential energy of, 50
Degaussing of ships, 215, 216
Degradation of energy, 107
Degree day, 98
Demagnetization, 214
Density, 63
Depolarizer, 164
Deposit, sedimentary, 156
Desalting of sea water, 169, 171, 174
Diamagnetic substance, 207
Dielectric constant, 183, 184, 185
Dielectric material, 185
Diesel engine, 111, 112
Difference of potential, 181, 182
Diffusion, 149
Digestive mechanism, 261
Disintegration of the nucleus, 235, 236, 237
Disposal of fission products, 247
Dissipation of power, 194
Distillation, 173
Distortion, elastic, 49
Distributor, 228
Distribution, energy, power, 227
  of velocities, 77
Distribution curve, 77
  for velocity, 78
Domain, magnetic, 209, 210
Domestic appliances, 195
Domestic heating, 97, 254, 256
Dry cell, 164
Dynamite, 149
Dyne, 38

E = MC², 239, 241
Ear, human, 138, 139
Earpiece, telephone, 138
Earth, 24, 25, 256
    energy reaching surface of, 126
    radius of, 28
    rotation of, 34, 93, 263
Earth's atmosphere, 27, 78, 256
Earth's axis, tilt of, 128
Earth's gravitational attraction, 78
Earth's magnetic field, 203, 207
Economics, 255, 263
Eddy current, 228, 229
Effect, Peltier, 198
    photoelectric, 200
    Seebeck, 196, 198
Effects, thermoelectric, 196
Efficiency, 107
    actual, 109, 110
    of energy storage, 52, 54
    of engine, 110
    of food production, 262
    of heat engines, 104, 106
    ideal, 109
    inherent limitation of, 253
    of lamps, 137
    of power generation, 134
    of thermoelectric converter, 198
    overall, 134
    theoretical, 109, 110
Efficiency limitation of heat engine, 254
Einstein, 237
Elastic deformation, 50
Elastic distortion, 49
Elastic energy, 49, 55, 181
Electric bell, 214
Electric circuit, 188
Electric current, 147, 159, 166, 188, 256,
    265
Electric generator, 225
Electric lamp, 192
    filament type, 137
Electric meter, 229
Electric motor, 216, 219, 220, 225, 253,
    256
Electric range, 195
Electrical energy, 47, 89, 151, 165, 166, 167,
    168, 169, 176, 186, 188, 254, 255, 256,
    257
Electrical heating, 132

Electricity, 103, 142, 160, 251, 253
    conduction of, 92
    negative, 179
    positive, 179
Electrification by friction, 185
Electrochemical potential, 162
Electrode, 161, 166
Electrolysis, 166, 167
Electrolyte, 164, 169
Electromagnet, 214, 221, 226
Electromagnetic damping, 229
Electromagnetic induction, 226, 230
Electromagnetic spectrum, 118
Electron, 92, 142, 145, 146, 147, 159, 160,
    176, 179, 181, 192
Electron volt, 237
Electronic flash, 186
Electroplating, 166, 256
Electroscope, 177, 178
Electrostatic attraction, 148
Electrostatic charge, 142, 176, 205
Electrostatic energy, 184
Electrostatic field, 182, 187, 238
Electrostatic force, 142, 145, 146, 147, 159,
    176, 180, 181
Electrostatic motor, 232
Electrostatic spray gun, 186
Element(s), 141, 142, 143, 145, 148
    abundance of, 141
Elevator, 11, 27, 47
    free-falling, 27
Elliptical orbit, 25
Emissivity, 120, 121, 128
Energy, 1, 46, 48, 49, 54, 80
    available, 151
    availability of, 107
    chemical, 141, 151, 152, 154, 155, 156,
        157, 159, 166, 188, 254, 260
    conservation of, 43, 44, 107, 255
    consumption, 256, 260
        distribution of, 259
        United States, 267
    conversion, 159, 193, 197, 251
        by muscle, 155
        processes of, 252
    cost of, 170, 253, 254
    of a current, 203
    degradation of, 107
    distribution of, 76, 80
    elastic, 49, 55

electrical, 47, 151, 165, 166, 169, 176, 186, 188, 225, 254, 256, 257
electrostatic, 184
of food, 155, 260
free, 151
of fuels and foods, 157
geothermal, 263
heat, 43
household use of, 259
kinetic, 40, 41, 42, 43, 55, 56, 57, 75, 80, 91, 148
of molecules, 85
maximum, wavelength of, 122
mechanical, 43
molecular, 80
of motion, 40
nuclear, 235, 249, 256, 263
potential, 40, 41, 42, 43, 46, 47, 48, 49, 56, 80, 148, 181, 183
radiant, 115
radiation of, 120
reaching surface of earth, 126
relationship between mass and, 239
solar, 130, 133, 152, 156, 174, 249, 254, 263, 265
conversion of, 201, 202
of sound, 138
sources of, 251, 263
for spaceships, 255
storage, 54, 55
efficiency of, 52, 54
in a compressed liquid, 52
in a solid, 53
stored, 50, 52, 53, 156
tidal, 263
uses of, 251
world consumption of, 267
of vibration, 80
Engine, aircraft, 112
automobile, 112, 149
diesel, 111, 112
efficiency of, 110
four-cycle, 111
gas turbine, 113
gasoline, 111, 158
heat, 108, 134, 149, 156, 198
heat, efficiency of, 104
internal combustion, 111, 251
overall efficiency of, 112
jet, 35, 113

jet-prop, 113
marine, 112
reciprocating, 108
steam, 253
reciprocating, 108, 109, 110
turbine, 108
turboprop, 35
English system of units, 1
Enriched reactor, 248
Equilibrium, 170
Equatorial regions, 127
Era, carboniferous, 156, 265
Erg, 38, 40
Error, experimental, 42
Escape velocity, 78, 79, 256
Evaporation, 64, 80, 81, 91, 94, 173
cooling by, 80, 81
Explosion, 149
External combustion engine, 108

Fabrication, 256
Fahrenheit, 60
Falling object, 7
Farad, 183
Fat, 155
Ferromagnetic, 207, 209, 210
Fertilizer, 263
Fiberglas insulation, 100
Fibrous material as a thermal insulator, 99
Field earth's magnetic, 203
electrostatic, 182, 187, 238
gravitational, 182
magnetic, 203, 204, 205, 206, 207
Filament, 192
Filament type electric lamp, 137
Fire extinguisher, carbon dioxide, 36
First law of motion, 7, 18
Fish, 156
Fission, 239, 241, 242, 248, 256, 263, 267
Fissile material, 247
Fission product, 242, 244, 247
Fission reactor, 249
Fissionable material, 248
Fixed points, 60, 61
Flash, electronic, 186
Flashlight battery, 253
Flask, vacuum, 99
Flight, 21, 251
orbital, 27
ultra-high-speed, 100

Flow of heat, 91
  spontaneous, 105, 106
Fluorescent lamps, 137
Fluorescent lighting, 202
Flywheel, 56, 104
Focal point, 119
Fog, 130
Food, 153, 154, 156, 157, 253
Food energy, 155, 260
Food production, efficiency of, 262
  per acre, 263
  world, 262
Food shortage, 262
Food supply, world, 260
Foot, 1
Foot candle, 137, 138
Foot-pound, 38, 40, 48
Foot-poundal, 38, 40
Force(s), 7, 8, 9, 10, 12, 25, 29, 30, 38, 40,
  44
  of attraction, 80
  between magnetic field and current, 217
  between magnetic poles, 204
  between magnets, 206
  centrifugal, 21, 22, 23, 25, 57
  centripetal, 21, 23, 24, 26
  coercive, 213
  component of, 45
  electrostatic, 142, 145, 146, 159, 176, 180,
    181
  frictional, 23, 30
  gravitational, 25, 129
  of gravity, 8, 11, 19, 25, 30, 34, 47, 181
  moment of a, 13, 14
  net, 12
  normal, 23
  resolution of, 13
  resultant, 12, 29
Forest, carboniferous, 156
Formula, chemical, 145, 148
Fossil fuel, 156, 157, 174, 265, 267
Four-cycle engine, 111
Free energy, 107, 151
Freezing, 173
Freezing point, 64, 65
  of water, 60
Freon, 86, 88
Frequency, 138
Fresh water, 169

Friction, 1, 7, 9, 10, 16, 17, 18, 19, 23, 25,
  30, 32, 33, 34, 44, 47, 50, 84, 107, 193
  of air, 100
  coefficient of, 23, 24
  electrification by, 185
Fuel(s), 34, 35, 157, 257
  chemical energy of, 167
  combustion of, 103, 107
  consumption, 1
  fossil, 156, 157, 174, 265, 267
  internal combustion, 257
  natural, 169, 253, 254
  nuclear, 174
  world reserves, 267
Fuel cell, 167, 168, 169, 251, 254
  bacterial, 169
  hydrogen, 169
Fuel element, 246, 247
Fuel rod, 245
Fulcrum, 14
Fungi, 261
Furnace, blast, 150
  solar, 132
Fuse, 195
Fusion, latent heat of, 64, 65, 132
  nuclear, 239, 248, 249, 263, 265, 267

G, 11, 22
Galvanometer, 223
Gamma ray, 117, 118, 235, 237, 247
Gas, 49, 267
  compressed, 50
  kinetic energy of, 75
  liquefaction of, 73
  natural, 156, 265, 266
  nature of, 67
  "perfect," 74
  pressure of, 65, 68
  temperature of, 74
  turbine, 112, 113
  volume of a, 67
Gas-cooled reactor, 246
Gaseous state, 65
Gasoline, 253, 257
Gasoline engine, 111, 158
Gauss, 207
Gear train, 17
Gear wheels, 17
Generator, electric, 216, 224, 225, 228
  hydroelectric, 130

MHD, 230
Van de Graaff, 187
Genetic damage, 237
Geothermal energy, 263
Glauber salts, 132
Government, energy consumption by, 259
Graphical construction, 20, 23
Gravitation, 24, 181
universal, 24
Gravitational attraction, 7, 8, 26, 30, 33, 79
of the earth, 78
moon's, 27
Gravitational field, 182
Gravitational force, 25, 129
Gravity, 9, 18, 19, 26, 27, 35, 38, 41, 49
acceleration of, 7, 21, 22, 27
force of, 8, 11, 19, 25, 30, 34, 47, 181
of moon, 8, 256
Greenhouse as heat trap, 129
Greenhouse effect, 131
Growth of plants, 130

Half-life, 236
Heat, 1, 6, 65, 79, 148, 265
capacity, 63, 102, 132
conduction of, 92, 95, 198
of combustion, 149
conversion of work into, 82, 83
energy, 43
flow of, 91
good conductors of, 92
insulation, 99
latent, 64, 65, 80
mechanical equivalent of, 82, 83, 84
radiant, 117
of reaction, 148, 151
sensible, 65
specific, 62, 63
spontaneous flow of, 105, 106
unit of, 62
white, 123
Heat engine, 103, 104, 105, 106, 107, 108, 134, 149, 156, 198
efficiency of, 104, 106
limitation of, 253
Heat pump, 86, 87, 89, 198, 254
Heat sink, 105, 106, 107
Heat source, 105
Heat storage system, 131
Heat transfer, 91

Heat transmission coefficient, 97, 98
Heat trap, atmosphere as, 129
greenhouse as, 129
Heating, aerodynamic, 100, 101
domestic, 97, 254, 256
due to the sun, 93
effect of a current, 192
electrical, 132
house, 85
radio frequency, 202
requirement, for a house, 99
solar, 131, 132
Heating unit, domestic, 88, 89, 90
Heavy hydrogen, 248
Helium, 73
Hibernation, 155
High explosive, 149
High-speed flight, 100
Horsepower, 46, 47, 48, 49, 52, 54, 114, 185
human, 47
Horsepower-hour, 48, 52, 185
Household use of energy, 259
Human body, 195
capacitance of, 185
Human ear, 138, 139
Human life, 260
Human metabolism, 81
Human skin, pigmentation of, 117
Humidity, 80, 81, 87
relative, 81
Hydrocarbon, 152
Hydroelectric generator, 130
Hydroelectric power, 167, 265
Hydrogen, heavy, 248
Hydrogen bomb, 249
Hydrogen fuel cell, 169
Hydrogen molecule, average velocity of, 75
Hysteresis loop, 214, 226

Ice, latent heat of fusion of, 65
Ice, thermal conductivity of, 99
Ice skater, 34
Ideal efficiency, 109
Ideal mechanical advantage 16, 17, 18
Industry, energy consumption in, 259
Ignition coil, 228
Ignition system, 186
automobile, 228
Illumination, 136
intensity of, 137

Immersion heater, 193
Impact, 31, 32
Increase of mass with velocity, 237, 238
Induced voltage, 226
Induction, 179
  electromagnetic, 226, 230
  magnetic, 207, 208, 212
Induction coil, 229
Industrial development, 256
Industrial processes, 256
Inertia, 40
  moment of, 14, 33, 34
Infrared radiation, 117, 118, 129, 136
Infrared region, 122
Insects, 261
Insulation, 228
  Fiberglas, 100
  heat, 99
Insulator, 92, 178, 185
  thermal, 99
Intensity of illumination, 137
  of magnetization, 207
  of sound, 139
Interest, 255
Internal combustion engine, 108, 111, 251
  overall efficiency of, 112
Internal combustion fuel, 257
Inverse square law, 129, 181
Ion, 146, 147, 148, 164, 230
Ionosphere, 118
Ion propulsion motor, 233
Irrigation, 263
Isotope, 239, 240, 241
Isotopic mass, 240

Jet, 35
Jet engine, 35, 113
Jet-prop engine, 113
Joule, 38, 40
Jupiter, 256

Kelvin scale, 74
Kerosene, 157, 257
Kilocalorie, 61
Kilogram, 1
Kiloton, 244
Kilowatt, 46, 47
Kilowatt-hour, 47, 48
Kinetic energy, 40, 41, 42, 43, 55, 56, 57,
  75, 76, 80, 91, 148

of gas, 75
of molecules, 73, 74, 75, 85
of vibration, 56

Lamps, efficiency of, 137
  electric, 192
  fluorescent, 137
Latent heat, 64, 65, 80
  of fusion, 64, 65, 132
  of ice, 65
  of vaporization, 64, 102
Law, inverse square, 129, 181
  of universal gravitation, 24
Leclanche cell, 163
Length, 1
Lever, 14, 16, 43
Life, animal, 153
  chemical energy and, 150
  sustenance of (in space), 255
Light, 115, 136
  brightness of, 136
  neon, 202
  parallel beam of, 119
  sodium, 202
  sources of, temperatures of, 123
  velocity of, 238, 239
  visible, 118
  white, 117
Light meter, 200
Light waves, 235
Lighting, 256
  fluorescent, 202
Lightning, 182, 230
Line of force, 205, 210, 211, 216, 223, 225
Liquefaction of gases, 73
Liquid(s), 49, 79, 145
  compressibility of, 52
Liquid coolant, 101
Livermore Laboratory, University of Cali-
  fornia, 249
Living matter, 151, 152
Locomotive, steam, 110
Loop, hysteresis, 214
Loud speaker, 138, 219
  moving coil, 218
Lubricant, 23
Lumen, 137

Machine, 16, 43, 103
  perpetual motion, 45

Machinery, 266, 267
Magnet(s), 203, 205
  bar, 204
  force between, 206
  permanent, 218
Magnetic domain, 209, 210
Magnetic effect of a current, 202
Magnetic field, 203, 204, 205, 206, 207
  in a coil, 211
  due to current, 210, 211
  earth's, 207
  force between current and, 217
  field in a solenoid, 212
Magnetic induction, 207, 208, 212
Magnetic mine, 215, 216
Magnetic pole(s), 203, 205, 206, 213
  force between, 204
  strength of, 206₁
Magnetic saturation, 213
Magnetically hard material, 208
Magnetically soft material, 209, 210
Magnetization, effect of temperature on, 209
  intensity of, 207
  remanent, 213, 214
Magneto hydrodynamics (see MHD), 230
Man, 27
Manufacture of steel, 150
Marine engine, 112
Marine propulsion, 249
Mass, 1, 9, 29
  critical, 243, 244, 249
  increase of with velocity, 237, 238
  isotopic, 240
  relationship between energy and, 239
Mass number, 239, 240
Massachusetts winter, 99
Material, dielectric, 185
  fissile, 247
  fissionable, 248
  magnetically hard, 208
  magnetically soft, 209, 210
Mean free path, 78, 79
Mechanical advantage, 16, 44
  ideal, 16, 17, 18
  real, 16
  theoretical, 16
Mechanical energy, 43
Mechanical equivalent of heat, 82, 83, 84
Mechanical work, 256

Mercury, 79, 256
Mercury thermometer, 59
Metabolism, human, 81
Metal, 146, 159, 196
  base, 163
  noble, 162, 163
Meteor, 100
Meteorite, 100
Meteorology, 8
Meter, 1
  electric light, 229
  light, 200
Metric system, 1
MHD, 230, 249
MHD generator, 230
MHD motor, 230, 231
Microfarad, 183
Microwave, 117, 118, 202
Microwave receiver, 119
Microwave region, 120
Microwave transmitter, 119
Moderator, 245, 246
Mole, 74, 75, 148
Molecule(s), 67, 74, 75, 145, 146, 148
  collisions between, 76
  hydrogen, average velocity of, 75
  kinetic energy of, 73, 74, 76, 85
  momentum of, 68, 71
  organic, 152
  velocity of, 71
  vibrations of, 80
Molecular energies, 80
Molecular weight, 74, 75, 148
Moment of a force, 13, 14, 33
Moment of inertia, 14, 33, 34
  momentum, 29, 30, 31, 32, 33, 34, 35, 67, 76
  angular, 33, 34
  change of, 68
  conservation of, 30, 32, 33
  of a molecule, 68, 71
Monkey on the rope, 11
Moon, 9, 24, 25, 256
  gravity of, 8, 27, 256
Motion, 2
  circular, 21
  energy of, 40
  first law of, 7, 18
  perpetual, 44
  second law of, 8, 9

third law of, 30
  wave, 115
Motor, 228
  electric, 216, 219, 220, 225, 253, 256
  electrostatic, 232
  ion propulsion, 233
  MHD, 230
  nuclear, 256
  outboard, 35
Motor scooter, 185
Moving coil loud speaker, 218
Muscle, 156, 251
  energy conversion by, 155
Muscular work, 155
Mutation, 237
  spontaneous, 237

National income per capita, 260
Natural fuels, 169, 253, 254
Natural gas, 156, 169, 253, 265, 266
Natural uranium, 244
Navigation (in space), 255
Negative electricity, 179
Negative pole, 162
Neon light, 202
Neon tube, 119
Neptunium, 244
Net force, 12
Neutron, 241, 243, 244, 245, 247
Newton, 7, 8, 30
Newton's first law of motion, 7, 18
Newton's law of cooling, 94
Newton's laws of motion, 21
Newton's second law of motion, 8, 9, 18
Newton's third law of motion, 30
newton, 9, 38
Noble metal, 162, 163
Non-randomness, 107
Normal force, 23
Norway, 130
Nose cone, 101
Nuclear energy, 235, 249, 256, 263, 267
Nuclear fission, 267
Nuclear fuels, 174
Nuclear fusion, 267
Nuclear motor, 256
Nuclear reactor, 245, 247
Nucleus, 142, 159, 176, 235
  disintegration of, 235, 237

unstable, 237
Nutrition, 260, 262

Obliquity of sun's rays, 127, 128
Oceans, algae from, 267
Oersted, 205, 207
Ohm, 189, 190
Oil, 156, 169, 249, 253, 265, 266, 267
Orbit, 27
  circular, 25
  elliptical, 25
Orbital flight, 27
Organic compound, 151, 152
Organic molecule, 152
Osmosis, 170, 171, 173
Overall efficiency, 134
  of internal combustion engine, 112

Packing fraction, 240, 242, 244, 248
Parabola, 20
Parachute, 8
Parallel beam of light, 119
Parallel connection, 190
Paramagnetic substance, 207
Particle, radioactive, 242
Peltier effect, 198
Pendulum, 41, 42, 80
Per capita energy consumption, 260
Per capita national income, 260
"Perfect" gas, 74
Permanent magnet, 218
Permanant magnet material, 208
Permeability, 207, 208, 212
Perpetual motion, 44
Perpetual motion machine, 45
Perspiration, 81
Pests, 262
Photoelectric converter, 134
Photoelectric effect, 200
Photodiode, selenium, 200, 201
  silicon, 201, 202
Photosynthesis, 152, 153, 156, 159, 260,
  265, 267
Pigmentation of human skin, 117
Pilot, 22
Pitch, 138
Planets, 9, 24, 25, 79, 129, 256
  atmospheres of, 79
Plant, 152
Plant growth, 130

Plant life, 117
Plasma, 230
Plutonium, 244, 245, 247, 248
Polar regions, 127
Polarization, 163
Pole(s), 205
  magnetic, 203, 205, 206
    force between, 204
    unit, 205
Population, 156
  world, 260
"Portable energy," 253
Positive electricity, 179
Potential, 181
  electrochemical, 162
  sparking, 185
Potential difference, 182, 184
Potential energy, 40, 41, 42, 43, 46, 47, 48, 49, 56, 80, 148, 181, 183
  of deformation, 50
  of the tides, 49
Pound, 1, 9
Poundal, 9, 38
Power, 1, 46, 47, 49, 52
  hydroelectric, 167, 265
  per worker, 259
  tidal, 46
  water, 46
Power dissipation, 194
Power distribution, 227
Power generation, efficiency of, 134
  from solar energy, 134
Pressure, 49, 68, 69, 71
  air, 67
  atmospheric, 50, 52, 60, 65, 66, 67, 78, 81
  effect of temperature upon, 69
  of gas, 65, 68
  of a tire, 73
  vapor, 81
Pressure cooker, 82
Primary coil, 226
Prism, 115
Probability, 106
Production of aluminum, 167
Productivity per head, 259
Projectile, 27
Propeller, 35
Propeller-driven aircraft, 35
Propulsion, 256
  of automobiles by batteries, 253

marine, 249
reaction, 36
rocket, 34
Protein, 153, 260
Proton, 240, 241
Pulley, 17
Pump, heat, 49, 86, 87, 89, 198, 254

Rabbits, 261
Radar, 117
  radian, 3, 21
Radiant energy, 115
Radiant heat, 117
Radiation, 91, 93, 101, 117, 242
  cooling by, rate of, 123
  cosmic, 237
  of energy, 120
  infrared, 117, 118, 129, 136
  mutation induced by, 237
  solar, 125
  sun's, 123, 152, 153, 156, 255
  ultraviolet, 117, 136
Radiation damage, 237
Radiator, 93
Radio, 118, 202
Radio frequency cooking, 202
Radio frequency heating, 202
Radio telescope, 120
Radio transmitter, 201
Radio waves, 117, 118, 235
Radioactive decay, 236, 244, 247
Radioactive particle, 242
Radioactive substance, 236
Radioactivity, 235, 247
Radiography, 118
Radium, 235
Radius, earth's, 28
Rain, 8, 93, 130
Rainbow, 115
Raindrops, 8, 115
Rainfall, 169, 173, 263
Range, 20
Rate of cooling by radiation, 123
Rate of working, 47
Ray, gamma, 117, 118, 235, 237
Reaction, 30, 35, 148, 160
  chain, 147, 150, 151, 242, 244
  heat of, 148, 151
Reaction propulsion, 36
Reactor, air-cooled, 246

critical size of, 247
enriched, 248
fission, 249
gas-cooled, 246
nuclear, 245, 247
Real mechanical advantage, 16
Receiver, microwave, 119
Reciprocating engine, 108
Reciprocating steam engine, 108, 109, 110
Red hot, 123
Reduction, 150
Re-entry, 100, 101, 256
Reflection, 117
Reflector, 119
Refrigeration, 85, 251, 256
Refrigerator, 86, 87, 88, 199
Region, infrared, 122
    microwave, 120
Relationship between mass and energy, 239
Relative humidity, 81
Relativity, 239
Remanent magnetization, 213, 214
Resistance, 189, 190
    of the air, 35
    specific, 190
Resistivity, 190, 191, 198
Resolution of force, 13
Resources, world's water, 130
Resultant force, 12, 29
Resultant of two forces, 13
Retro-rocket, 256
Return of spaceships, 100
Rifle bullet, 19
Rocket(s), 149
    motor, 34
    nose of, 100
    propulsion, 34
    return of, 100
Rollerskates, 32
Rope, monkey on the, 11
Rotation, 3, 13, 25, 43
Rotation, axis of, 34
    of the earth, 34, 93, 263
    center of, 13
    maximum speed of, 57
Roughness, 23
Rust, 150

Sailing ship, 131
Satellite, 25, 26, 133, 134

artificial, 25, 201
    temperature of, 134, 136
Saturation, 80
    magnetic, 213
Saturation vapor pressure, 170
Scale of temperature, 60, 61
Sea water, conversion plant, 174
    desalting of, 169, 174
Second, 1
Second law of motion, 8, 9, 18
Secondary coil, 226
Sedimentary deposit, 156
Seebeck effect, 196, 198
Selenium photodiode, 200, 201
Semiconductor, 197, 198
Semi-permeable membrane, 171, 173
Sensation of touch, 100
Series, connection in, 165, 189
Shadow, 118
Shielding, 247, 248
Ship, sailing, 131
Shortage of food, 262
Silicon photodiode, 201, 202
Simple cell, 160
Skidding, 23
Sliding, 30
Smoothness, 23
Snow, 130
    thermal conductivity of, 99
Sodium light, 202
"Soft landing," 256
Solar battery, 201
Solar constant, 125
Solar cooking, 133
Solar energy, 130, 133, 152, 156, 174, 249,
        254, 263, 265
    conversion of, 201, 202
    power generation from, 134
    for spaceships, 134
Solar furnace, 132
Solar heating, 131, 132
Solar radiation, 125
Solar system, 237, 255
Solenoid, magnetic field in, 212
Solenoid valve, 215
Solid, 50, 79
    crystalline, 79
    energy storage in a, 53
Solvent extraction, 173
Sound, 138

speed of, 138
Sound barrier, 100
Sound energy, 138
Sound intensity, 139
Sources of energy, 251, 263
Space, 9, 115
Space flight, 231
    controlled, 256
Space ship(s), 133, 134, 198, 231, 233
    energy for, 255
    return of, 100
    solar energy for, 134
Space travel, 26, 255
Space vehicle, 256
Spark, 182, 185, 186, 188, 228
Spark plug, 111, 228
Sparking potential, 185
Speaking voice, 138
Specific heat, 62, 63, 131
Specific resistance, 190
Spectrum, 115
    electromagnetic, 118
    visible, 117
Speed, 1, 2, 21, 29
    of sound, 138
Spontaneous mutation, 237
Spray gun, electrostatic, 186
Spring, 40, 53, 54
    coiled, 39
Standard candle, 136
Stars, 115
"Static," 186
Steam, 251
Steam engine, 253
    reciprocating, 108, 109, 110
Steam locomotive, 110
Steam turbine, 110
Steam turbine plant, 112
Steel, manufacture of, 150
    maximum strength of, 57
Step-down transformer, 226
Step-up transformer, 226
Stopping time, minimum, 24
Storage battery, 164, 165, 166, 201, 253
Storage system, heat, 131
Stored energy, 53, 156
Strength, magnetic pole, 206
String, violin, 138
Submarine, 249
Substance, diamagnetic, 207

ferromagnetic, 207
paramagnetic, 207
radioactive, 236
transparent, 117
Summer, 128
    difference between winter and, 127
Sun, 24, 93, 115
    heating due to, 93
    radiation from, 123, 152, 153, 156, 255
    rays, obliquity of, 127, 128
    surface temperature of, 125
Surface, 23
Surface temperature, 126
    of the sun, 125
Susceptibility, 207, 208
Switzerland, 130
Symbol, chemical, 142

Telephone earpiece, 138
Telephone repeater circuit, 201
Telescope, radio, 120
Temperature, 59, 79, 191
    absolute, 76
        scale of, 71
        zero of, 71
    color, 123
    conversion, 60
    Curie, 209
    effect on magnetization, 209
    of a gas, 74
    measurement of, 197
    of a satellite, 134, 136
    scale of, 60, 61
    of sources of light, 123
    surface, 126
Tension, 13
Terminal velocity, 8
Terrestrial objects, 25
Theoretical efficiency, 109, 110
Thermal capacity, 63, 64
Thermal conductivity, 95, 99, 197
    of ice, 99
    of snow, 99
Thermal insulators, 99
    air as, 99
    cellular material as, 99
    fibrous material as, 99
    vacuum as a, 99
Thermionic conversion, 199, 200, 201, 202
Thermionic converter, 134

Thermocouple, 197
Thermoelectric conversion, 201, 202, 251
Thermoelectric converter, 134, 198, 200
Thermoelectric cooling, 198, 199
Thermoelectric device, 198
Thermeolectric effects, 196
Thermoelectric power, 197
Thermojunction, 197, 199
Thermometer, 60
  alcohol, 61
  mercury, 59
  wet and dry bulb, 80
Thermopile, 196, 197
Thermos flask, 99, 193
Third law of motion, 30
Thorium, 248
Thrust, 34, 36, 113, 114
Thunder-cloud, 93
Tidal energy, 263
Tidal power, 46
Tide(s), 27, 28, 46
  potential energy of, 49
Time, 1
Tires, automobile, 24
  pressure of, 73
Torque, 14, 17, 22, 33
Torsion, 54
Torsion spring, 54
Touch, sensation of, 100
Trajectory, 18, 20, 27, 33, 42
  free, 27
Transformer, 118, 216, 225, 226, 228, 229
Transmitter, microwave, 119
  radio, 201
Transparent substances, 117
Transportation, 251, 256
  energy consumption, 259
Tube, neon, 119
Turbine, 35
  gas, 112
  steam, 110, 112
Turbine engine, 108
Turboprop engine, 35

Ultra-high-speed flight, 100
Ultraviolet, 118
Ultraviolet radiation, 117, 136
Unit, 1, 59
United Kingdom, power per worker, 259

United States, consumption of energy in, 256, 260
  energy generated in, 130
  power per worker, 259
Unit magnetic pole, 205
Universal gravitational constant, 25
University of California, Livermore Laboratory, 249
Unstable nucleus, 237
Uranium, 241, 247, 248
  natural, 244

Vacuum, 192
  as a thermal insulator, 99
Vacuum flask, 99
Valency, 151, 152
Valve, solenoid, 215
Van de Graaff generator, 187
Vapor, water, 130
Vapor pressure, 81
  saturation, 170
Vaporization, latent heat of, 64, 102
Vegetable matter, 159
Velocity, 2, 6, 20, 21, 29, 31, 32, 33, 40, 41
  angular, 3, 21
  average, 77
  distribution curve for, 78
  distribution of, 77
  escape, 78, 79
  of the hydrogen molecule, 75
  instantaneous, 2
  of light, 238, 239
  mean, 79
  of molecules, 71
  terminal, 8
Vibration(s), of atoms, 80
  energy of, 80
  kinetic energy of, 56
  of molecules, 80
Violin string, 138
Visible light, 118
Visible spectrum, 117
Vitamin, 153, 260
Voice, speaking, 138
Volt, 161, 184
Volt meter, 188
Voltage, 161, 162, 164, 181
  induced, 226
Voltage drop, 189

Volume, 1
  of a gas, 67

Water, boiling point of, 60, 81
  compressibility of, 52
Water drop, 8
Water mill, 46
Water power, 46
Water resources, world's, 130
Water use per person, 170
Water vapor, 80, 130
Watt, 46, 48
Wattage, 193
Wavelength, 115, 117, 118
  of maximum energy, 122
Wave motion, 115, 138
Waves, light, 235
  radio, 117, 118, 235
Weight, 9, 10
  apparent, 11
  molecular, 74, 75
  sensation of, 27
Weightlessness, 26, 27
Wet and dry bulb thermometer, 80

White heat, 123
Wind, 93, 131
Windmill, 33, 131
Winter, Massachusetts, 99
  difference between summer and, 127
Wood, 253, 257, 265, 267
Work, 1, 38, 39, 40, 43, 44, 46, 48, 49, 50,
  53, 103, 265
  conversion of heat into, 103
  conversion into heat, 82, 83
  done by animals, 266
  mechanical, 256
  muscular, 155
Working, rate of, 47
World energy consumption, 260, 267
World food production, 262
World food supply, 260
World fuel reserves, 267
World population, 260
World water resources, 130

X-rays, 117, 118, 235

"Yo-yo," 43